Landscape Design, Construction, and Maintenance

Revised Third Edition

RONALD J. BIONDO

Landscape Designer and Educator
Naperville, Illinois

CHARLES B. SCHROEDER

Landscaper and Professor Emeritus
Danville Area Community College
Danville, Illinois

materials, and constructing hardscape features such as fences, decks, and patios are discussed in detail.

Part Three of this book focuses on the maintenance of landscapes. The latest findings from scientific research on plant care direct the writings on landscape maintenance. Major topics covered include establishing and maintaining turfgrass; fertilizing, watering, and mulching plants; pruning woody plants; and controlling plant pests.

This book is the result of the combined talents of two highly successful horticulture authors. The authors have applied their experiences in both the landscape industry and the horticulture classroom. The Second Edition expanded information on water gardens, irrigation, and perennial gardens. New information has been included on selecting trees, turfgrass establishment, pesticide safety, and integrated pest management. The Third Edition and Revised Third Edition have further expanded content in these and other areas. Statistical information has been updated. Expanded information has been introduced on student development.

DISCLAIMER CLAUSE / STATEMENT OF WARRANTY

The authors and publisher are in no way responsible for the application or use of the chemicals mentioned or described herein. They make no warranties, express or implied, as to the accuracy or adequacy of any of the information presented about various chemicals in this book, nor do they guarantee the current status of registered uses of any of these chemicals with the U.S. Environmental Protection Agency. Also, by the omission, either unintentionally or from lack of space, of certain trade names and of some of the formulated products available to the public, the authors are not endorsing those companies whose brand names or products are listed.

Preface— Revised Third Edition

Landscape Design, Construction, and Maintenance is the new title of a book that has offered a practical approach for students and teachers for three prior editions as ***Introduction to Landscaping: Design, Construction, and Maintenance***. It has been the leading book for learning and teaching the establishment and maintenance of residential landscapes. It is intended to introduce the various aspects of the landscape industry to students of horticulture and agriculture. The authors have carefully written and revised this book from a horticultural perspective. Plant selection and care are the foundation of this book. This book has been organized in three distinct parts— landscape design, landscape construction, and landscape maintenance.

Landscaping has been one of the fastest growing segments of the horticulture industry! The design of new landscapes, the building of landscapes, and the maintenance of existing landscapes are in high demand. People appreciate well-planned landscapes. Well-planned landscapes are attractive and easily enjoyed. They are also functional, allowing many leisure time uses.

The steps to developing a complete and functional landscape plan for the residential setting are identified and explained in an easy to understand writing style. Part One covers the principles of art as they relate to the design process in landscaping. The student is guided through the process of designing landscape projects from establishing customer needs to preparing and costing out the plan.

Tools and products used in landscape construction are explained in Part Two of this book. Procedures for preparing planting beds, installing plant

v

Special thanks goes to Robert Hursthouse, R.S. Hursthouse & Associates, Inc., and John Mitten, Church Landscape, for extensive interviews concerning the operations of businesses in the landscape industry.

Hannah McKay of Education Images, Inc., is acknowledged for her photography assistance as indicated in caption courtesy lines throughout the book and for the Part Three divider page image.

Acknowledgment also goes to the teachers and students throughout the United States who have used previous editions of this book and provided suggestions for additional improvements.

Acknowledgments

The authors of *Landscape Design, Construction, and Maintenance* are grateful to many individuals for their assistance with this book. Some are acknowledged here. Others are recognized within the text.

Special acknowledgment is due to those who reviewed the manuscript. They include:

- Julian Smith, Horticulture Teacher, Bear Creek, North Carolina

- Ken Godfrey, Agriculture Department Chair, Riverside, California

- Gail Komoto, Agriculture Teacher, Vancouver, Washington

- Deborah Swafford, Horticulture Teacher, Moore, Oklahoma

- Norman Hammond, State FFA advisor, North Scituate, Rhode Island

- Doug Prevette, Horticulture Teacher, Olin, North Carolina

- Susan Kelly, Program Specialist, Orlando, Florida

Other individuals receiving special acknowledgment for assistance with photographs follow: Robert Hursthouse, R.S. Hursthouse & Associates, Inc.; John Mitten, Church Landscape; Lorin Reicks, LANDCADD Division of Eagle Point Software; Patricia Cassady, Illinois Landscape Contractors Association; Greg Stack, University of Illinois Cooperative Extension Service; Kathy Freeland, Midwest Groundcovers; Harold Hoover, City of Elmhurst Forestry Department; Joe Karr, Joe Karr and Associates; Frank Mariani, Mariani Landscape; David Van Zelst, Van Zelst, Inc.; Dave Peters, Pavestone Company; Rex Bastion, Hendricksen The Care of Trees.

Landscape Design, Construction, and Maintenance

Revised Third Edition

Previously published as *Introduction to Landscaping: Design, Construction, and Maintenance, Third Edition*

Pearson® is a trademark, in the U.S. and/or in other countries, of Pearson plc or its affiliates.

Interstate™ is a trademark, in the U.S. and/or in other countries, of Pearson Education, Inc., or its affiliates.

Cover photo courtesy of Western DuPage Landscaping, Inc.

ISBN-13: 978-0-13-362638-4
ISBN-10: 0-13-362638-5

1 2 3 4 5 6 7 8 9 10   12 11 10 09 08

Landscape Design, Construction, and Maintenance

Revised Third Edition

Interstate
AgriScience
& Technology
Series

Jasper S. Lee — Series Editor

PEARSON

Boston, Massachusetts
Chandler, Arizona
Glenview, Illinois
Upper Saddle River, New Jersey

Contents

PART ONE—Landscape Design

PART TWO—Landscape Construction

PART THREE—Landscape Maintenance

PART ONE

Landscape Design

CHAPTER 1

Landscape Methods

OBJECTIVES

1 Define landscaping and its benefits.

2 Identify the purposes of landscape design.

3 Describe the scope of landscape construction.

4 Recognize the need for landscape maintenance.

5 Identify careers found in the landscape industry.

6 Report on desirable workplace skills.

7 Discuss general safety rules in the workplace.

8 Recognize the value of supervised experience programs.

9 Explain related opportunities found in student youth organizations.

TERMS

aesthetic value
arboretum
botanical garden
career success
design/build landscape
    companies
garden center
golf course design and
    maintenance
green industry
hardscape

horticultural garden
landscape architect
landscape construction
landscape contractor
landscape design
landscape designer
landscape maintenance
landscape supervisor
landscaping
leadership
National FFA Organization

National Junior Horticultural
    Association (NJHA)
nursery production
ornamental horticulture
personal growth
sod production
supervised agricultural
    experience programs
    (SAEP)

1-1. More people take interest in beautiful landscape settings than ever before. (Courtesy, Church Landscape)

HAVE you ever mowed the lawn? Have you ever planted flowers in the yard? Have you tended a vegetable garden? If you have done these activities, you have touched upon the landscape industry. Many people enjoy these gardening activities. In fact, national polls show gardening to be the most popular outdoor leisure activity in the United States.

Some people like landscape activities so much they devote their professional career to the landscaping industry. The industry involving the design, construction, and maintenance of landscapes shows rapid growth. More people take interest in beautiful landscape settings than ever before. As a result, job opportunities are abundant.

LANDSCAPING

Landscaping is a part of the ornamental horticulture industry. The **ornamental horticulture** industry uses plants and other materials for decorative purposes. Ornamental horticulture combines the principles of art with the science of growing plants. In addition to landscaping, ornamental horticulture claims the areas of floral design, greenhouse management, and nursery management. Sometimes the ornamental horticulture industry is referred to as the "**green industry**" because of the use of green plants.

TIP: According to realtors and appraisers, a beautifully landscaped house sells faster and for more money than its neighbors.

1-2. Landscaping surrounds us in the United States. (a.) schools and universities, (b.) churches, (c.) corporate offices, (d.) golf courses , (e.) cemeteries, (f.) government buildings, (g.) parks, (h.) residential housing, (i.) shopping malls.

LANDSCAPING DEFINED

Landscaping is the segment of the green industry that focuses on the beautification of outdoor terrain and, to some extent, interior settings. Landscaping usually begins with the sculpting of the soil and natural lay of the land. Landscaping involves the planting of ornamental trees, shrubs, vines, ground covers (including grasses), perennial flowers, annual flowers, and bulbs. Landscaping involves physical features or **hardscape**. Hardscape includes fences, terraces, retaining walls, patios, walks, drives, irrigation systems, lighting, and water features.

Achieving an attractive landscape requires planning, proper construction techniques, and regular maintenance. It is not an easy task. Landscape professionals are challenged with every job. Landscaping is actually a practical application of problem solving. The challenge is for the landscape professional to determine the best method to beautify a piece of land.

Professional landscapers must consider many factors during the work on a landscape job. Some factors that influence landscapes are the terrain; the climate; the houses, buildings, and other physical structures; the intended use of the property; and the client's wants. The challenge for the landscaper is to allow for all the factors while developing a landscape that is both attractive and functional. The challenge created with the landscape process can often become quite complex.

1-3. This series of photos show the house, the landscape plan, and a scene from the completed landscape. (Courtesy, Illinois Landscape Contractors Association)

1-4. Hardscape involves physical elements such as stone walls. (Courtesy, Church Landscape)

1-5. Landscaping involves problem solving. (Courtesy, Church Landscape)

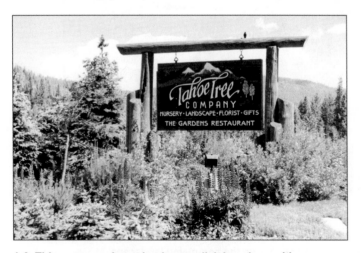

1-6. This company has a landscape division along with a nursery, garden center, florist, and restaurant.

This book will focus primarily on residential landscapes and the three major segments of landscaping. The first segment, landscape design, deals with the planning of a landscape project. Once a design is prepared, work can begin on the second segment, installation or construction of the project. The third aspect involves the maintenance of the landscape so it will continue to be attractive over a long period.

Landscape companies can be grouped based on the type of services they offer. ***Design/build landscape companies*** involve themselves with both the design and the installation of landscapes. They are quite common. They employ a landscape designer or a landscape architect to work with the client to design a landscape plan. In addition, landscape companies may be classified as construction, maintenance, arborist, irrigation, garden center, and nursery. Some businesses have multiple capabilities. For instance, a company might provide design/build, garden center, and landscape maintenance services.

Landscaping Is Profitable

Landscape horticulture is a billion-dollar industry in the United States. The Gallup Organization conducted a survey on behalf of the National Gardening Association in a recent year. It was found that homeowners in the United States spent 50.9 billion dollars to install, improve, and maintain their landscapes and gardens. These figures show that millions of Americans value a beautiful outdoor environment.

In 2000, nursery production was measured by the USDA to be at $3.3 billion nationally. Deciduous shrubs accounted for 23 percent of total sales, broadleaf evergreens 18%, coniferous evergreens 12%, deciduous trees 12 %, propagative material 11%, fruit and nut plants 9%, deciduous flowering trees 7%, vegetable transplants 4%, and Christmas trees 4%.

LANDSCAPE BENEFITS

What are the benefits from well-landscaped residential properties? The obvious benefit is enjoyment given to the homeowner. Attractive or aesthetic views are pleasing. The beauty of a landscape is sometimes referred to as ***aesthetic value***. Plants in the landscape convey warmth, protection, and comfort. Landscapes designed with function in mind also lend themselves well to many activities. You might enjoy using the landscape for volleyball, entertainment at a cookout, or for growing fresh vegetables.

Homeowners polled by the Gallup Organization in a survey for the National Gardening Association ranked the benefits of a well-maintained lawn and landscape as follows:

- Beauty and relaxation for the family, employees, or visitors (54.0 percent)

- Reflects positively on its owner (53.2 percent)

- Comfortable place to entertain, work at, or visit (47.4 percent)

- Increased real estate market value (44.1 percent)

- Helps to beautify the neighborhood (43.3 percent)

- Provides a safe, high-quality play area for children (36.7 percent)

- Provides an exercise area for pets (21.3 percent)

- Helps to purify the air (19.9 percent)

- Helps to cool the air (17.8 percent)

- Provides a natural water filter to protect water quality and the environment (13.5 percent)

The time and money put into establishing a nice landscape pay dividends when selling a house. A study by Weyerhaeuser Nursery Products Division estimated that landscaping can add as much as 15 percent to the resale value of a home. The landscape provides the first impression prospective buyers have of a home. Attractive land-

1-7. Landscaping can add as much as 15 percent to the value of a home.

1-8. These planters in Chicago reduce pollutants in the air, reduce noise from the traffic, and provide a pleasant view.

1-9. Design is one segment of landscaping. (Courtesy, Joe Karr & Associates)

scapes draw buyers out of their cars and into the house. According to realtors and appraisers, a beautifully landscaped house sells faster and for more money than its neighbors.

Landscape plants are good for the environment. The photosynthetic process in a leaf uses carbon dioxide and releases oxygen. Studies have shown that a 2,500 square foot area of turf releases enough oxygen for a family of four. Plants and soil organisms also scrub the air of pollutants, such as ammonia, benzene, toluene, trichloroethylene, and xylene.

Landscape trees play a major role in cooling the air. Shaded areas are naturally cooler than those in the direct sun. Well-placed trees cut cooling costs up to 20 percent. Carefully located landscape plantings also cut winter heating costs.

Well-landscaped properties reduce noise pollution. Noise from busy streets, railroad activity, and other sources is absorbed or deflected by landscape materials. The same barriers help to screen unwanted views and provide privacy.

LANDSCAPE DESIGN

A well thought-out plan simplifies problems confronted by landscapers. A good analogy to a landscape plan is the use of a road map on a cross-country trip. On such a trip, you would refer to a map as you traveled on roads you had not traveled on before. The road map gives you direction and removes guesswork from your travel decisions. Landscape planning removes guesswork, too. Carefully planned projects are more likely to be attractive and functional than those with poor planning.

Landscape design is the practice of creating a plan to make the best use of available space in the most attractive way. Consideration is given to the relationships between the land, buildings, plants, and people. Professional designers have two main purposes in mind when designing landscape plans for a home or a building:

> **TIP:** Attractive landscapes are achieved through good planning, proper construction techniques, and regular maintenance.

1. Show off the home or building to its best advantage.
2. Create both an attractive and useful setting for the inhabitants.

QUALIFIED DESIGN PROFESSIONALS

People trained in the area of landscape design fall into one of two categories. The two professional titles are landscape architect and landscape designer. It is sometimes confusing to determine the difference between landscape architects and landscape designers. In general, landscape architects are educated to work on large scale projects, whereas, most landscape designers received education enabling them to develop plans for residential landscapes.

Landscape Architect

Landscape architects are trained in engineering, graphic arts, and architectural technology. They are skilled in designing functional plans based on the interrelationship of people and their surroundings. They use their creative talents to design projects ranging from small gardens to entire cities. The vast majority of their work involves large-scale projects, such as parks, golf

1-10. The landscape should show off the home to its best advantage. (Courtesy, Western DuPage Landscaping, Inc.)

1-11 Landscape design is the practice of creating a plan to make the best use of available space in the most attractive way. (Courtesy, R.S. Hursthouse & Associates, Inc.)

1-12. Landscape architects are skilled with large-scale projects. (Courtesy, Church Landscape)

courses, community planning, and large corporate complexes. Some landscape architects find employment designing plans for residential homes.

Most states require landscape architects to be licensed before they can practice. Formal training for landscape architects is the first step. Those interested in landscape architecture study for a degree in landscape architecture from an accredited college or university. Upon graduation, they gain experience as an apprentice for a professional landscape architect. Finally, the landscape architect must pass a state licensing examination. For most landscape architects, education does not end. Many seek further degrees to improve their skills.

1-13. Landscape designers are trained in the art of design and the science of growing horticultural plants.

Landscape Designer

Landscape designers are trained in the art of design and the science of growing horticultural plants. Landscape designers work primarily with residential home designs and small commercial sites. They are often employed by landscaping companies or by garden centers and nurseries that offer landscape installation services. Knowledge of plant identification, cultural requirements for plants, construction practices, and the principles of design are required to be a successful designer. Landscape designers must also develop their personal skills. They must effectively communicate with the client about the landscape plan and with construction crews to see that the job is installed as designed.

Formal education beyond high school is needed for landscape designers. Some landscape designers gain their education through an associate's degree from a community college. Others earn a bachelors degree in ornamental horticulture from a four-year college or university. Further education is helpful.

1-14. An example of a landscape design.

LANDSCAPE CONSTRUCTION

Once a design has been drawn for a landscape project, work can begin on construction. **Landscape construction** is the segment of landscaping that involves the installation of materials identified in the landscape design. Construction projects range from being very simple, such as planting a tree, to very elaborate. Large projects may involve moving soil, installing drainage systems, building permanent structures, such as walls, walks and drives, and planting numerous plants.

LANDSCAPE CONTRACTOR

The construction of the project is performed by a **landscape contractor**. Landscape contractors are hired to install the landscape. Their job is to transfer the design provided on paper to the actual landscape. Therefore, landscape contractors must be able to read and understand the landscape plans.

The landscape designer and the contractor may work for the same company. Sometimes, the contractor hires a designer. Sometimes, the contractor is trained in landscape design. The important consideration is that the contractor fully understands what the designer has intended with a design. It is equally important that the contractor communicate with the designer when part of the plan simply will not work. A good working arrangement eliminates many problems during the installation.

There are many aspects to the landscape contractor's job. Like any business, landscape contractors advertise their work and try to build a professional image with the public. They develop business contracts with clients. Contractors may be responsible for obtaining building permits, and they must install projects in accordance with munici-

1-15. Landscape construction is the segment of landscaping that involves the installation of materials identified in the landscape design.

pal codes. Contractors ensure that the materials called for in the landscape plan are ordered and that the necessary equipment is available and in working order. Landscape contractors must also hire qualified workers to do the physical installation.

Landscape contractors learn the profession while on the job and through school. It is common for an individual to start in this field as a crew member. As crew members, they gain practical experience. They can also improve their understanding of plant care, plant identification, business skills, construction practices, and landscape design through formal education at a community college or university. Additional training programs for landscape professionals are available through state and national landscape associations.

1-16. Installation of plant materials is a major aspect of landscaping. (Courtesy, Church Landscape)

LANDSCAPE SUPERVISOR

TIP: Good work habits involve job productivity and citizenship.

Landscape workers are usually organized in groups or crews. A **landscape supervisor** or crew chief has responsibility for the crew. The landscape supervisor provides leadership. This individual assigns tasks to the workers and usually works alongside them. Teamwork among the workers is extremely important. Working well with one another improves the quality of work as well as the speed in which it takes to complete a job.

1-17. The landscape supervisor provides leadership to the crew. (Courtesy, Church Landscape)

LANDSCAPE MAINTENANCE

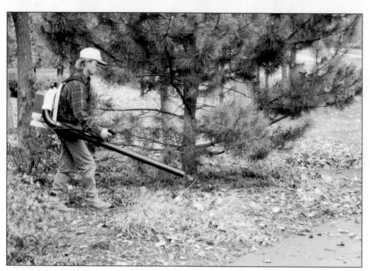

1-18. Landscape maintenance is the care and upkeep of the landscape materials after installation.

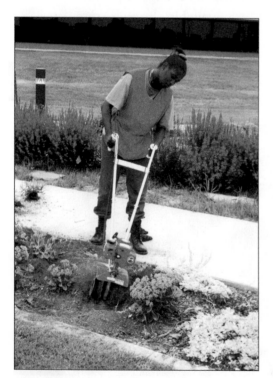

1-19. Maintenance involves weed control in planting beds.

Landscape maintenance is the care and upkeep of the landscape materials after installation. Landscape maintenance includes tasks, such as mowing grass, fertilizing landscape plants, pruning landscape plants, applying pest controls, planting and weeding flower beds, removing leaves in the fall, cultivating soil, and applying mulch to landscape planting beds. The goal of a good landscape maintenance program is to keep the landscape as attractive and functional as intended in the original landscape design. Jobs and occupations in landscape maintenance include crew supervisor, superintendent of operations, salesperson, and manager.

Most landscape companies focus on either construction or maintenance. There are several reasons for this. The specialized equipment required for each type of work differs. The workers are trained to do specific types of work and are familiar with certain equipment. Also, the types of projects performed call for different scheduling of workers. Some landscape companies do both construction and maintenance. However, those companies usually have some landscape crews assigned to construction and others to maintenance.

Landscape maintenance involves all types of landscape projects. A large portion of contracted landscape maintenance work is performed on large landscapes surrounding commercial office buildings, apartment buildings, townhouse associations, condominiums, etc. Most homeowners rely on professionals to do the more difficult installation and then maintain the landscape themselves. Other homeowners hire landscape professionals to attend to the

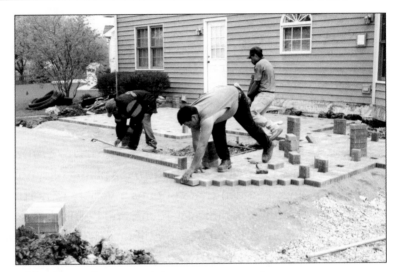

1-20 . These employees demonstrate teamwork in the construction of a patio.

upkeep of their landscape. Golf courses and large gardens requiring constant maintenance often employ workers year round.

RELATED CAREERS

Jobs and careers in the landscape industry can be in the position of employee or an entrepreneur. An employee is someone who works for someone else, while entrepreneurs work for themselves. Jobs and careers can be in nursery production, garden centers, arboretums, gardens, sod production, turfgrass establishment, and golf course management.

Nursery production involves growing plants in containers or fields. Plants can be grown from seed, cuttings, or grafting. Jobs and occupations in nursery production include propagator, inventory manager, field supervisor, manager, salesperson, sales manager, and shipping supervisor.

The plants and seeds used by commercial growers come from large operations. These large operations are able to mass produce seeds and plants. Examples of jobs and occupations related to this industry include

1-21. Automation is used by large nursery producers to economically produce large quantities of plants. (Courtesy, Education Images, Inc.)

plant breeder, propagator, independent grower, sales manager, and salesperson.

The heart of the retail nursery industry is the **garden center**. Garden centers offer consumers plant materials and supplies needed to maintain a garden or landscape. Jobs and occupations related to the retail nursery industry include buyer, plant technician, and manager.

Arboretums and botanical gardens offer both job and educational opportunities for people interested in horticulture. An **arboretum** is a natural setting of trees, shrubs, and vines. A **botanical garden** is a plant collection habitat. A **horticultural garden** is an arranged garden that contains a variety of horticulture plants. Jobs and careers related to arboretums, botanical gardens, and horticultural gardens include: writer, researcher, propagator, educational director, librarian, director, curator, and greenhouse manager.

Sod production is the mass production of turfgrass. Jobs and occupations related to the sod production industry include farm manager, assistant farm manager, spray technician, and staff leader.

Turfgrass establishment is a site where turfgrass has already been installed and requires maintenance. Examples of jobs and occupations in the turfgrass establishment industry include construction superintendent and planting superintendent.

Golf course design and maintenance involves the design and care for golf course landscapes. Jobs and occupations related to golf course maintenance and design include golf course architect, superintendent, assistant superintendent, irrigation technician, spray technician, landscape technician, and equipment operator.

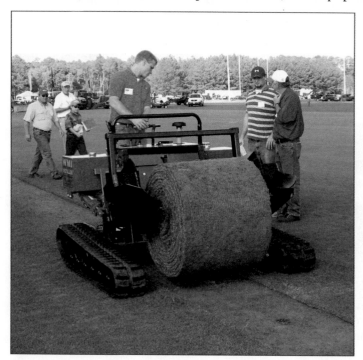

1-22. New sod harvesting equipment is being demonstrated at a field day. (Courtesy, Eddie Seagle, Abraham Baldwin Agricultural College)

WORKPLACE EXPECTATIONS

People who work for others are expected to have certain workplace skills. These skills go beyond technical skills such as how to plant a tree, design a landscape, or operate equipment. Employers look for common work habits in all their employees whether he or she is a designer, a foreman, or landscape maintenance technician. Good work habits involve job productivity and citizenship. Employers want employees who:

- Arrive to work on time everyday
- Dress appropriately for the job
- Stay on task
- Demonstrate loyalty to the employer
- Are honest
- Work well with co-workers as a team player
- Take pride in their work
- Work without errors
- Have a positive attitude
- Care for equipment and do not waste resources
- Communicate orally with others
- Follow written and oral instructions
- Ask questions about tasks
- Demonstrate a willingness to learn
- Are sensitive to cultural, sexual, and racial diversity
- Practice safety on the job

1-23. Safety is a major concern when working with large landscape equipment and heavy plant material.

SAFETY IN THE WORKPLACE

TIP: One of the most important workplace expectations involves safety.

One of the most important workplace expectations involves safety. Rules have been established to prevent injuries that can occur on the job. Laws have been passed that employers must observe to protect employees. Employees must follow those rules and other safety rules identified by the employer. Personal protective equipment designed to protect eyes, ears, hands, and other parts of the body are manufactured for use in the landscape industry and should be used.

Employees can follow general safety rules to reduce injury:

- Identify and follow safety rules and procedures
- Know how to operate tools and equipment safely
- Be aware of possible hazards to yourself, others around you, and the environment
- Use personal protective equipment
- Keep tools and equipment clean and in good working order
- Read and follow instructions
- Alert other people of potential hazards

Safety with Power Equipment and Tools

Much landscape work requires the use of power equipment and tools. Working with power equipment and tools is especially hazardous. Operators of equipment must know how to properly run equipment before attempting to use it. They should read the operator's manual, and if necessary, receive training. The operator should be aware of hazards associated with fuels, batteries, electricity, PTO and pulleys, cooling systems, and moving parts.

Common hand tools can cause personal injuries. Keep hand tools in proper working condition. Use hand tools properly and only as intended. Store hand tools when not in use. Also wear eye, hearing, skin, and respiratory protection when appropriate.

Electricity and electric power tools and equipment are a source of hazards. Electrical circuits are safety risks, particularly around water. All electrical devices should be installed according to the proper electrical code. Use ground fault circuit interrupters (GFCI) to protect all circuits. Only turn power on when tools are going to be in use.

SUPERVISED EXPERIENCE

Valuable work experiences can be obtained through ***supervised agricultural experience programs (SAEP)***. SAEs provide opportunities to apply classroom instruction through real-world experiences. Through SAEs students have an opportunity to explore the landscape industry.

Students practice specific job skills in one of four ways. They can have exploratory, placement, ownership, or research and experimentation projects. Common landscape oriented SAEs are placement or employment with a local business and ownership of a landscape operation.

The Agriculture/Horticulture instructor, the parents, and the employers provide supervision of the experience. These people are available to help plan a student's project and provide guidance as the experience progresses.

It is common for students to begin with a fairly simple SAE. As the student learns more the project may become more advanced. Student recognition for SAEs can be gained through the FFA Organization.

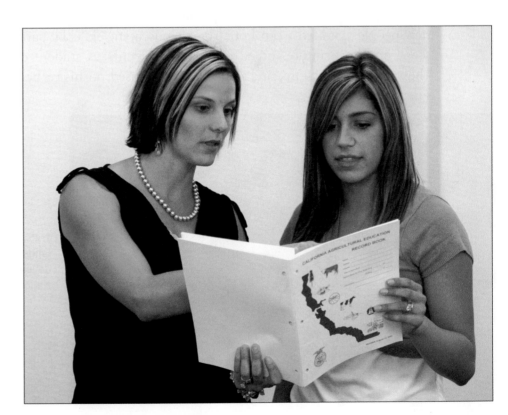

1-24. A student and her teacher are reviewing supervised experience records. (Courtesy, Education Images, Inc.)

STUDENT YOUTH ORGANIZATIONS

The National FFA Organization

The premier student organization for young people interested in the landscaping industry is the **National FFA Organization**. In fact, the FFA Organization is designed for students enrolled in Agriculture/Horticulture and is an integral part of the classroom instruction. The National FFA Organization is the largest student organization in the United States.

The focus of the FFA Organization is threefold. It is to promote premier leadership, personal development, and career success. **Leadership** is the ability to influence other people to meet individual or group goals. **Personal growth** deals with social skills, citizenship, and topics associated with self-esteem. **Career success** involves those things that will help a person succeed in the world of work. The employability skills mentioned in this chapter are addressed through the FFA Organization.

Many exciting experiences are possible through the FFA. Students can travel and meet new people. Students can hone their landscaping skills by participating in nursery/landscape and horticulture career development events. A student can also receive awards at chapter, regional, state, and national levels based on his or her proficiency in landscape management.

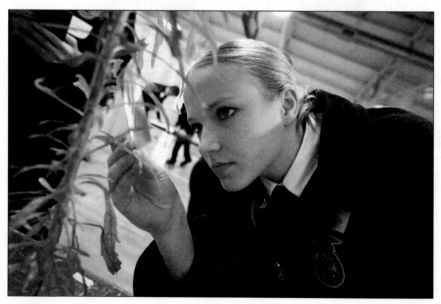

1-25. Students can test their landscape skills through FFA career development events. (Courtesy, The National FFA Organization)

The National Junior Horticultural Association

Another organization for young people interested in the landscape industry is the **National Junior Horticultural Association (NJHA)**. NJHA projects and activities are for youth 22 years of age and under. Membership in the NJHA is achieved by enrollment or participation in any NJHA project or activity.

The NJHA program focus is represented by the acronym HYCEL, which stands for Horticulture, Youth, Careers, Education, and Leadership. NJHA projects and activities are designed to work with existing programs, such as, but not limited to 4-H, FFA, scouts, horticulture/agriculture education, and youth gardening groups. Projects and activities are also designed for independent youth who participate directly in NJHA.

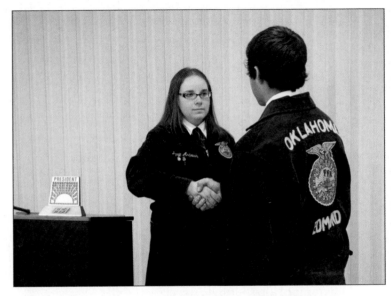

1-26. The FFA provides considerable opportunity for leadership and personal development. (Courtesy, Education Images, Inc.)

REVIEWING

MAIN IDEAS

Landscaping is a part of the ornamental horticulture industry, which uses plants and other materials for decorative purposes. Landscaping is challenging work centered on improving the appearance of land. Landscape horticulture is a billion-dollar industry in the United States. There are many benefits from well-landscaped residential properties.

Landscaping begins with a landscape plan or design. Landscape design is the practice of creating a plan to make the best use of available space in the most attractive way. The landscape plan is developed by either a landscape architect or a landscape designer. Landscape architects tend to work with large-scale landscape designs while designers concentrate on residential landscape projects. Knowledge in plant materials, plant cultural requirements, the principles of art, and interrelationships between people and their surroundings is valuable to landscape architects and designers.

Landscape construction is the segment of landscaping that involves the installation of materials identified in the landscape plan. Installation projects range from planting woody landscape plants to building fences, walls, and patios. The landscape contractor is the one hired to install the landscape as specified in the landscape plan. Landscape supervisors lead crews working as a team to complete the job.

Landscape maintenance is the care and upkeep given to a landscape after installation. Some tasks include mowing turf, pruning woody plants, fertilizing landscape plants, and removing leaves in the fall. Most companies focus on landscape construction or landscape maintenance.

There are numerous jobs and careers related to the landscape industry. Some jobs and careers are found in nursery production, garden centers, arboretums, gardens, sod production, turfgrass establishment, and golf course management.

Workplace skills and safety are important to landscape employers and employees. Workplace skills consist of good work habits that involve job productivity and citizenship. One of the most important workplace expectations is safety. Employees should follow general safety rules to reduce injury.

The premier student organization for young people interested in the landscape industry is the National FFA Organization. The FFA Organization is for students enrolled in Agriculture/Horticulture and is an integral part of the classroom instruction. It promotes premier leadership, personal development, and career success. Another organization for interested young people is the National Junior Horticultural Association (NJHA).

QUESTIONS

Answer the following questions using correct spelling and complete sentences.

1. What is landscaping?

2. Why is landscape design important?

3. How do landscape architects and landscape designers differ?

4. What are some skills beneficial to architects and designers?

5. What does landscape construction involve?

6. What are some jobs of a landscape contractor?

7. What does landscape maintenance involve?

8. What are considered to be good work habits?

9. What general safety rules should all employees follow?

10. How does participation in SAE, The National FFA Organization, and NJHA benefit young people?

CHAPTER SELF-CHECK

Match the term with the correct definition. Write the letter by the term in the blank provided.

a. landscape designer
b. landscape construction
c. landscaping
d. landscape contractor
e. hardscape
f. landscape maintenance
g. landscape design
h. landscape architect
i. landscape supervisor

_____1. Leader responsible for the landscape crew

_____2. Creating a plan to make the best use of available space in the most attractive way

_____3. An individual trained in making landscape plans with greater emphasis on large areas

_____4. An individual trained in making landscape plans with emphasis on residential landscapes

_____5. A company hired to install landscape projects

_____6. The care and upkeep of a landscape after installation

_____7. The installation of landscape materials identified in a landscape plan

_____8. The part of the ornamental horticulture industry that involves the beautification of outdoor terrain and, to some extent, interior settings

_____9. The portion of landscaping that involves physical features

EXPLORING

1. Interview local landscapers on the various aspects of their jobs. Learn the scopes of the businesses. Do they undertake design work, construction work, maintenance work, or a combination of these? Ask what landscapers like most about their work and what they dislike.

2. Visit a university or community college that offers a program in landscape architecture or landscape design. Find out what course work is recommended to obtain a degree.

CHAPTER 2

Working with the Customer

OBJECTIVES

1 Explain the landscape sales process.

2 Describe the family inventory survey and how it is used.

3 Explain the difference between a proposal and a contract.

TERMS

closing
communication
contract
family inventory survey

landscape proposal
opening
portfolio
preparation

presentation
probing
sales

2-1. The designer on the left reviews a plan for his client in the design studio.

BEFORE a design is drawn, a shrub is planted, or a blade of grass mowed, an agreement must be reached between the customer and the landscaper. Without an agreement, how would the customer know what services were to be provided and at what cost? How would the landscaper know what work is to be performed?

Reaching an agreement is necessary in the business world. How is this accomplished? It happens when the landscaper makes an effort to communicate in a cooperative way with the customer. This open communication usually starts with a meeting between the designer and the customer.

THE SALES PROCESS

Landscaping is a service industry. The landscape company provides the client with a well-planned design, a professionally installed landscape, or maintenance of the client's landscape. Fair dealings with the customer and quality work are beneficial to both the customer and the landscaper. The customer receives quality services and goods in exchange for money. The landscaper generates money to maintain a healthy business and wins endorsements that lead to additional jobs later.

Of course, the landscaper must first persuade the client to purchase services. Landscape projects begin with the sales process. A **sale** is the exchange of goods or services at a price mutually agreed upon by the parties involved. The one landscape employee in the best position to make a sale is the designer. It is the designer who applies the wants and needs of the customer to a landscape design. The designer also knows through experience what work the company can perform.

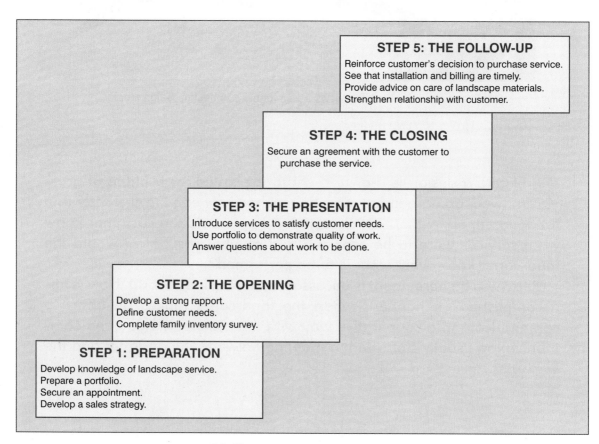

STEP 5: THE FOLLOW-UP
Reinforce customer's decision to purchase service.
See that installation and billing are timely.
Provide advice on care of landscape materials.
Strengthen relationship with customer.

STEP 4: THE CLOSING
Secure an agreement with the customer to purchase the service.

STEP 3: THE PRESENTATION
Introduce services to satisfy customer needs.
Use portfolio to demonstrate quality of work.
Answer questions about work to be done.

STEP 2: THE OPENING
Develop a strong rapport.
Define customer needs.
Complete family inventory survey.

STEP 1: PREPARATION
Develop knowledge of landscape service.
Prepare a portfolio.
Secure an appointment.
Develop a sales strategy.

2-2. Five steps to a landscape sale.

Other employees of landscape businesses are involved directly or indirectly in sales. It is common for the owners of businesses to be actively involved in the sales process. In some companies, the owner is the sales person. The owner has direct contact with the customer and relates the customer's needs. Crew leaders and workers also contribute to making sales. Their professionalism and the way they conduct themselves on the job attract the attention of potential customers. Sometimes, their contact with potential customers leaves either a positive or negative impression.

Making the sale is a problem-solving process. Sales differ because of the people involved and their needs. Knowing this, the designer must be flexible as the sale unfolds. An understanding of the sales process enables the designer to adjust to the challenge presented with each customer. Completing a successful sale usually depends on executing five steps in the sales process referred to as preparation, opening, presentation, closing, and follow-up.

PREPARATION

The saying "Prior planning prevents poor performance" holds true in the sales process. A prepared salesperson anticipates the questions and concerns of the customer and addresses them accordingly. **Preparation** involves a number of factors before the sale is actually conducted.

First, new customers need to be located. In the landscape industry, it would be better to say the landscape company needs to be located. This is because the customers usually make the initial contact with the landscape company. These customers need land-

2-3. Many customers learn of landscape services through the telephone book and make the first contact by telephone.

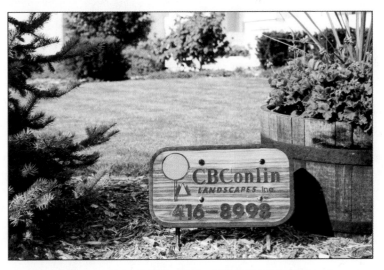

2-4. This landscape company promotes its work by placing a sign in a newly completed landscape.

scape services they cannot or do not want to do themselves. They may need a complete landscape installed. They may want an area of the existing landscape improved.

It is up to the landscape company to market their company to potential customers. Many customers learn of the company from telephone book advertisements, through newspaper advertisements, word of mouth, or from flyers distributed by the company. A well-prepared website can attract and inform potential customers.

Landscape companies can also promote their services by doing work for house contractors, placing signs at construction sites (i.e., "Landscaping by AJB Landscape Company"), sponsoring community events, or participating in home shows. Established landscape companies, known for high quality work, often survive entirely by referrals and repeat customers and do little advertising.

> **TIP:** Prior to a sales meeting develop a strategy based on what is known about the customer's needs.

Once the contact is made, the designer has the responsibility of setting up an appointment with the customer. Typically, the meeting is held at the customer's home so the designer can see the site being discussed. Prior to the meeting, the designer develops a sales strategy based on what is known about the customer's needs. The designer must also be prepared to explain the landscape goods and services available for sale to the customer.

> **TIP:** Greet the customer with a warm smile, a firm handshake, and establish eye contact.

THE OPENING

Opening a sale is the first meeting of the designer and customer. The opening of a sale has two primary purposes. One is to develop a strong rapport or a relationship with the customer. The other is to define the needs of the customer through carefully planned questions. The opening phase takes place during the first meeting with the customer.

The initial meeting with the customer is critical as it provides the first impressions about the designer and the professionalism of the company. First impressions are lasting impressions. Poor impressions at the first meeting are difficult to change. Some things contribute to making a good impression. Examples are politeness, dressing

2-5. Greeting the customer with a smile creates a good first impression.

according to the situation, smiling, acting confidently without being arrogant, speaking clearly, showing an interest in what the customer has to say, and looking the customer in the eye.

Throughout the meeting it is important to communicate with the customer. Effective **communication** requires that both individuals participate in exchanging information. This gives both parties an opportunity to get to know one another. The result is an easing of tension and awkwardness and a building of trust.

After the initial introductions, build rapport with light conversation before diving into the business at hand. The weather, sporting events, and holidays are topics in which a wide range of people take interest. In fact, when strangers meet they often talk about something both have in common, such as the weather. As they become more comfortable with one another, they move on to other topics. Experience helps designers determine the appropriate time to move on to the purpose of the visit.

At this point, it is helpful to probe for customer needs. Probing is a practice of thoroughly investigating a customer's wants, needs, and problems. Probing involves asking appropriate questions through a customer interview to discover the needs. Knowing the needs of the customer allows the salesperson to adjust his or her sales effort to address those needs. If the sale is made, the landscaper is better able to provide the exact goods and services that will meet the needs uncovered during the probe.

2-6. Probing involves asking careful questions to learn more about the customer's landscape needs.

Family Inventory Survey

Landscape design is complex and there are many factors to consider during the design process. Therefore, a written family inventory survey is a useful tool in the probing process. The **family inventory survey** is a form on which the

2-7. This family is completing a family inventory survey.

FAMILY INVENTORY SURVEY

FAMILY MEMBERS:

Name	Age	Sex	Hobbies
_____	_____	_____	_____
_____	_____	_____	_____
_____	_____	_____	_____
_____	_____	_____	_____
_____	_____	_____	_____
_____	_____	_____	_____

PUBLIC AREA (front of the house):

Driveway needs _____

Number of cars owned by family _____

Off-street parking needed _____

Entry garden _____

Landscape lighting _____

Privacy from the street _____

Structures, such as fences, walls, brick pavers, etc. _____

OUTDOOR LIVING AREA (rear of the house):

How much time do you want to spend maintaining the landscape?

Minimal _____ Moderate _____ Quite a bit _____

What are your gardening interests? Describe preferences.

Vegetable garden _____

Perennial garden _____

Annual flowers _____

Rose garden _____

Small fruits (raspberries, strawberries, grapes, etc.)_____

Large fruits (apples, peaches, etc.) _____

What favorite plants would you like included in the design?_____

_____

_____

_____

_____

List any plants you do **not** want in your landscape: _____

_____

2-8 A family interest survey.

FAMILY INVENTORY SURVEY (continued)

What size groups do you anticipate entertaining? _____

    Patio _____ Deck _____ Gazebo _____

    Patio materials (brick pavers, flagstone, concrete, etc.) _____

    Permanent seating _____

Will you have a grill? _____

    Gas _____ Gas line from the house? _____

    Charcoal _____

Sink _____ Water _____ Electrical outlets _____ Storage _____

Swimming pool _____ Dressing facility _____ Storage _____

    Portable _____

    Permanent _____ Size _____ Shape _____

        Decking _____ Material _____

        Enclosure _____

            Lighting _____

Hot tub _____

Lawn Games _____

_____

SERVICE AREA:

Vegetable garden _____ Size _____

Compost bin _____ Cold frames _____

Greenhouse _____ Size _____

Lawn and garden tool storage _____ Size? _____

Dog run _____ Size _____ Dog house _____

Clothesline _____ Permanent _____ Portable _____

Garbage cans _____ Number _____ Preferred location _____

Play area for children _____

    Outdoor gym _____ Size _____

    Preferred surface material (sand, wood chips, grass, etc.) _____

    Shade desired _____

Other features you would like included with your landscape:

    Statuary _____

    Water features _____

            Fountain _____ Pool _____ Fish _____ Aquatic plants _____

    Bird features _____

            Feeder(s) _____ Bath(s) _____ House(s) _____

            Bird attracting plants _____

Other notes or comments: _____

_____

_____

_____

2-8 A family interest survey. (continued)

customer provides information on factors that affect the landscape project. Sometimes, it is helpful if the designer is present. On other occasions, the family can complete the survey as the designer analyzes the site. A third possibility is to let the family complete the survey at their leisure and return it to the designer before design work begins.

Through the use of the family inventory survey the designer can learn about the family. Information collected should include the number and ages of family members, family hobbies (i.e., baseball, gardening, badminton), and pets. Each of these things may influence the design. The gardening interests of the family should be determined. The designer should find out if the clients want a vegetable garden, annual garden, bulb garden, or other landscape features. The amount of time a client is willing to spend in the yard doing maintenance should be established. The level of entertainment planned by the family influences the size of the patio or deck. A pool or plenty of open lawn space for games may need to be incorporated into the design based on the client's wishes. The designer should ask if the client has any favorite plants he or she would like included in the landscape. They should also find out if there are any plants that should be avoided.

2-9 A family inventory survey would reveal a client's interest in having a feature such as a gazebo included in their landscape plan.

Presentation

Presentation is the step where the designer introduces the service or product that meets the customer's needs identified earlier in the sales process. The presentation should do three things. It should introduce the service or product the landscaper can provide to solve the landscape need. It should convince the customer that the plan suggested by the landscape company will work. Third, it should create a desire in the customer to buy the goods and services offered by the landscape company.

Supportive materials are extremely useful during the presentation. A ***portfolio*** of design work and photos of previous landscape projects can be shown to a customer. When the customer sees the landscaper's work, he or she can more easily determine if they will benefit. It is also helpful to provide a list of references or former customers. These materials add credibility to the designer's claims by showing the quality of the work performed. The landscaper also demonstrates an openness about the work performed. After viewing portfolio materials and contacting references, the customer feels more confident in the services he or she is buying.

During the presentation, it is likely the customer will want to discuss the cost of the landscape project. Rough figures for previous jobs can help to answer those questions. A truly accurate figure for the entire project is difficult to provide until the design is drawn.

The amount of money the customer is willing to invest in the landscape influences the design. Many people envision a beautiful landscape and are shocked to learn what their ideas cost to install. During these situations, it is up to the designer to reinforce the value of the service. It is also helpful for the designer to establish the customer's financial limits. Having openly discussed the budget for the landscape project, the designer can adjust the design work accordingly.

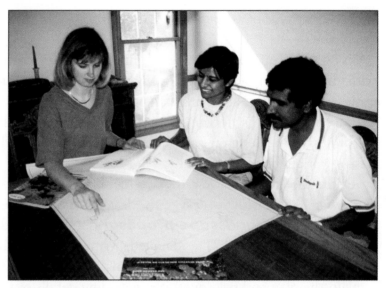

2-10. This designer is using portfolio materials to help the customer visualize landscape possibilities.

2-11. It is up to the designer to convince the customer he or she will receive high quality service for the price paid.

Closing

The *closing* of the landscape sale interview is the agreement between the customer and the designer to begin work on the design. Usually, this happens after the designer has reviewed the type of work the company has done and offered some ideas for the customer's landscape.

In the landscape industry, it is a common practice to complete the design work and meet with the customer again to go over the costs of installation. For the design itself, some designers may charge an hourly rate, while others may charge a flat fee. It is also a common practice to provide a free design if the landscape is installed by the designer's company. Regardless of the design fee structure, the customer should be asked to sign a contract for design work to be completed.

During a second interview, the designer meets with the customer to discuss the details of the design. Along with the design, the designer should present a prepared proposal for landscape services. A **landscape proposal** is a complete description of the materials and services to be provided. The detailed, written proposal helps the customer understand exactly what services and costs are being agreed upon. At this point, the designer can explain the plan and field questions regarding details of the design and installation costs. Adjustments to the landscape plans can be made, if necessary, to satisfy the customer. The next step in the sale is to obtain a signed contract for the construction of the landscape project. A **contract** is a legal document representing an agreement between two parties.

There are differing methods to close a landscape sale. In some cases, the designer may, in a straightforward manner, want to request that the customer buy their company's services. This method is simple and direct. An example is, "Would you like me to begin the design process for your new landscape?"

A second method is the assumed close. In this case, the designer takes for granted the customer is going to buy his or her services. This closing is common when the reputation of the landscape company precedes the sales interview. Sometimes, the customer will make comments early in the sales interview indicating that the designer's services will be purchased. In these situations, the designer may simply say, "When would you be available to meet again to go over the preliminary design work?"

A third closing strategy involves the summary of the sales interview. Major

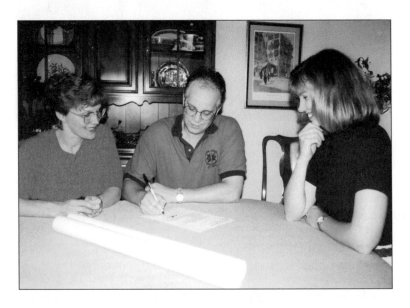

2-12. Signing a contract completes the sale.

AJB Landscapes, Inc.

February 28, 2009

LANDSCAPE PROPOSAL

Front Entry Walk and Courtyard:

• Remove and dispose of existing concrete front walk.

• Pour concrete to enlarge the front step to be surfaced in bullnosed pattern bluestone.

• Construct the front entry walk and courtyard out of patterned bluestone, as designed.

$11,780.00

Public Area Foundation Plantings:

• Remove and dispose of existing plant material that is dead or in decline.

• Prepare planting beds with premium blend compost.

• Install the following plant material:

3	Bigleaf Wintercreeper Euonymus	18"	15	Assorted Hosta	1 gal.
1	Winged Euonymus	36"	1	White Fringetree	6'
11	Dense Yew	30"	3	Cardinal Hydrangea	24"
1	Clump Linden	12'	1	European Black Alder	Transplant
5	Juddi Viburnum	30"	3	Miss Kim Lilac	30"
2	Canadian Hemlock	7'	1	River Birch	18'
3	Dwarf Fothergilla	24"	165 sq. ft.	Assorted Perennials	1 gal.
1	Shadblow Serviceberry	8'	655 sq. ft.	Pachysandra 'Green Carpet'	3" pot
3	'Green Velvet' Boxwood	18"			

$13,220.00

Outdoor Living Area Plantings:

• Prepare planting beds with a premium blend compost.

• Install following plant material:

1	Canadian Hemlock	7'	3	Dense Yew	30"
3	Tautoni Yew	24"	1	White Fringetree	6'
7	Winged Euonymus	36"	1	Bradford Callery Pear	3"
6	Dwarf Korean Lilac	24"	225 sq. ft.	Assorted Roses	1-3 gal.
7	Dwarf Fountain Grass	5 gal.	525 sq. ft.	Assorted Perennials	1 gal.
1	Honeylocust	6"	280 sq. ft.	Pachysandra 'Green Carpet'	3" pot

$11,595.00

Landscape Illumination:

• Illuminate the Alders, Shadblow, Linden, Honeylocust, and existing Honeylocust and Maple with halogen well fixtures.

• Illuminate the existing Honeylocust with four tree mounted halogen fixtures.

• Illuminate the front walk and courtyard with six copper walk fixtures.

• Power all fixtures with a 500 Watt photocell/timer transformer and a 300 Watt photocell/timer transformer.

$6, 560.00

Total $43,155.00

Respectfully submitted,

2-13. A landscape proposal.

AJB Landscapes, Inc.

February 28, 2009

LANDSCAPE CONTRACT

AJB Landscapes, Inc. agrees to furnish and install the items specified on order number 44908 dated February 14, 2009 in the sum of $43,155.00.

- - - Forty-Three Thousand One Hundred Fifty-Five and 00/100 dollars - - -

Payment is to be made as follows:

   $14,385.00   Down payment due with contract

   $14,385.00   Due at start up

   $14,385.00   Due upon completion

AJB Landscapes, Inc. shall not be responsible for "Acts of God" or any other conditions beyond their direct control but otherwise guarantees all material specified herein for a period of one year unless neglected by the purchasers.

Authorized Signature _____

AJB Landscapes, Inc.

Accepted _____

Date _____

2-14. A simple contract for work to be performed.

points of the sales presentation are restated by the designer. The summary may go something like this: "Let me summarize our discussion. Once I receive your family inventory survey, I will design a landscape plan that will be attractive, require low maintenance, and is functional. Two weeks from now, we will meet again to discuss details of the plan and make changes if you feel some are necessary. Also, at that time I will provide you with a proposal for installation costs."

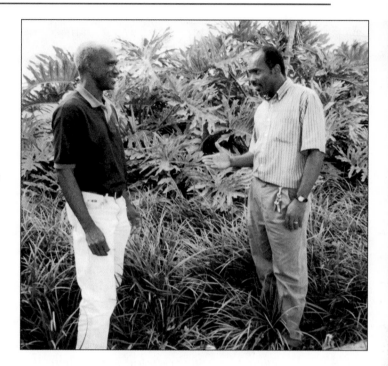

2-15. The follow-up helps to retain customer loyalty and to achieve future sales.

The Follow-Up

Throughout the landscape project, it is important to communicate with the customer. Remember, the designer is providing a service to the customer. The service being sold is not completed in one day. Often, landscape projects last several months. Continued contact with the customer ensures the wants and needs of the customer are met.

TIP: Follow-up after the sale is complete helps retain customer loyalty and to achieve future sales.

Follow-up after the sale is complete is equally important. This helps retain customer loyalty and to achieve future sales. Quality workmanship and follow-up procedures create new customers by referral and result in repeat customers. To create a positive influence and build a strong relationship with the customer, certain activities should occur:

- Work is completed as scheduled.
- Bills are handled in a timely fashion.
- Advice on plant care is given.
- Installation work is completed properly.
- The customer is frequently asked if he or she is satisfied with the work.
- Care is taken to avoid disturbing or damaging non-landscaped areas and features.

REVIEWING

MAIN IDEAS

Landscaping is a service industry including the design of landscape plans, the installation of new landscapes, and the maintenance of existing landscapes. The health of a landscape company depends on its ability to attract customers and sell them services. Usually, the designer is in the best position to make the sales for landscape services. The success of the designer often is determined by his or her understanding of the basic steps in the sales process.

Five steps identified in the sales process include preparation, the opening, the presentation, the closing, and the follow-up. Preparation involves planning for a meeting with the customer based on what is known at that time. The opening provides a chance for the customer and designer to get to know one another through open communication. In this step, the designer probes to learn more about the customer's needs and uses a family inventory survey as a tool. The presentation step is when the designer presents possible solutions for the customer's landscape needs. Use of portfolio materials is helpful during the presentation. At some point, the sales interview comes to a close with the signing of a contract for work. There are several methods to close a sale including the straightforward method, the assumed close, and the summary. The fifth step involves follow-up procedures demonstrating a concern for customer satisfaction. Follow-up procedures build customer loyalty and lead to future sales.

QUESTIONS

Answer the following questions using correct spelling and complete sentences.

1. What is a sale?

2. Why does the landscape designer often have the responsibility for conducting the sale?

3. What are the major steps of the sales process?

4. What are some ways landscapers can promote their business to attract customers?

5. Why is the opening critical in the sales process?

6. What is probing?

7. Why is the family inventory survey useful?

8. What takes place in the presentation portion of the sales interview?

9. What are three methods to close a sale?

10. What are some practices used in the follow-up sales step?

CHAPTER SELF-CHECK

Match the term with the correct definition. Write the letter by the term in the blank provided.

a. portfolio   d. presentation   g. communication
b. probing   e. sales   h. closing
c. opening   f. family inventory survey

_____1.   An exchange of goods or services at a price mutually agreed upon by the parties involved

_____2.   A form on which the customer provides written information on factors that affect the landscape project

_____3.   Design work and photos of previous work that can be shown to a customer

_____4.   The end of the landscape sale interview in which an agreement is reached between the customer and the designer

_____5.   The step where the designer introduces the service or product that meets the customer's needs identified earlier in the sales process

_____6.   Both individuals participate in exchanging information, which gives both parties an opportunity to get to know one another

_____7.   When the designer and customer first meet and begin to get to know one another

_____8.   A practice of thoroughly investigating a customer's wants, needs, and problems

EXPLORING

1. Role play a landscape sales interview in the classroom. Practice the five sales steps identified in this chapter. Arrange to have the interview videotaped so you can review your performance.

2. With the help of your teacher, identify a family that would like to have their house landscaped. Ask them to complete a family inventory survey that can be used in the design process.

CHAPTER 3

Analyzing the Landscape Site

OBJECTIVES

1 Identify steps in the landscape design process.

2 Describe equipment used in the drafting process.

3 Explain the purpose and components of a site analysis

TERMS

Ames lettering instrument
architect's scale
base plan
circle template
compass
computer assisted design
    (CAD)
contour lines
drawing paper
elevation view
engineer's scale

erasure shield
French curve
grade
hardpan
hardware
macroclimate
microclimate
native plant
ornamental plant
plan view
plat of survey

site analysis plan
software
soil structure
soil texture
subsoil
topography
topsoil
trash paper
video imaging

3-1. Analyzing the site is critical to a well-planned design.

IMAGINE being asked to develop a landscape design for a house. The owner has invited you to look at the property. You ask yourself "What am I going to look for? What is important to note before I begin the drafting work? How am I going to remember what I see?"

Skill in analyzing the site can be the difference between a great design and one that fails miserably. This is because landscape design is more than a pretty drawing. A landscape designer's work involves live plants, complex soil characteristics, climate extremes, and of course, people and their interactions with the landscape.

STEPS IN THE DESIGN PROCESS

Landscape design is a process. It involves an orderly approach to solve landscape problems. Landscape design can be simplified by following steps to reach a final plan. This book offers a step-by-step method in preparing landscape designs. The major steps are as follows:

1. Meet the customer
2. Have the customer complete a family inventory survey
3. Draw the base plan
4. Prepare a site analysis plan
5. Develop a goose egg plan
6. Establish bed patterns including patios, decks, and walks
7. Locate trees on the plan
8. Draw shrubs within planting beds by size and function
9. Locate perennials and ground covers
10. Assign desired textures and colors to the trees, shrubs, perennials, and ground covers
11. Select plants based on size, texture, color, and function determined in steps 7-10
12. Trace the plan on good quality vellum or use computer software
13. Label the plan
14. Price the plan

3-2. The landscaper must take the natural features of the site into account. (Courtesy, Church Landscape)

The design process begins with gathering information that is crucial for the design work. Client needs, as discussed in the previous chapter, are important. Also, preparation for the design work requires details, such as the dimensions of the house, the height of the windows, the size of the lot, orientation to North, etc.

One key to successful landscaping is to consider the features of the site and the surrounding area. You will need to study the property before any design takes place. Designers note site characteristics, such as the drainage of water, the slope of the land, soil conditions, existing vegetation, views to and from surrounding areas, existing structures, and climate. Knowing what the site has to offer helps the designer enhance the positive features and correct the negative ones.

THE BASE PLAN

The first drawing in the landscape design process involves a base plan. The **base plan** is an accurate representation of the house on the lot. This drawing can be on a large sheet of paper or entered into the computer. The base plan shows the plan view of the house as it sits within property lines. The **plan view** is a view from above looking down as opposed to a drawing of the front of a house known as the **elevation view**. The base plan should include property lines, easements, doors, windows, and existing hardscapes, such as sidewalks, driveways, and patios. When placing the base plan on paper, orient the house so that north is toward the top of the paper.

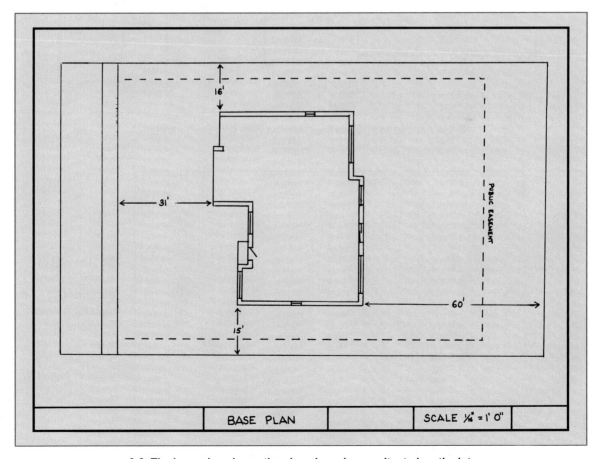

3-3. The base plan shows the plan view—house situated on the lot.

3-4. A house shown from the elevation view with the floor plan.

3-5. The plat of survey is a legal document indicating exact locations of physical structures on a piece of property.

Helpful tools in preparing the base plan are a plat of survey and house plans. A *plat of survey* is a legal document indicating the exact locations of physical structures on a piece of property and the exact dimensions of the property. It can be used for the proper placement of the house, property lines, and easements. A blue line copy of the house plans gives valuable information concerning the floor plan, room uses and sizes, and the locations and sizes of doors and windows. Visit the site to obtain exact measurements of features that may not be included on the plat of survey or the house plans, such as the driveway, patio, walks, and fences.

DRAFTING EQUIPMENT

Landscape designs may be produced with the simplest equipment or sophisticated computer technology. Whether low tech or high tech equipment is used, the needs of the customer and the principles of design must be followed in the design process.

COMPUTER ASSISTED DESIGN (CAD)

As the cost of technology continues to decrease and computers become simpler to use, more landscape designers will use them in their design work. The term *computer assisted design (CAD)* refers to the use of computer hardware and software to produce drawings. *Software* is the programs (instructions) which make the equipment function. *Hardware* describes the computer equipment. Hardware includes input devices which allow the designer to enter information into the computer. These devices may include a standard computer keyboard, mouse, pen plotter, and more.

TIP: One of the major advantages of CAD system is the ease with which designs can be edited to satisfy changes desired by the customer.

Video imaging is a technique that uses computer technology to superimpose a landscape design over a photograph of the customer's undeveloped landscape. Video imaging software may require a scanner, a special camera and input device, or a video input device. A

3-6. Landscape designs may be produced with video imaging using computer technology.

3-7. A CAD site plan with contours and design. (Courtesy, LANDCADD Division of Eagle Point Software)

computer specialist should be consulted when hardware is being selected for a video imaging system. Documentation on minimum hardware requirements is provided with the software by most CAD and video imaging software suppliers.

Designers need training and practice to master computer design systems. Learning how to use computer assisted design systems, however, does not make someone a landscape designer or landscape architect anymore than knowing how to use a calculator makes someone a mathematician. Knowing the fundamentals such as design principles, plant materials, grading and drainage, and hardscape materials are essential. A CAD system is a tool to help the landscape designer.

One of the major advantages of a CAD system is the ease with which designs can be edited to satisfy changes desired by the customer. It is particularly useful for making changes to large, complex designs. Changes to small, less complex designs seldom call for re-drawing the plan.

3-8. A CAD perspective view of a hole on a golf course. (Courtesy, LANDCADD Division of Eagle Point Software)

DRAWING THE PLAN

Many designers of residential landscapes prefer to draw plans by hand for several reasons. Designers often claim that the hand-drawn designs provide a personal touch that customers like. The drafting equipment needed is inexpensive. Many designers are comfortable with pencil and paper designs. In addition, customers of residential projects seldom require drastic changes to plans. Small changes can easily be made by hand.

A simple, low cost setup might include the following drafting equipment:

Drawing board—At least one side must be true and the surface must be smooth (minimum size 20" × 24"). It is the surface on which drafting paper is affixed.

T-square—The working edge of the T-square must be straight and 90 degrees to the edge of the drawing board. When drawing, hold the T-square firmly to the edge of the board. Use the top edge of the T-square to draw horizontal lines.

> **TIP:** Hold the T-square firmly to the edge of the board, and use the top edge of the T-square to draw horizontal lines.

Drawing paper—White vellum or tracing paper is commonly used. Drawing paper is translucent. Lines can be seen through the paper. Many sizes are available. Use the T-square to line up the top edge of the paper on the drawing board. It is important that the paper is square. Then, fasten the free

3-9. A CAD planting plan for a residential site. (Courtesy, LANDCADD Division of Eagle Point Software)

3-10. Attractive, functional landscape plans can be produced using low cost drafting equipment.

3-11. This designer uses trash paper on which she sketches ideas without marking the work she wants to save.

TIP: Keep your pencil sharp, and roll the pencil slowly between your thumb and forefinger to maintain uniform lines.

TIP: Pull the pencil across the paper while holding the pencil at a 60-degree angle to the paper.

TIP: Tip: Hold the triangle firmly on the top side of the T-square and use the edge to draw 90-, 60-, 45-, and 30-degree lines.

corners with 1 to 2 inch lengths of drafting tape. Smooth the paper from the center with your fingernails to avoid smudging the paper and secure the remaining corners. Check the squareness of the paper after it has been secured, and make adjustments if needed.

Trash paper—Often a buff color, this tracing paper is lightweight and inexpensive. The designer can sketch ideas on trash paper laid on top of the base plan without marking the quality tracing paper beneath.

Drafting tape—Drafting tape is used to secure drawing paper because it is less sticky than masking tape.

Drawing pencils—Select medium grade pencils for drawing: 3H, 2H, H, F, HB, and B. 3H grade pencils have harder lead than a B pencil and, thus, provide a lighter line. HB pencils have a medium softness and can be used effectively for most drawing. Always keep your pencil sharp to maintain uniform lines. Hold the pencil at a 60-degree angle to the paper. Another tip is to pull the pencil across the paper rather than pushing the pencil. Roll the pencil slowly between your thumb and forefinger. Rolling the pencil helps to maintain a uniform line.

Triangles—Two triangles commonly used are the 45-degree triangle and the 30-degree _ 60-degree triangle. Hold the triangle firmly on the top side of the T-square and use the edge to draw 90-, 60-, 45-, and 30-degree lines. Be sure to hold the T-square snug to the side of the drawing board as you draw.

Eraser and erasure shield—Use these tools to remove unwanted lines. The ***erasure shield*** is a thin metal plate used to protect lines while erasing. To avoid a messy, smudged drawing think about every line before it is drawn and erase completely when necessary.

Scale—Two types of scales are used in landscape design work. The most commonly used is the architect's scale. The ***architect's scale*** can easily be used for scale measurements of 1/16", 1/8", and 1/4". It is also preferred because the homeowner can use a ruler to read the plan. The other scale used is the engineer's scale. The **engineer's scale** is divided by tenths and is used to produce 1/10, 1/20, 1/50, 1/100 scale drawings. It is useful to have an engineer's scale on hand to convert plat of survey measurements, normally drawn using an engineer's scale, to the base

> **TIP:** Tip: Select a scale that will provide the largest image possible on the tracing paper and still be attractive.

plan. Engineer's scales are used in large-scale projects drawn by landscape architects. Never use the edge of the scale to draw lines.

Circle template—This instrument is used as a guide to draw circles and curves on the landscape plan.

Compass—The compass is a tool used to make large circles and curves not possible when using the circle template.

French curves—Irregular curves can be drawn with the French curve.

Ames lettering instrument—The Ames lettering instrument is used to draw light parallel guidelines for lettering. The space between the lines can be adjusted depending on the size of letters desired. Place a well-sharpened pencil in a hole and slide the lettering instrument along the top edge of the T-square. Move the pencil to the next hole and repeat the process.

Drawing a Plan to Scale

Base plan drawings are made to scale. Scale is a measure of dimensions. Scale allows the designer to shrink the house, the lot, and the landscape plan to a size that is manageable and will fit on a piece of paper. The preferred scale for most landscape design work is 1/8, 1/10, or 1/4 inch. In the case of 1/8 scale, 1/8 of an inch on the plan represents 1 foot at the site. Another way to express this is one inch on the plan is equal to 8 feet at the site (1 inch equals 8 x 1/8 or 8/8s). By following a strict 1/8 inch scale all measurements will be accurate.

Select a scale that will provide the largest image possible on the tracing paper and still be attractive. Most normal size lots can be drawn at 1/8 scale. Smaller lots can be drawn larger at 1/4 scale.

3-12. Scale is a measure of dimensions. One foot in the landscape would be drawn 1/8 of an inch wide on paper at 1/8 inch scale.

Lots that cannot fit on a standard piece of tracing paper at 1/8 inch scale must be drawn at a smaller scale. Scales of 1/16, 1/10, and 1/20 are used in order to fit larger properties on standard size paper. Of course, plans drawn at larger scales, such as 1/8 and 1/4, are easier to read than plans drawn at 1/16 scale.

SITE ANALYSIS

It is important for the designer to visit and study the landscape site and to record observations. Often an initial site analysis is conducted during the same visit at which the client is asked to complete the family inventory survey. Several visits often reveal information that might be overlooked with just one visit. Visits at different times of the day and under different weather conditions are helpful. Materials needed during these visits might include a clipboard, pencil, 100' measuring tape, camera, and an accurate drawing of the house and the lot. Sometimes, notes can be recorded on a duplicate of the plat of survey. Photographs taken of the site are great as a reference during the design process.

TIP: Make notes on the site analysis regarding the orientation of the house, the lay of the land, soil, existing vegetation, natural features, climate, and views.

Prior to the on-site visit, contact the utility locating service to mark existing utility lines. Make notes as to where the lines run. The utility lines could influence where certain design elements, such as large trees, ponds, and patios are located.

Carefully transfer observations made during the visits to a site analysis plan. The **site analysis plan** is a piece of paper with an accurate sketch of the house and lot on which

3-13. New home construction generates landscape work and the housing sites call for careful analysis. (Courtesy, Natural Resources Conservation Service)

observations are recorded. Trace the base plan through to the site analysis paper. The site analysis plan can then be referred to throughout the design process.

Some of the features to be noted on a site analysis plan follow.

ORIENTATION OF THE HOUSE

Note on the site analysis plan the orientation of the house on the lot. Knowing which direction is north is vital to designing a functional plan. The exposure of walls to the sun's rays influences plantings. The orientation of the house is a factor in locating activity areas. Orientation of the house also has tremendous impact on plant selection and location due to shade requirements or exposure to wind.

THE LAY OF THE LAND

The lay of the land in terms of hills, valleys, and flat areas is referred to as *topography*. Note on the site analysis plan the topography of the site to be landscaped. This can be done with the

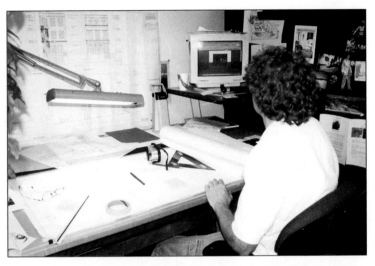
3-14. This designer refers to photographs taken with a digital camera during the site analysis while he prepares the design at his drawing

3-15. It is important for the designer to make an on-site visit to gather information.

use of arrows and written notes. It is also helpful to obtain plans from the developer or soil survey agencies that show the topography of the site with contour lines. Surveyors use **contour lines** to represent the vertical rise or fall of the land. Each line represents a certain elevation. The lines are labeled in a break in the line or on the high side of the contour. Each contour line connects all of the points of equal elevation on the map. Steep slopes are shown by closely spaced lines. Gentle slopes are identified by more widely spaced lines.

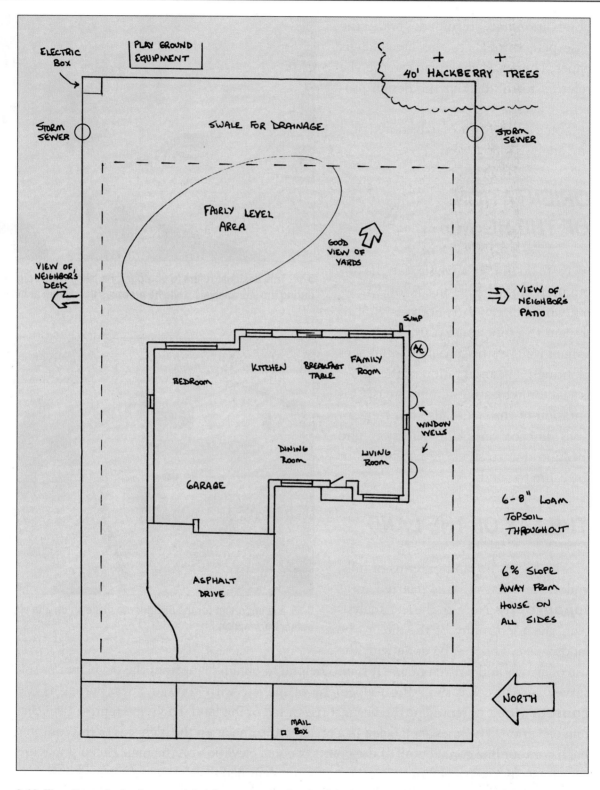

3-16. The site analysis plan consists of an accurate sketch of the house and lot on which observations are recorded.

The natural **grade**, or slope, of the land is usually changed to some extent when a home is built. Changing the grade usually results in a change to the natural drainage patterns. If not addressed, the outcome can be flooded basements. Another problem that can arise is poorly drained soils. Most plants require well-drained soils to survive. Poorly drained soils limit the types of plants that can be grown.

Study the grade of the land surrounding the house. Determine the drainage patterns. Ask yourself questions regarding the drainage. Does water flow quickly away from the structure? Are there areas on the lot where water stands after a rainfall? Do the neighboring properties present a drainage problem? Will drainage tile or regrading be required?

Heavy construction equipment damages soil structure. This is especially true when wet soils are involved. Often a **hardpan** or densely compacted layer of soil under the soil surface results. Hardpans inhibit the flow of water through the soil. They can also inhibit root growth. You will find that many construction companies have little knowledge or concern for soil and the importance of soil for healthy plant growth.

3-17. Measure the height and width of windows during the site analysis.

3-18. Poor drainage can be improved with the installation of drain tile. (Courtesy, Eddie Seagle, Abraham Baldwin Agricultural College)

3-19. Heavy equipment used in construction can seriously damage soil structure and drainage patterns.

3-20. Construction equipment has compacted this soil greatly slowing water drainage.

One goal of landscaping is to limit changes to the natural land form and slope of the property so the new landscape remains consistent with the surrounding properties. Drastic changes to the site can make the property "stick out like a sore thumb." Note on the site analysis features of the land, such as a large flat area, a rock outcrop, or estimated percent of slope. These notes will influence the design of the three major landscape areas addressed in later chapters.

In different parts of the country, the natural appearance of the terrain differs. For example, the Northeastern States tend to be wooded and hilly, plains and woodlands dominate the Midwestern States, and the Rocky Mountain States are rocky and dry. Within each region, there are a variety of terrains. Wherever the house may be located, the landscape should be designed to give the house the appearance that it belongs with the landscape. Well-designed landscapes provide a natural setting for the structures. As the site is analyzed, observe the predominate land form in the region and in the area surrounding the house.

3-21. Note the land form where the house is located.

SOIL

The soil found on the landscape site provides plants with water, air, nutrients, and support. These characteristics, important to plant growth, vary with the type of soil. Both soil

3-22. Components of a good soil.

3-23. Soil texture is the proportion of sand, silt, and clay particles in the soil.

texture and soil structure influence the availability of water, air, and nutrients for plant growth. **Soil texture** is the proportion of different sized particles in the soil described as sand, silt, and clay. **Soil structure** is the arrangement of soil aggregates in the soil. Soil with poor drainage, low nutrient-holding ability, and poor water-holding ability can lead to the death of the plants. Use this information to select plants based on the soil conditions or to amend the soil.

The soil found near the surface, known as the **topsoil**, is most valued for healthy plant growth. Depending on the location in the country, the topsoil may be a few inches to several

3-24. The wind toppled this pin oak (*Quercus palustris*) revealing the majority of the tree's roots were growing within the top 2 feet of soil.

feet deep. Most plant roots are found in the top two feet of soil and benefit from a thick top-soil layer. It is in the topsoil layer that the best combination of nutrients, air, and moisture for plant growth is found. Even large trees have most of their roots in the top two feet of soil. The topsoil is usually dark in color due to a high content of organic matter. Organic matter consists of decomposed and partially decomposed plants and animals.

Table 3-1. Characteristics of the Various Soil Classes

Soil Property	Sand	Silt Loam	Clay
Looseness	Good	Fair	Poor
Air Space	Good	Fair to Good	Poor
Drainage	Good	Fair to Good	Poor
Tendency to Form Clods	Poor	Fair	Good
Ease of Working	Good	Fair to Good	Poor
Moisture Holding Ability	Poor	Fair to Good	Good
Fertility	Poor	Fair to Good	Fair to Good

Below the topsoil is a lighter colored layer of soil known as the **subsoil**. Subsoil can vary in color based on soil series, from yellow to brown to red. The subsoil is considered of much lower quality than topsoil for growing plants. It lacks a good combination of nutrients, air exchange, and moisture, and the amount of organic matter is very low.

Grading of soil around house construction sites disturbs the layers of soils. A common practice is to remove the topsoil, construct the home, and return the topsoil when construction is completed. Although good in theory, it often results in the damage to soil structure and the complex relationships between the soil layers. As is often the case, a homeowner is left with a thin layer of top-soil in which to grow their plants. Some of the same problems can occur if the landscaping project itself calls for the moving of large amounts of soil.

Note on the site analysis plan the type of soil. Determine the texture of the soil and the depth of the topsoil and record this information on the plan. It is also a good idea to have the soil tested by a university

3-25. This topsoil is dark in color due to a high percentage of organic matter.

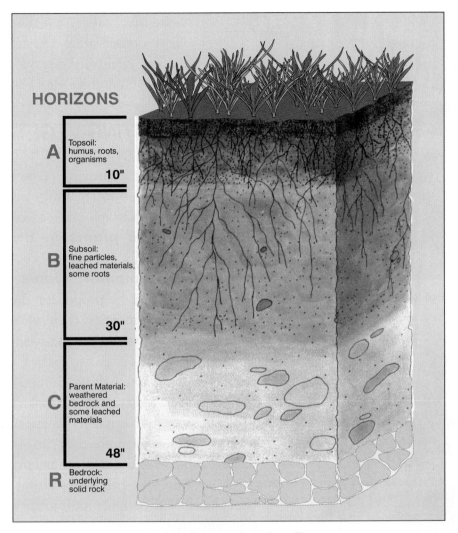

HORIZONS

A Topsoil: humus, roots, organisms
10"

B Subsoil: fine particles, leached materials, some roots
30"

C Parent Material: weathered bedrock and some leached materials
48"

R Bedrock: underlying solid rock

3-26. A diagram of a soil profile.

3-27. A common construction practice by developers is to remove and stockpile topsoil until work is complete.

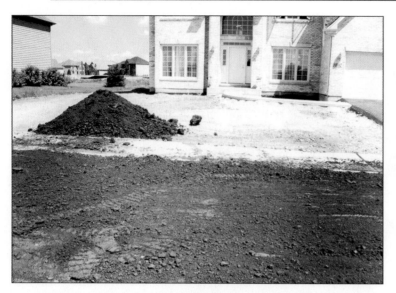

3-28. Topsoil is returned to a site and spread over the subsoil.

3-29. Developers have placed fencing below the drip line of this existing Green ash (*Fraxinus pennsylvanica*) to protect the tree and its roots during construction.

extension office, the United States Soil Conservation Department, or a private soil-testing service for nutrient levels and textural classification.

EXISTING VEGETATION

Existing vegetation includes native plants or ornamental plants found in the landscape prior to construction. **Native plants** are those growing naturally, not introduced by people. **Ornamental plants** are those planted by people for the attractive characteristics they possess. Ornamental plants often are not native to the area. Many landscape plants grown in the United States were imported from Asia or Europe. Determine the value of existing plants and make note on the site analysis plan. Native plants are often valued for the natural appearance they can give to a landscape. Sometimes, existing ornamental trees and shrubs are large or especially beautiful and cannot be replaced. The designer must judge whether it is cost effective to save the existing plants and whether the plants fit into the design. In some cases, the recommendation is to transplant existing vegetation from one part of the site to another.

Inspect existing plants to determine their value. Identify the plants. Some plant species have greater ornamental value than others. Correct identification will reveal the potential size of the plant, health problems, and other attributes related to plant quality. The age of the existing plant is important. Older, more mature plants may be in decline. Consider the shape and form of the plants. One-sided or oddly shaped plants are not as valuable as full, symmetrical plants.

Construction crews must be careful not to disturb drainage patterns or compact soil if existing vegetation is to be preserved. Native plants often die within a few years if not protected from construction traffic or from changes in drainage patterns. A good example involves old oak trees in the Midwest. People pay top dollar for a lot with large oak trees on which to build their home. Construction traffic compacts the soil around the tree roots, roots are cut when installing basements and utilities, and the grade is altered affecting drainage patterns. Years after the home is completed, the homeowners are left wondering why their beautiful trees are dying.

3-30. The oak trees in this photograph are dying as a result of damage to the root zone during construction of the house.

NATURAL FEATURES

Rocks, earth, and water found on the site are considered natural features. When worked into the designed landscape, they add to the visual appeal. While conducting the site analysis, determine which natural features have value and are to be preserved. The challenge in the design process is to incorporate these features into the plan without losing their natural appearance. Avoid any changes to the site that destroy the natural character of the land.

CLIMATE

Climate greatly influences the landscape design and plant selection. Climate is broken down into two categories, macroclimate and microclimate. **Macroclimate** concerns the temperature, precipitation, humidity, and wind over large areas or regions. **Microclimate** is the temperature, precipitation, humidity, and wind on the landscape site.

Research on the macroclimate is extremely helpful in the landscape design process. Note the average temperatures in summer and winter for the region. The high and low temperatures determine which plants can be grown based on their ability to withstand heat and cold. The summer high temperatures play a role in determining how best to achieve a comfort level for the owners. The amount of annual precipitation also influences the selection of plant materials and decisions on the need for an irrigation system. Plants grown in regions

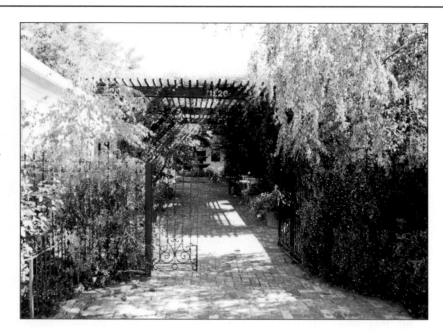

3-31. The walls enclosing this courtyard and the arbor influence the microclimate and the type of plants that can be grown.

with high humidity tend to have more disease problems than those in dryer climates. Also, note on the site analysis the prevailing wind direction. The landscape can be designed to take advantage of cool summer breezes and to block cold winter winds.

The microclimate is influenced by buildings, plants, and landscape structures. Each of these or a combination of these can alter the typical macroclimate conditions. For example, a planting area surrounded on two or three sides by the walls of a building often allows for the planting and survival of plants adapted to warmer climates. The walls protect the plant from freezing winds and cold temperatures.

VIEWS

Study and make note on the site analysis plan views to and from the landscape site. Those living in a house will frequently look away from their property to the surrounding areas. If some views are particularly attractive, make note of them. Views worth maintaining might include golf courses, nearby woods, mountains or bodies of water, and well-maintained land-

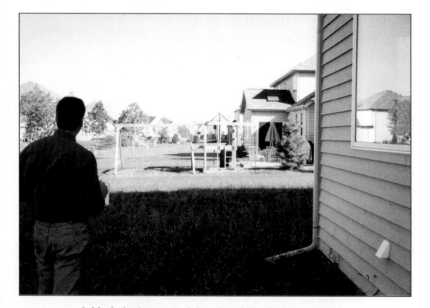

3-32. A designer studying the views from a property.

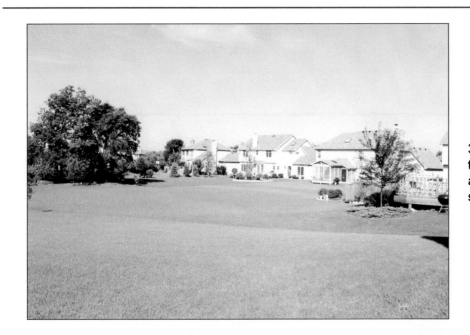

3-33. The view across these backyards is attractive and is one that should be preserved.

scapes. These views can add to the value of the property and to the pleasure of the owners. Other views may be eyesores, such as a parking lot, a well-traveled road or expressway, or even a neighbor's yard.

The other major views to consider are those from off the property. People generally approach the public area of the house in one or two directions. Note on the site analysis plan these directions so the view of the home can be enhanced. In other cases, views from off the property may not be welcome to the homeowner. Maybe a neighbor's deck is in line of sight with a large window or the owner's own deck. Public traffic that has open views of the back-yard living area may need to be screened to maintain the owner's privacy.

3-34. Some views are not attractive, such as this cluttered yard.

REVIEWING

MAIN IDEAS

Landscape design is a process. It involves an orderly approach to solve landscape problems. Landscape design can be simplified by following a step-by-step method in preparing landscape designs.

The design process begins with the gathering of information from the client and the site. The first drawing is the base plan showing the house as it is situated on the lot. This is drawn to scale, usually 1/8 or 1/4 inch equals one foot. Designers draw plans using simple equipment or computer assisted design (CAD) systems. The base plan is then used as a guide for the site analysis plan.

The site analysis plan is a record of observations made on a piece of paper with an accurate sketch of the house and lot. The information recorded on the site analysis plan is obtained during visits to the site. Some observations to be recorded are the grade or slope of the land, which affects drainage of water; soil type and quality, which influences plant growth and water drainage; and existing vegetation. Occasionally, it is worthwhile to try to save plants on the site during the construction process. Also noted on the site analysis survey are natural features, the macroclimate and microclimate, and good and poor views.

QUESTIONS

Answer the following questions using correct spelling and complete sentences.

1. What are the steps in the design process as identified in this chapter?

2. What is the base plan?

3. What are the advantages and disadvantages to drawing a landscape plan by hand?

4. What are the advantages and disadvantages of using computer assisted design equipment?

5. What is the site analysis plan?

6. Why is a site analysis plan important?

7. What should be noted on a site analysis plan?

8. Why is the grade around a house important?

9. What are the soil characteristics that should be noted?

10. What notes should be recorded in terms of existing vegetation?

11. How do macroclimate and microclimate differ?

12. Why are views to and from a landscape site important?

CHAPTER SELF-CHECK

Match the term with the correct definition. Write the letter by the term in the blank provided.

a. topsoil   e. scale   i. plat of survey
b. soil texture   f. T-square   j. grade
c. site analysis plan   g. plan view   k. base plan
d. microclimate   h. ornamental plants   l. drawing paper

_____1. Planted by people for the attractive characteristics they possess

_____2. A piece of drafting equipment held firmly to the drafting board and used to draw horizontal lines

_____3. A piece of paper with an accurate sketch of the house and lot on which observations are recorded

_____4. The proportions of sand, silt, and clay particles in the soil

_____5. The drawing of the plan view of the home oriented on the lot

_____6. The soil found near the surface

_____7. The slope of the land

_____8. A view of the house and landscape from above looking down

_____9. A legal document indicating the exact locations of physical structures on a piece of property and the exact dimensions of the property

_____10. A measure of dimensions

_____11. Translucent white vellum or tracing paper used for drafting landscape plans

_____12. The temperature, precipitation, humidity, and wind on the landscape site

EXPLORING

1. Select a house in need of a landscape design. Obtain a plat of survey for the house and visit the site for additional measurements. Use the information collected to draw a base plan from the plan view. Practice the drafting tips discussed in this chapter.

2. Go to the house site identified in Exploring Activity 1, and make observations related to the grade, soil characteristics, climate, natural features, and views. Using the base plan, trace the house and lot onto another sheet of paper. This will serve as the site analysis plan. Record your observations on the site analysis plan. You may want to use colored markers to represent different observations.

Designing the Landscape

TERMS

corner planting
deck
doorway planting
enclosures
entry garden

focal point
garden accessory
high interest planting
outdoor living area
patios

private area
public area
service area

4-1. This house appears to belong in the landscape. (Courtesy, Church Landscape)

IF you were to ask 100 artists to paint the same view of a street scene, would any two of the paintings be the same? It is doubtful. Each artist views the scene differently. The colors they use would vary. Their brush strokes would differ. Even the painting style (modern art, impressionist, etc.) would differ. Is it possible then that all 100 of the paintings would be attractive? Of course, it would be possible.

The same holds true in designing the landscape. Each landscape design project has multiple solutions to the design. As you design your landscapes, do not worry about the design being perfect. Follow the guidelines in this book and do your best to provide a functional and attractive landscape plan for the homeowner.

THE PUBLIC AREA

4-2. The home landscape has three main areas.

Before work with the pencil and paper begins, it helps to have a good understanding of landscape areas to be designed. The good residential landscape design has three main areas: the public area, the outdoor living area, and the service area. Understanding the purpose of each area aids the designer in creating a landscape plan that will meet the needs of the customer. Different functions or activities are designated to occur in each of these areas.

THE PUBLIC AREA

The **public area** is the portion of the property that is in full view of the public. It includes the area between the house and the road. It provides people their first impression of the house. For that reason, the public area is designed with the appearance of the house in mind. In the cinema, you often see one or two star actors. The stars are surrounded by a supporting cast of many other actors. In a similar way, the house is the star of the public area, surrounded by a supporting cast of landscape elements (trees, shrubs, etc.). In the movies, the supporting cast never outshines the star. In the landscape, the house should outshine all landscape elements.

> **TIP:** Design landscapes to improve the appearance of the house and to focus attention on the front door.

4-3. A little color helps draw the viewer's attention to the focal point of the landscape, the front door.

Design the public area so people passing by look at and appreciate the house. A well-designed landscape improves the appearance of the house and focuses attention on the front door. The front door is the most important aspect of the public area. The front door is the ***focal point***, or point of emphasis, of a well-designed landscape. The focal point captures the attention of the viewer.

Keep three main goals in mind as you design the public area for a house:

1. Soften the architectural lines of the house.

2. Frame the house with trees.

3. Maintain open lawn areas.

Architectural Features

Houses are artificial structures placed in natural settings. Standing alone, they appear rigid. The lines produced by the architecture of the house are straight. Vertical lines created at the corners of houses are particularly harsh in appearance. Make it a priority to design the public area so the sharp architectural lines are softened with plant materials.

Study the architecture of the house to be landscaped. Note the dominant architectural lines. Consider the masses of the house. It is sometimes helpful to sketch the house in the elevation view. Properly locate the windows, doors, and porches on the drawing. Then, indicate the dominant lines and masses on the sketch with colored pencils.

> **TIP:** Repeat the dominant lines of the house by using plant materials that have similar lines.

The dominant lines of the house should be repeated in the plant materials. Select trees and shrubs

4-4. The house should outshine all landscape elements.

4-5. The vertical lines of this house need to be softened with plantings.

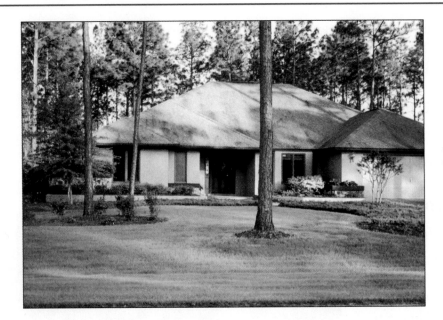

4-6. Select trees and shrubs that repeat the dominant lines of the house.

with horizontal branching habits if the house has dominant horizontal lines. Houses with dominant pyramidal forms, such as peaks, call for trees with pyramidal growth habits. Limit the use of trees with pyramidal growth habits in the public area to houses with pyramidal forms. This practice supports the goal to have the house appear that it belongs with its surroundings.

The dominant architectural masses of the house contribute to visual balance or imbalance of the house. Study the masses and determine how proper placement and massing of plant materials can achieve better balance. Strive to design landscape plantings that repeat the architectural masses at the end of the house opposite of the planting. For example, the right side of the house might appear as a large blocky mass. In this case, a large blocky mass

4-7. Repeat the architectural masses of the house at the opposite side of the house with masses of plant materials.

of plants should be installed to the left side of the house. This reversal of location promotes a balanced view.

Architectural detail of the house influences the landscape design. Different-sized windows, randomly located shutters, wrought iron railings, roof supports, and changes in building materials and colors lead to a busy appearance. When the house has abundant architectural details, avoid adding to the visual confusion. Design simple plantings with neutral green colors and rounded forms. Houses with equal-sized, evenly spaced windows and little detailing permit greater variety in the landscape plantings.

4-8. Design simple plantings when the house has abundant architectural details.

Four elements that make up the public area are 1) walks, driveways, and parking areas; 2) tree plantings; 3) shrub plantings; and 4) lawn or ground cover areas. Together, the elements of the public area contribute to a functional and attractive landscape.

Walks, Driveways, and Parking Areas

The walks and driveway are important considerations in the design process. They need to be functional, permitting

TIP: Design entry walks to follow a direct line and be wide enough for two people to walk side by side.

4-9. Walks and drives make up one element of the public area. (Courtesy, R.S. Hursthouse & Associates, Inc.)

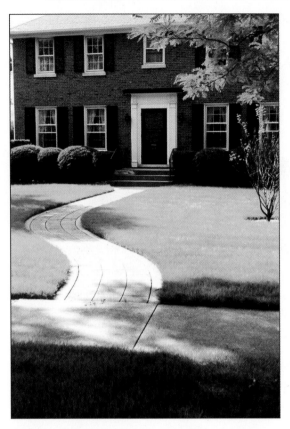

4-10. Avoid designing walks that divide the lawn area or that snake through the lawn.

easy access to the house. Well-designed walks and drives appear to blend into the landscape. Poorly designed walks and drives draw attention away from the house.

The entry walk leads guests to the front door. Therefore, it should follow a direct line and be wide enough for two people to walk side by side. Careful design prevents the walk from attracting the attention of the viewer. Sometimes people try to get "fancy" with their entry walk by making it serpentine through the front lawn. The unusual shape of that type of walk actually calls attention to itself. Also, walks that bisect the lawn take away from the overall appearance of the house. Lawns that are undivided give a more spacious appearance and provide an attractive setting for the home. The best walk design is one that parallels the front of the house and connects with the driveway.

Large expansive driveways and circle drives can draw attention from the home. These drives often dominate the view of the landscape by their size alone. Design the driveway so it will meet the needs of the customer without being excessive. A driveway for a

4-11. Here is a driveway that also serves as an entry walk.

single car should be a minimum 10 feet wide. A driveway for two cars should be 18 feet wide. Driveways that also serve as a walk, connecting the entry to the street, should be 11 feet, 8 inches wide. Circle drives need to be 14 to 18 feet wide depending on the curve.

The Role of Trees

Trees play many roles in the landscape. In the public area, well-positioned trees frame the house much as a picture frame frames the picture. Most people view the house at roughly a 30- to 45-degree angle. Therefore, locate trees so they will frame the house at a 30- to 45-degree angle from the street. Refer to the site analysis plan for the primary direction of traffic passing the front of the house. Sometimes, the house cannot be framed from more than one direction. In those cases, choose the direction from which most people will view the house.

The sizes of the framing trees are also important. Select large trees whose mature size will match the size of the house. For instance, a two-story house requires larger trees for effective

4-12. The earth tones of this gravel driveway provide a natural appearance to the landscape.

TIP: Position trees to frame the house, much as a picture frame frames the picture.

4-13. Frame the house with trees at a 30- to 45-degree angle from the street.

4-14. This house has been framed with trees.

4-15. Within only ten years these poorly placed trees have screened the view of the house and its front door.

framing than a single-story house. Trees in scale with the house help to balance the overall view. Also, select trees that have growth habits that repeat the dominant lines of the house.

Trees have other functions in the public area. They can provide shade in the summer. They can also be used to mask or screen awkward architectural features. For example, a tree could be used to screen a point where brick color changed slightly as the result of an addition to the house. Other examples of awkward features include a large roof mounted antenna, a chimney, an uneven roof line, or a satellite dish. However, trees should not block the signals to a satellite dish.

Shrub Plantings

Shrubs are used in the public area to tie the house to the landscape. They help to soften the vertical lines of a house and hide the foundation. Softening of architectural lines can be accomplished by placing shrubs at the foundation of the house. Use foundation plants at the corners of the house and at the doorway. They are also helpful in hiding the foundation walls or in breaking up a broad expanse of wall. Because evergreen plants lend color to the landscape throughout the year, they often work well as foundation plants. However, deciduous plants also work effectively.

Select foundation plants that have natural forms that will complement the architectural style of the house. Plants with natural, open forms soften architectural lines. A common mistake is the failure to consider the mature size of the plants used. As a result, the home-owner is forced to prune the plants frequently to prevent them from covering windows,

4-16. Shrubs are used in the public area to tie the house to the landscape. (Courtesy, Church Landscape)

walks, and doors. The resulting appearance is a series of plants pruned into tight, geometric shapes that do little to soften architectural lines. Avoid this mistake by drawing plants at their mature size on the landscape plan.

Severe pruning of foundation plants contributes to another common mistake. Many people share a mistaken belief that plants pruned into green meatballs, poodle bushes, and other unnatural shapes improve the appearance of the house. These do not belong in the public area. Their unusual shapes grab the viewer's attention from the house.

4-17. Plants pruned in unnatural shapes do not belong in the public area.

The severe pruning needed to maintain the shapes also places stress on the plants by reducing total leaf-surface area.

If the house has wide overhangs, locate the plants at least one foot beyond the drip line of the house. Plants located beneath the overhangs often do not get enough light or water.

TIP: Select plants for corner plantings that will not grow taller than two-thirds the distance from the ground to the eaves.

Corner Plantings

Special attention needs to be given to plants placed at the corners of the house. These plants are referred to as ***corner plantings***. Use plants with rounded forms, and arrange them in group plantings. The grouping should consist of several different plant species that complement one another. It is a good practice to select plants for corner plantings that will not grow taller than two-thirds the distance from the ground to the eaves.

4-18. Select plants for corner plantings that will not grow taller than two-thirds the distance from the ground to the eaves.

Overhead drawing of a corner planting

2/3

4-19. A small tree has been used in the corner planting of this 2-story house.

Selecting and placing plants that cause the viewer's eye to step down from the tallest plant to the shortest plant is an effective technique. Corner plantings contribute greatly to the overall appearance of the house. They help unite the house with the landscape. This is accomplished by softening of the harsh vertical lines created by the corners of the house. A well-done corner planting provides a scene whereby the house blends into its natural surroundings. Corner plantings hide the foundation of the house. The stepping down from the tallest plants also leads the viewer's attention to the front door.

Doorway Plantings

Another important planting arrangement, known as the **doorway plantings**, is located on either side of the entry door. These plantings may be identical if the architecture of the house has formal balance. Most houses, however, have informal or asymmetrical balance. In the case of houses with asymmetrical architecture, use different plantings on either side of the doorway.

Use shorter plants for doorway plantings. The height of the plants is determined by following a line from the threshold of the door to a point at the corners of the house that is two-thirds the distance from the ground to the eaves. Choose plants that have a mature height at or below this line. The doorway plants are usually no taller than one-fourth to one-third the distance from the ground to the eaves. Placing of the taller plants at the corners and shorter plants at the doorway has the

4-20. How well do the plantings at this house tie it to the natural surroundings?

4-21. Shorter plants near the doorway draw the eye toward the door of this North Carolina landscape.

4-22. The doorway plants are usually no taller than one-fourth to one-third the distance from the ground to the eaves.

4-23. The use of plant material and hardscape help to draw the viewer's eye to the door of this house.

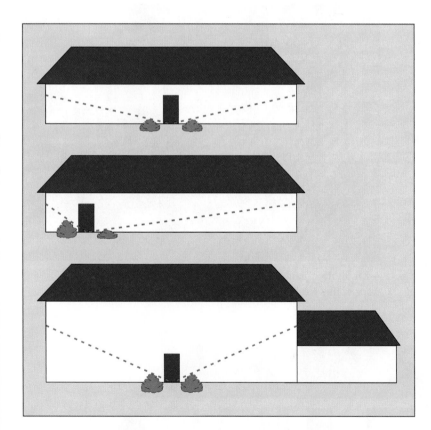

4-24. The height of corner and doorway plants can be determined by drawing a line from the point two-thirds the distance from the ground to the eaves at each corner to a point at the center of the threshold.

visual effect of drawing the viewer's eye toward the door. The outline of the corner and doorway plants sloping to the door draws the attention of the eye inward.

Another way to draw attention to the door is to use specimen plants. Specimen plants, due to their high visual quality, help pull the viewer's eye toward the door. They also provide high visual interest to visitors as they approach the doorway. Additional interest can be created for visitors with the use of entry gardens. An **entry garden** consists of plantings at the entrance of the house that are more developed than a typical doorway planting. The space of the entry garden can be established with a low fence, wall, or hedge. Plantings and garden accessories are placed within the defined space. The fence or hedge also plays a role in screening the view of the high interest plantings from passerbys on the street, whose attention should be drawn to the door.

TIP: Avoid dividing the lawn with walks, drives, and island plantings.

4-25. A white picket fence goes well with the architecture of this house and effectively creates space for a small entry garden.

Lawn Areas

Lawn or grass areas unite all elements of the public area. The lawn also provides a broad expansive setting for the house. These qualities improve the overall appearance of the landscape and the house. It is important to maintain a large unbroken expanse of lawn area. Avoid dividing the lawn with walks, drives, and island plantings. Place all shrubs in planting beds. Shrubs scattered throughout the lawn create a design that appears unorganized.

4-26. The lawn serves to unite all elements of the public area and provides a broad expansive setting to the house.

THE OUTDOOR LIVING AREA

The outdoor living area is designed differently than the public area for several reasons. The **outdoor living area** includes all the property to the rear of the house except the service area. It is out of sight of the public. For this reason, some landscapers call this area the **private area**. Views in the outdoor living area tend to be away from the house.

4-27. The outdoor living area is designed with games and entertainment in mind.

Therefore, the house is not the focus of attention. Instead, the design of the outdoor living area focuses on utility and beauty. The outdoor living area is designed with the family's gardening interests and entertainment activities taken into consideration. Several design elements satisfy the needs and interests of the family. They include the following:

- **Enclosures**—including fences, walls, or plants create walls for the outdoor living room.

- **Surfaced areas**—such as walks, paths, sitting areas, patios, and decks comprise one element of the outdoor living area.

- **Plantings**—shrubs, trees, perennials, annuals, and ground covers enhance the appearance of the outdoor living area.

- **Garden accessories**—used to add interest include sculptures, pools, fountains, rocks, furniture, and lighting.

The outdoor living area has grown in importance over the years. More people are spending a greater proportion of their leisure time to the rear of the house. This trend has resulted in a greater desire from customers to landscape their outdoor living area. The lifestyle of the customer, whether it is entertaining guests or providing room for the play of children, calls for well-designed outdoor living space.

Consider the outdoor living area as an extension of the indoor living space. The landscape is a room. Trees and the sky function as the ceiling. Plants and fences serve as the walls. The ground is the floor. The space of the outdoor living area can be divided into sub-spaces, with each space designed with different activities in mind.

The Ceiling

The ceiling in the outdoor living area involves overhead features. Except in heavily wooded lots the sky composes most of the ceiling. This is rightfully so, as the sky is a beautiful feature that should be enjoyed. Maintain open areas in the design to view the sky. Trees provide the next most common ceiling element. The limbs of shade trees planted near the patio become part of the ceiling in the outdoor living room. Trees also provide shade for a

4-28. The sky composes most of the ceiling in the outdoor living room.

play area or the patio. Studies have shown there is a psychological comfort to be gained relaxing by a tree. If given a choice, people will sit near a tree with overhead protection rather than sit in a wide-open area. Patio umbrellas and other physical structures protect people from the sun's rays and provide a sense of overhead protection.

4-29. Trees provide a sense of overhead protection. (Courtesy, R. S. Hursthouse & Associates, Inc.)

The Walls

The walls, or **enclosures**, of the outdoor living room serve several purposes. They help to define space. They screen views. They provide privacy. They can serve as backdrops to flowering plants, and they can provide protection from winds. Base the location and height of enclosures on the information gathered through the site analysis survey. The height of the enclosure may vary depending on its function. For privacy purposes and wind protection, an enclosure of 6 feet or more is recommended. Other functions, such as defining space or screening a vegetable garden, could be accomplished with shorter enclosures.

Enclosures can be established with plant materials. Plant materials are frequently used because of their natural appearance in the landscape. They have a softer appearance than the physical structures. In addition, establishing an enclosure with plant materials is less

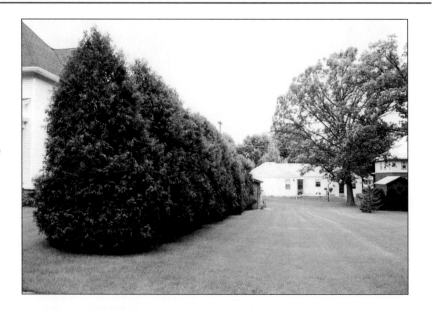

4-30. Enclosures of columnar plant materials contribute to the natural appearance of the landscape.

expensive than enclosures made of other materials. One disadvantage of using plant material for screens is they take up ground space. A columnar plant 6 to 10 feet tall will likely take up 4 to 6 feet of ground space. Because of their width, enclosures with plant materials should be limited to larger spaces.

Design masses of one type of vertical plant material to establish the enclosure. A mix of different species conflicts with the principles of design discussed in Chapter 6. Shrubs grown close to one another as clipped or un-clipped hedges form living walls. A clipped hedge requires pruning several times a year to maintain the desired shape. Clipped hedges have a formal appearance. An un-clipped hedge is allowed to grow naturally and is considered low maintenance.

Wood fences are another popular enclosure solution. A fence often is the most efficient way to provide enclosure. Fences take a small amount of square footage, thus, maximizing yard space. Another advantage is fences are useful in keeping animals from entering or leaving the yard.

A variety of fence styles can be used in the outdoor living area for different purposes. For example, a small solid fence might be used to enclose the vegetable garden or

4-31. Wood fences are popular for enclosure purposes. (Courtesy, Illinois Landscape Contractors Association)

screen garbage cans, while a wood board on board fence might enclose the property. Also, consideration must be given to the effect fences might have on breezes that cool the living area. Fence styles that let air pass are sometimes desirable for this purpose.

Fence construction influences the design of the landscape. Never have two different fence types or sizes meet at the corner of the yard. The obvious difference between the two attracts the viewer's attention. Also, when installing a fence, see that the top of the fence is level. In

4-32. This ornate fence and plant material provide enclosure. (Courtesy, Illinois Landscape Contractors Association)

the case of hilly terrain, step the fence down the hill. A level fence projects a sense of stability.

A third material used for enclosure purposes involves stone or brick. Walls constructed of these materials give a sense of permanence. Cost of walls constructed of these materials is high, but maintenance is very low. Walls tend to easily blend into the landscape.

4-33. Walls constructed of stone or brick give a sense of permanence to this Oklahoma landscape.

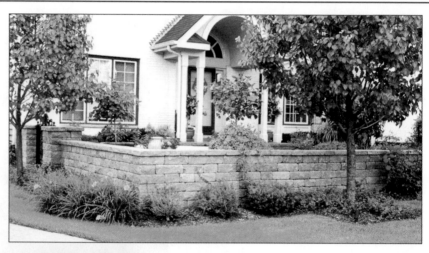

4-34. This low stone wall encloses an entry garden. (Courtesy, Western DuPage Landscaping)

4-35. Pavers lend themselves well to walks and patios.

4-36. Exposed aggregate concrete is the surface material used with this patio. (Courtesy, Illinois Landscape Contractors Association)

The Floor

The floor, or surface of the outdoor living area, is made of many materials. The most common surfacing material is a grass lawn. Other surfaces include ground cover plants, organic mulches, inorganic mulches, concrete, stone, and brick pavers. Surfacing materials can be used to strengthen the bed pattern designs. Base the selection of the material on the function it is to serve. For instance, grass is attractive, green, cool, and soft, making it a good play surface. Unfortunately, it requires regular care. Brick pavers, flagstone, and concrete are hard, durable materials that lend themselves well to walks and patios. Ground covers and mulches function well as low elements in planting beds. They fill spaces between trees and shrubs and tie the differing units together.

Nearly every house built today is constructed with a patio or deck in mind. *Patios* are built with hard permanent materials and are level with the ground. Brick pavers, concrete, and flagstone are

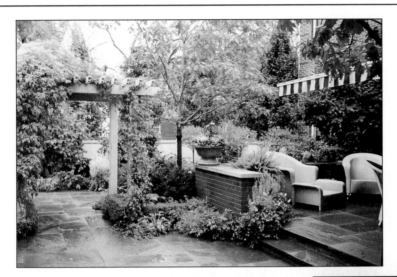

4-37. Bluestone is a very attractive surfacing material. (Courtesy, Illinois Landscape Contractors Association)

common surface materials for patios. **Decks** are wooden surface areas raised above the ground level. Cedar, redwood, and wood treated to resist decay are used in deck construction. Decks require more maintenance than patios. Washing and staining a deck every three to four years, depending on the severity of the weather and the wood used, extends the life of the deck.

Patios and decks serve as a transition from the interior of the house to the out-doors. Also, because of the activities that take place on a patio or deck (cooking meals, entertaining guests, etc.), ease of movement is important. Locate the patio or deck adjacent to the house. This will allow it to be easily accessed through a door to the house. It is preferable to locate the patio or deck nearest to the kitchen if more than one door is available. Sometimes they are located a short distance from the house, but connected to the house with a surfaced walkway.

4-38. Decks are wooden surface areas raised above the ground. (Courtesy, R.S. Hursthouse & Associates, Inc.)

4-39. Locate the patio or deck adjacent to the house so it can be easily accessed through a door. (Courtesy, R.S. Hursthouse & Associates, Inc.)

4-40. This simple walk connects the patio with the public area. (Courtesy, R.S. Hursthouse & Associates, Inc.)

4-41. This paver walk is very comfortable to use. (Courtesy, Illinois Landscape Contractors Association)

Walkways serve to make passage in and around the landscape easy. Brick pavers, concrete, flagstone, gravel, wood chips, and cross sections of logs are some materials used for walkways. Walkways designed to connect the public area to the outdoor living area allow guests to reach the patio or deck without entering the house. Walkways also make movement around the landscape easier for the homeowner.

The patio or deck is the center of activity in the outdoor living area. Therefore, the pattern design of the patio or deck should dictate the bed pattern style used in the rest of the living area. If the patio has lines 90 degrees to the house, use 90-degree bed patterns for the planting beds. Also, locate plantings and enclosures to benefit those on the patio or deck. High interest plantings within view of the patio or deck provide enjoyment for the viewers.

4-42. The pattern design of this patio is the same as the bed pattern style used in the rest of the living area.

Plantings

Plants in the outdoor living area serve many functions. The primary function of plants is to provide pleasure for the

homeowner. Well-designed shrub borders provide viewer interest from the deck or patio, as well as from indoors. Annual and perennial gardens give a splash of color to the landscape. Trees provide shade and a ceiling for the outdoor living space.

Some plantings called **high interest plantings** are designed to capture the attention of the viewer and to provide interest to the garden. Place high interest plantings in full view of the patio or deck. In locating these high interest plantings, also consider the views from the inside. Carefully designed plantings provide interest throughout the year for those inside.

4-43. This Indiana landscape has high interest plantings close to the seating area in the gazebo and an open area surfaced with grass for lawn games.

Some yards are large with distant views. Location of an interesting planting area in the distance gives the viewer something on which to focus attention. Garden accessories placed within the planting can help provide emphasis.

Garden Accessories

Garden accessories are items in the landscape that attract attention and provide interest. Because they draw the attention of the viewer, they have limited use in the public area. Remember, one of the rules of landscaping is to make the house the center of attention. However, in the outdoor living area, garden accessories can be used as focal points. Some accessories used with great success include sculptures, pools, and lawn ornaments.

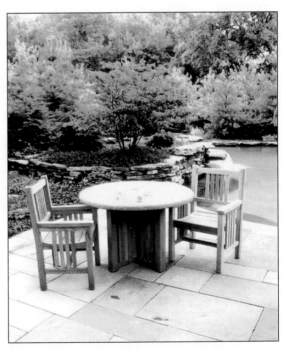

4-44. A high interest planting is placed close to this patio. (Courtesy, R.S. Hursthouse & Associates, Inc.)

4-45. Garden accessories include statues and water features.

It is not required that a design have garden accessories. Sometimes, the customers request accessory placement in the landscape. When asked to utilize garden accessories in the landscape, work them into the plan where they can be fully appreciated. It is often effective to locate accessories within the high interest planting area. Avoid locating the accessories haphazardly in the design.

4-46. Pots planted with annuals and perennials make good movable garden accessories.

4-47. This birdbath has been placed just outside a window in full view. (Courtesy, Church Landscaping)

THE SERVICE AREA

Areas to the rear or the side of the house set aside for strictly functional purposes make up the service area. Garbage cans, garden storage sheds, clotheslines, compost piles, and vegetable gardens are some activities that occur in a service area. Most service area activities are screened from view due to the nature of the activities. Work the service area activities into the rest of the plan. For example, the vegetable garden and compost pile could fit nicely inside a planting bed.

4-48. This vegetable garden has been located in the service area of the landscape.

PLAY AREAS

Design play areas to blend in with the landscape. If placed in the center of the yard, they attract attention due to the size of the structures and bright colors of the toys or equipment. It is best to place the play areas where they are less noticeable. At the same time be sure to design an open line of site to the patio and from a room indoors. In sunny, warm climates, provide overhead protection with well-placed shade trees.

4-49. This play area has been located away from the patio and the high interest planting area. (Courtesy, R.S. Hursthouse & Associates, Inc.)

REVIEWING

MAIN IDEAS

The residential landscape has three major areas of design. The areas are the public area, the outdoor living area, and the service area. Each is designed differently based on the functions the area will serve.

The main purpose of the public area design is to enhance the appearance of the house. Three main practices help to achieve a more attractive public area. The first is to soften the architectural lines of the house. Design the landscape with foundation plantings at the corners and doorway. Shrubs at the corners should be no taller than two-thirds the distance from the ground to the eaves. Those at the doorway should be no taller than one-fourth to one-third the distance from the ground to the eaves. Select foundation plants based on their mature size, growth habit, and their design qualities. Second, frame the house with trees. In doing so, use trees with growth habits that reflect the dominant lines of the house. Third, maintain a broad expanse of lawn. An open, uncluttered lawn area provides a grand setting to the house and ties other landscape elements together.

The design goals for the outdoor living area revolve around the family's interests and entertainment needs. Consider the outdoor living area to be an extension of the indoor living space. The ceiling of the outdoor living room consists of the sky, trees, and artificial elements. The walls or enclosures of the room include living plant materials, wood fences, and stone or brick walls. Enclosures serve several functions that include furnishing a backdrop for flowering plants, providing privacy, screening views, and defining space. The major flooring material in the outdoor living room is grass. Other materials used are mulches, concrete, brick pavers, stone, and wood. Durable flooring material is used for decks and patios. Locate decks and patios close to the door leading into the house.

The service area is the portion of the property used for utility purposes. Some common activities are storage of garbage cans, clotheslines, work sheds, and vegetable gardens. Often this area is screened from view due to the nature of the activities and vegetable gardens.

QUESTIONS

Answer the following questions using correct spelling and complete sentences.

1. What are the three main goals in designing the public area?
2. How are foundation plants used in the public area?
3. Why is it important to consider size in the selection of foundation plants?
4. What role do trees have in the public area?
5. How do the major architectural lines of a house influence plant selection?
6. What is the advantage to keeping open lawn in the public area?
7. What are some examples of materials that make up the ceiling, walls, and floor of the outdoor living area?
8. What functions do enclosures serve?
9. Where should patios and decks be located? Explain why.
10. What function does the service area have?

CHAPTER SELF-CHECK

Match the term with the correct definition. Write the letter by the term in the blank provided.

a. outdoor living area
b. focal point
c. public area
d. patios

e. high interest plantings
f. garden accessories
g. corner plantings

h. doorway plantings
i. decks
j. service area

_____1. Plants placed at the corners of the house

_____2. Located on either side of the entry door

_____3. Built with hard permanent materials and level with the ground

_____4. Areas to the rear or the side of the house set aside for strictly functional purposes

_____5. Walls of the outdoor living room

_____6. Plantings designed to capture the attention of the viewer and to provide interest to the garden

_____7. Point of emphasis of a well-designed landscape

_____8. All the property to the rear of the house except for the service area

_____9. Wooden surface areas raised above the ground level

_____10. The portion of the property that is in full view of the public

EXPLORING

1. Tour a residential neighborhood. Ask yourself a series of questions:

   Does the public area design show off the house?

   Do the homeowners use rounded plant forms to soften architectural lines?

   Are the lawns broad and expansive?

   Has an effort been made to frame the house with trees?

   Are the doors the focal point of the designs?

   Are the doorway plants one-fourth to one-third the distance from the ground to the eaves?

   Do the growth habits of the plants repeat the dominant lines of the houses?

   Are the views of the houses balanced by reversing the plant masses?

2. Visit the backyards of family or friends. Ask yourself:

   Is the patio or deck large enough for the entertainment needs?

   Is the patio or deck located near a rear entry to the house?

   Are poor views screened from view?

   Are there interesting plantings within view of the patio or deck and the indoors?

   Are the bed patterns for the plantings the same as the outline of the patio or deck?

CHAPTER 5

Starting with a Plan

1 Explain how to begin designing a landscape.

2 Describe how activity areas can be organized with goose egg plans.

3 Describe bed pattern designs for landscape plantings.

4 Explain principles of design as applied to surfaced areas.

5 Explain how to locate trees in the plan.

6 Explain how to plan an energy-efficient landscape.

TERMS

bed pattern
deciduous
evergreen

goose egg plan
lines of force
stomata

sun calculator

5-1. A functional landscape begins with planning.

ASK landscape designers what they like about their work and you might get many different answers. Some would say they like working with the customers. Some enjoy the creativity that goes into a beautiful landscape design. Others might love the challenge offered with each new job. All would agree that they like to see the transformation that takes place to a landscape because of their efforts.

Producing an attractive landscape that is functional for the client requires a plan. The process in creating a plan can be broken down into a number of steps. Initial steps in the design process, including the gathering of information about the project, were discussed in Chapter 3. The next steps in the design process are presented in this chapter.

BEGINNING THE DESIGN WORK

Once information has been gathered, work can begin on creating a design. The family inventory survey completed by the customer provides information on his or her wants and needs. The site analysis survey shows features on the site that will influence the design. Together with the base plan, they provide enough information to begin creating a design.

5-2. Consider the lot as room. (Courtesy, University of Illinois Cooperative Extension Service)

As work on the design progresses, apply three considerations:

1. Consider the lot on which the house sits to be like a room. A well-designed landscape becomes an extension of the indoor living space.

2. Consider the floor plan of the house. Locations of various rooms within the house impact the design of the landscape. For instance, locating a patio near the family breakfast area is very practical. Also, placing a high interest planting within view of those seated in the living room increases the value of the landscape.

3. Consider the landscape as viewed by neighbors and those who pass by.

GOOSE EGG PLANNING

Plan the location where activities will occur to achieve a well-organized landscape. It is important to understand that various activities are best located in different areas of the landscape. A good way to organize activity areas is to quickly draw small sketches of the house and the lot similar to the dimensions on the base plan. Each of these might only be 4 to 5 inches in size. Then, sketch rough ovals or circles on the small drawings to represent activities. The activities will likely overlap so allow the circles and ovals to overlap as well. These odd shapes are sometimes referred to as the ***goose egg plan***, or functional diagrams. Some examples of activities or land uses sketched on the plan include lawn games, play areas for children, patio or deck, vegetable garden, plantings, shed, screen, water garden, service area, and public area. Label the different goose egg shapes as to the activity intended.

It is often helpful for the designer to make the goose egg plan more detailed. Because the landscape is designed with function in mind, draw arrows indicating the major traffic patterns. The flow of traffic has a major impact of where certain activities should be located. Also, the patio or deck might warrant its own functional diagram. Plan the deck or patio by subdividing the space with different areas for seating, traffic flow, food preparation, etc.

Try to be open-minded when working on the goose egg plan. Consider a wide range of possible solutions. Exact, detailed work will come later. In fact, it is better to let yourself be creative. Forcing yourself to work quickly is often helpful in this step.

After several sketches are made, look at the plans carefully and choose the plan that appears to be the most practical. Some things to consider are whether

5-3. A goose egg plan helps to locate where certain activities will occur.

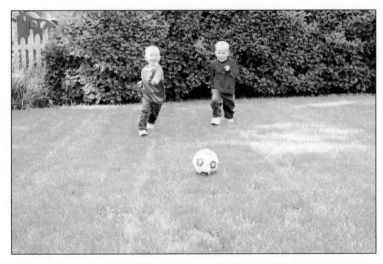

5-4. Open lawn was designed into this landscape with play in mind.

TIP: Place all shrubs, ground covers, perennials, and annuals within planting beds to keep maintenance in and around the plants at a minimum.

the activities are compatible to one another. For instance, you would not want the children's play area right next to the patio. You would not want the patio located away from an entry to the house either. Also, consider how the microclimate, macroclimate, soil conditions, views, and existing vegetation might affect each activity. It would be a mistake to locate a vegetable garden in the shade of existing trees or to obscure a beautiful view with plantings.

The value of the goose egg plan is it provides a general guide for the landscape design. It encourages the designer to be creative. It is not a rigid plan. If something does not work, the plan can be changed so it will work. All design work that follows reflects the location of the activities sketched in the goose egg plan.

ESTABLISHING BED PATTERNS

The design step that follows goose egg planning is the establishment of bed patterns. The bed patterns form the framework for the design. A **bed pattern** is a border that outlines where plants are planted. The border separates the lawn from the plantings within the bed. By placing all shrubs, ground covers, perennials, and annuals within a planting bed, maintenance in and around the plants is kept to a minimum. Imagine how much extra work would be involved to control weeds and cut grass if shrubs, ground covers, and annuals were planted at random on the property. Also, by locating plants within a planting bed it is much easier to follow the principles of design that will be discussed in Chapter 6.

TIP: Design bold bed patterns and use a consistent style throughout the landscape.

5-5. Can you determine the lines of force created by this house?

Lines of Force

Bed patterns are influenced by lines of force. With any architectural structure, there are dominant lines created by such features as corners, windows, chimneys, and doors. These lines have visual energy that extend into the landscape, hence the term **lines of force**. Bed patterns are designed with lines of force in mind. Draw lines of the patio, deck or planting beds in harmony with the lines of force. For instance, start a bed pattern at the corner of the house or edge of a window. The edge of the deck or patio might line up with a jog in the wall or the frame of a door. Following this practice helps to connect the house with the landscape.

Bed Pattern Styles

The eyes of the viewer tend to follow the outline of the bed patterns. Therefore, it is important to design bold patterns that are consistent throughout the landscape. Three main styles are commonly used for bed patterns. They are curved lines, straight lines at 90 degrees to the house, and straight lines at 45 degrees to the house.

> **TIP:** Where bed patterns meet the house or another physical structure, be sure to draw the lines at a 90-degree angle to the structure.

5-6. A bed pattern is a border that outlines where plants are planted and separates the lawn from the plantings within the bed.

The lines of a curved plan flow smoothly through the landscape and lend themselves well to a natural appearance. Curved bed patterns are influenced the least by architectural lines of force. Design bold curves. Little squiggles through the landscape confuse the viewer and lack clear definition. Often, this style is a mix of arcs and straight lines tangent to those arcs.

5-7. The three main bed pattern styles are (A) straight lines at 90 degrees to the house, (B) straight lines at 45 degrees to the house, and (C) curved lines.

5-8. Curved bed patterns lend themselves well to a natural appearance. (Courtesy, Illinois Landscape Contractors Association)

5-9. Quick sketches of possible bed patterns.

The 90-degree patterns reflect the architectural lines of the house. They give the impression of greater control over the landscape. Many famous formal gardens benefit from the symmetrical look provided by 90-degree bed patterns. Symmetrical landscapes have the same bed patterns and plants on each side of an axis. Select 90-degree patterns for a formal, rigid look to the landscape. Bed patterns of 90 degrees work with asymmetrical designs, as well. As with the curved bed patterns, these should be designed to appear bold.

The 45-degree patterns also reflect the architectural lines of the house. However, the 45-degree lines can be used to provide an asymmetrical look to the landscape. The asymmetrical appearance created with 45-degree patterns tends to be more dynamic and hold more interest for the viewer than the formal, 90-degree plan. Bed patterns of 45-degree angles work very well with houses of contemporary design.

Start by drawing rough sketches of possible bed patterns. Sketch the house and the property lines. Several of these could be drawn on a standard size sheet of paper. Now, try different bed pattern ideas including the curved, 90-degree and 45-degree styles. Use the goose egg plan as a guide for locating the various activity areas. Work quickly taking no more than a few moments for each. Be consistent with your patterns. Only one style of bed pattern should be used for the outdoor living area or the public area. Changing a bed pattern style within one of these areas appears disruptive. Because it is unlikely anyone could view both the outdoor living area and the public area at the same time, the bed pattern style used in each area may differ.

After a number of sketches have been drawn, choose the best plan for the landscape project. Ask yourself if the plan addresses the needs of the family. Does it have visual interest? Are the bed patterns appropriate for the site or will changes need to be made?

The pattern selected is then enlarged and placed on tracing paper laid over the base plan or entered into the computer. You may find that during this transfer process you will need to make slight adjustments to your bed patterns. During this phase, take care to draw accurate lines.

Whichever style is used, start and finish the planting beds at architectural features of the house that create lines of force. Some examples are the edge of a window, a jog in a wall, and a change in building material. On wall surfaces lacking architectural features, begin the bed one-third or two-thirds the distance across the wall. Also, where bed patterns meet the house or another physical structure, be sure to draw the lines at a 90-degree angle to the structure. This touch gives a clean appearance and keeps maintenance low.

5-10. On wall surfaces devoid of architectural features, begin the bed pattern one-third or two-thirds the distance across the wall.

DESIGNING PATIOS, DECKS, WALKS, AND DRIVES

Design surfaced areas to follow the same pattern as the planting beds. If the bed pattern style used in the outdoor living area is curved, the deck or patio should have curves in its outline as well. A square patio conflicts visually with curved bed patterns. Where the home has an existing deck, it may be advisable to let its shape dictate the style of bed patterns used.

Refer to the family inventory survey to help determine the size of the deck or patio. The minimum size should be 300

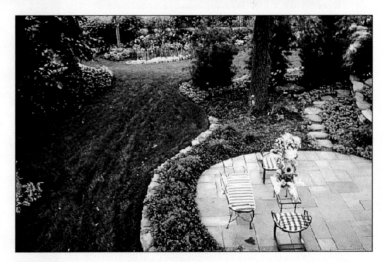

5-11. Design patios and decks to follow the same pattern as that used in the planting beds. (Courtesy, R.S. Hursthouse & Associates, Inc.)

TIP: | Allow for a traffic flow pattern through the deck or patio.

square feet. Of course, if the family entertains large groups, you will want to design a larger surface area. Calculate the square footage of the surface area drawn with the bed patterns and make adjustments as necessary.

Determine the traffic flow patterns before designing the size and shape of the deck or patio. Allow for traffic to move through the deck or patio from one area to another. A primary avenue is usually from the entrance of the house to the lawn area. In most cases, the flow is a direct line from one point to another. Once identified, the patterns will indicate where patio furniture can be placed without obstructing traffic. Place the seating area away from the main flow of traffic to limit disturbance to people seated.

Also, at this stage of the design process, locate walks or pathways. A walk from the public area to the outdoor living area is often necessary. Guests do not

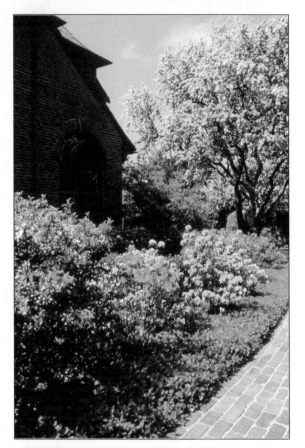

5-12. This walk connects the front of the house to the outdoor living area. (Courtesy, Illinois Landscape Contractors Association)

have to trek through the house for outside functions. Furthermore, a surfaced walk is easier to walk across than grass. Usually, this type of walk is located on the garage side of the house. Walks in the landscape can be narrower than public walks or walks to the front door. Two feet in width is acceptable. Stepping stones with grass between the stones also make an effective walk.

5-13. The minimum size of a patio should be 300 square feet.

LOCATING TREES IN THE PLAN

The customer may be fortunate to have existing trees on the property. However, most new homes do not have older trees if they have any trees at all. Usually, it is up to the landscaper to install trees. Trees provide shade, a backdrop to the house, screening of poor views, framing of good views, and a sense of permanency to the landscape.

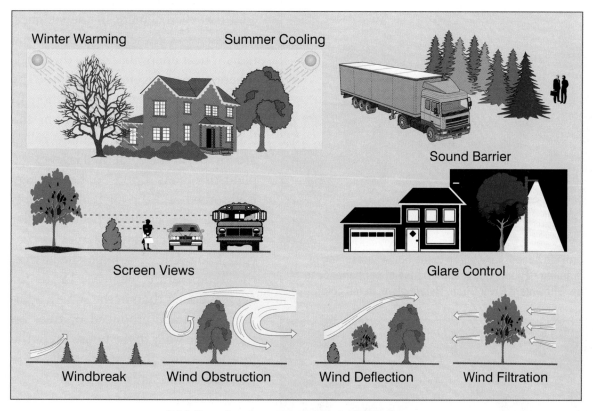

5-14. Trees have many purposes in the landscape.

Trees are the largest element of the landscape. Locate them on the plan once the bed patterns have been established. At this point do not select the specific trees. Selection of specific trees comes later in the design process. Rather, choose the location of the tree and a basic size—small, medium, or large. The location and size should be determined by family needs and site conditions. Some examples of where to place trees include: a patio that requires shade from a tree, a poor view that can be screened only with the placement of a tree, and the main approach to the house, which calls for framing with trees.

DESIGNING AN ENERGY-EFFICIENT LANDSCAPE

Trees have a tremendous impact on the microclimate around a house. When carefully located, trees soften harsh weather conditions. The result is an improved comfort level for the family. Also, energy requirements to heat and cool the house can be reduced.

5-15. Trees provide shade, a backdrop to the house, screening of poor views, framing of good views, and a sense of permanency to the landscape. Shown are River Birch, *Betula nigra*, in fall color.

5-16. Shade trees help to keep this house cool in the heat of summer.

Deciduous trees, or those that lose their leaves in the fall, can be used to cool the microclimate in the summer. The leaves of these trees reflect some radiant heat energy back into the atmosphere. Some heat energy is absorbed by the tree through evapo-transpiration. In this case, water evaporates from the leaves through the pore openings, called **stomata**, in the epidermal layer of the plant tissue. As it does so, heat energy is absorbed and the air temperature is lowered. This cooling effect is similar to the way perspiration serves to cool your body. Under a large shade tree, the temperature can be 15 to 25 degrees cooler than in the sun. In addition, the shade produced by trees on the outside walls of the house keeps the interior cooler than if the walls were exposed to the sun's rays.

PROTECTION FROM THE SUN'S HEAT

The first step in locating trees in the landscape for cooling purposes is to learn the direction from which the sun's rays hit the house. The angle of the sun changes with the seasons. As

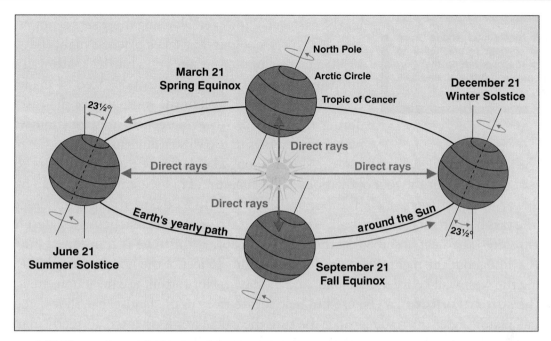

5-17. The rotation of the earth on its axis and its orbit around the sun cause seasonal change.

the earth rotates on its axis the seasons change.

In the winter months, the sun is farther south on the horizon. The sun's rays hit primarily the south wall. By allowing these winter rays to hit the house and enter windows on the south wall, the interior of the house is warmed. *Evergreen* trees keep their leaves year round, and when planted south of the house block these rays Deciduous trees, on the other hand, let most of the rays pass.

In summer, the sun is farther to the north. The walls that receive the greatest amount of radiant energy in the summer months are the east and west walls. As the sun rises, the rays

5-18. Deciduous trees allow the sun's rays to warm the house in the winter.

TIP: Place deciduous shade trees within 25 feet of the house to block the rays hitting the west wall between 3:00 P.M. and 5:00 P.M.

hit the east wall. However, blocking these rays is not necessary due to the cooling that takes place at night. Between 11:00 a.m. and noon, the sun's rays hit the south wall with intensity. Consider placing a deciduous tree to shade the east end of the south wall or the south end of the east wall during that period. An evergreen in this location would block wanted rays in the winter months.

The sun hits its highest point in the sky at noon. The angles of the rays are very steep. Most of these rays hit the roof of the house. The amount of radiant energy absorbed by the south wall at noon is very small. It is not until 1:00 p.m. to 2:00 p.m. that the sun descends and the rays begin to hit the west wall. At around 4:00 p.m. the sun reaches its greatest heating capacity. The heat absorbed by the west walls during this time is transferred into the house throughout the night. Place shade trees within 25 feet of the house to block the rays hitting the west wall between 3:00 p.m. and 5:00 p.m. Here again, use deciduous trees.

The **sun calculator** can be used to help locate trees in the landscape. Slide a copy of the calculator under the tracing paper. Be sure the calculator is oriented correctly in terms of north and south. Then, center the calculator on the wall or area (e.g., patio, play area) to be shaded. Locate your trees within the angles suggested to block the sun's rays for a particular time.

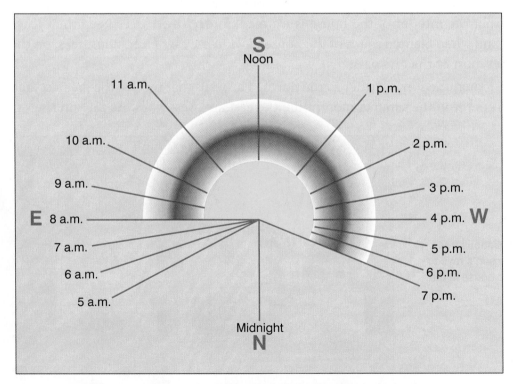

5-19. The sun calculator can be used to help locate trees in the landscape.

WIND PROTECTION

Trees also reduce the impact of harsh winds in the winter. Groups of evergreen trees planted in the path of the prevailing winter winds effectively cut the chill of the wind. In much of the United States, the prevailing winter winds come from the north and northwest.

Trees can be carefully located to block the prevailing winter winds that strike a house. The loss of heat is reduced resulting in lower heating costs. Another benefit is the wind speed is slowed, causing snow carried by the wind to fall to the ground rather than drift around the house. Benefits are also gained in the summer. Well-placed trees slow the wind speed and reduce the drying effect of hot summer winds.

The extent of wind protection can be calculated. A row of trees or shrubs provides protection for a distance twenty times the height of the plants. Measure the height of the windbreak and multiply by twenty. For example, a ten-foot high windbreak would provide protection for a distance of two hundred feet (10 × 20 = 200 feet).

5-20. Evergreen trees, such as these Douglasfir, *Pseudotsuga menziesii,* planted in the path of the prevailing winter winds effectively cut the wind chill. (Courtesy, University of Illinois Cooperative Extension

5-21. An Oklahoma teacher reviews an informal home landscape plan with a student. (Courtesy, Education Images, Inc.)

REVIEWING

MAIN IDEAS

Goose egg planning is a step in the landscape design process that helps the designer locate where activities will occur in the landscape. Goose egg planning involves quick sketches of ovals or circles that represent the activities. The location of activities and the activities themselves are influenced by the family inventory checklist and the site analysis survey.

Bed patterns are established following the goose egg planning. Bed patterns form the framework for the design. Shrub plantings, flowers, and ground covers are placed within planting beds. Three main bed patterns are used for planting beds: curved lines, straight lines 90 degrees to the house, and straight lines 45 degrees to the house. Quick sketches of possible bed patterns are drawn. The bed pattern best suited for the landscape project is selected and transferred to the master plan.

Trees are the largest element of the landscape. They are located on the plan after the bed patterns are established. Consider their use as shade providers, backdrops to the house, screens of poor views, and frames for the house when locating them. The sun calculator is helpful in locating trees for an energy-efficient landscape.

QUESTIONS

Answer the following questions using correct spelling and complete sentences.

1. What considerations are important as the initial landscape planning takes place?

2. Why is it important to organize the location of landscape activities?

3. How are goose egg plans developed?

4. Why are bed patterns important?

5. What are the major bed patterns?

6. How can trees be located in the landscape to provide areas with shade?

7. What can be done to reduce heat loss in the winter months?

CHAPTER SELF-CHECK

Match the term with the correct definition. Write the letter by the term in the blank provided.

a. goose egg plan   c. bed patterns   e. stomata
b. evergreen   d. deciduous   f. sun calculator

_____1. A border that outlines where plants are planted

_____2. Trees that keep their leaves year round

_____3. Trees that lose their leaves in the fall

_____4. Tool used to help locate trees for an energy-efficient landscape

_____5. Rough sketches of ovals or circles to represent locations of activities

_____6. Leaf openings

EXPLORING

1. Using the family inventory survey and the site analysis plan developed in the previous chapters, practice goose egg planning. Sketch a small version of the house on the lot. Reproduce this drawing. Now, based on the material provided, quickly draw four or five goose egg plans. Try to be creative as you sketch these plans.

2. Select the best goose egg plan. If there is not one that appears functional, draw some more. Next, using the small sketches of the house on the lot try drawing bed patterns that will accommodate the goose egg plan you have selected. Try two to three sketches of each of the three main bed pattern styles.

3. Transfer the bed pattern that you consider to be the best to the base plan drawn previously. Take care when enlarging, to draw the bed patterns accurately.

4. Locate trees on your plan. Use the sun calculator to place trees for an energy-efficient landscape. Give an oral report in class on your tree placement. Explain your reasoning based on site analysis and other features.

Using the Principles of Art

OBJECTIVES

1 Describe the design qualities of plants.

2 Explain the impact of line and form in design work.

3 Explain how texture influences designs.

4 Explain the visual impact of colors as a design quality.

5 Explain the principles of design as applied to the landscape.

TERMS

art	high visual energy	texture
balance	informal balance	unity
color	line	unity of three
emphasis	repetition	variety
form	scale	
formal balance	sequence	

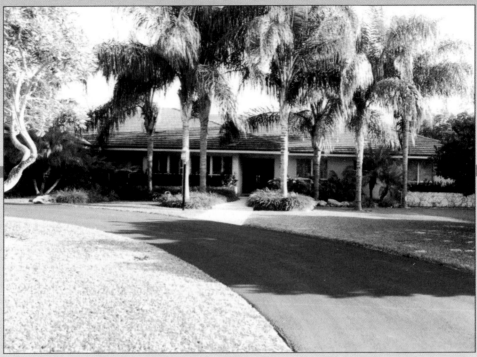

6-1. Beautiful landscape settings result from following the principles of art as shown in this Florida landscape.

VAN Gogh, Monet, and Renoir are names with which you are probably familiar. They were great artists, who by following principles of art, created masterful paintings. These artists applied colors to canvas as an expression of beauty. To do so, they followed guidelines or principles of art established by countless artists that have preceded them over the centuries. Landscape designers also follow principles of art. However, the landscape designer works with plants and hardscape materials rather than with paints and canvas.

Landscape design is primarily a visual art. Landscape designers produce views pleasing to the eye. They do this by carefully selecting and using plants and other landscape components in a way that follows basic principles of art. In this chapter, the principles of art, as applied to landscape design, will be examined.

THE ART AND SCIENCE OF PLANTS

Horticulture is often defined as the art and science of growing plants. Landscaping is the segment of horticulture pertaining to the art and science of growing plants in an outdoor setting. The science of growing plants involves botany and soil science. Plants are living organisms. Understanding what plants need to perform in certain situations and how to successfully grow them is a science. **Art** as defined by the *American College Dictionary* is the production or expression of what is beautiful, appealing.

Landscape design is primarily a visual art. Arranging plants and other design elements in a way that is pleasing to the eye is an art. Attractive landscapes can be achieved by following basic rules or the principles of art. These principles are the same as those considered by artists who paint and sculpt.

Selecting plants for use in the landscape is based on the ability of a plant to grow in cer-

6-2. An understanding of plant growth and care is important to ensure that the plants provide long-lasting pleasure in the landscape. (Courtesy, Illinois Landscape Contractors Association)

6-3. Natural and artificial features in the landscape have line.

tain situations and the principles of art and design. As a result, the plant selection process is often the most time-consuming step in producing a design. The plants used must fit with all the other elements of the design in a way that is attractive. The major design qualities to consider in selecting plants for the landscape are line, form, texture, and color.

Successful landscapers understand how plants grow and the conditions needed for plants to be healthy. Plant materials should be chosen that are adapted to the climate. Though a particular species adds immensely to a landscape, little has been accomplished if it is not adapted where it will be planted.

LINE AND FORM

Everything in the landscape has **line**, whether it is natural or artificial. The outlines of trees and shrubs have line. The edge separating lawn and planting beds has line. The patterns in patio and deck materials have line. Line gives the viewer's

6-4. The observer's eye follows the outline of an entire mass planting.

6-5. The eye tends to follow the outline of this planting and the outline of the foregound shrubs.

6-6. Horizontal lines, such as where the sky meets the ocean are relaxing and pleasant.

eye direction and movement. Whatever its source, the viewer's eye follows the line. For example, the eye may move up and down following the line of upright plants or the corner of a house. The eye follows the horizontal lines of spreading junipers. It also follows the outline of an entire mass planting.

Line creates emotional and psychological responses from the viewer. Vertical lines are severe and when used in excess, cause a feeling of tension and nervousness. Horizontal lines, on the other hand, provide a relaxing, pleasant emotional response. Doctors have been known to send patients with nervous breakdowns to ocean resorts or on cruises as therapy. The horizontal line where the sky meets the sea has a therapeutic, calming effect on the patient's nerves.

FORM

Form is the three-dimensional shape of the plant. The lines formed by the trunk and branches contribute to the form of the plant. Examples of forms or plant shapes include: columnar, oval, pyramidal, round, vase, and weeping. Extreme forms, such as columnar plants, have high visual energy. **High visual energy** implies the ability of a plant to attract attention. The more extreme the form, the more attention the plant will attract.

Different plant forms affect the viewer in different ways. Upright forms, common with many evergreens, provide accent to a design. They draw your attention. Upright forms are difficult to use in the landscape because they are so visually active. Horizontal or spreading forms emphasize the breadth of space. They are less visually active forms. Rounded forms are the most common forms found in nature. They lend themselves well to groupings and mass plantings.

TIP: Use a majority of rounded plant forms in the landscape to establish a natural, informal appearance.

6-7. Common plant forms: (a) horizontal: Pagoda Dogwood, *Cornus alternifolia;* (b) vase: American Elm, *Ulmus americana*; (c) columnar: Lombardy Black Poplar, *Populus nigra* 'Italica' ; (d) oval or oblong: American Sweetgum, *Liquidambar styraciflua;* (e) rounded: Bradford Callery Pear, *Pyrus calleryana* 'Bradford'; (f) weeping: Weeping European Beech, *Fagus sylvatica* 'Pendula'; (g) Pyramidal: Littleleaf Linden in youth, *Tilia cordata*

6-8. Form is the three-dimensional shape of the plant. Pictured is Annabelle Smooth Hydrangea, *Hydrangea arborescens* 'Annabelle.' (Courtesy, Midwest Groundcovers)

6-9. Upright forms provide accent to a design. Shown is a Blue Colorado Spruce, *Picea pungens* 'Glauca.'

6-10. Shrubs with rounded forms are common and lend themselves well to group plantings. Shown is a species of Cotoneaster.

Plant forms greatly influence a landscape design. Avoid using one form as the landscape can appear very monotonous. It is a good practice to use a majority of rounded forms. Using the rounded forms helps to establish a natural, informal appearance to the landscape. Add a few of the more extreme plant forms to the design for variety and interest.

TEXTURE

Texture is another design quality of plants to consider. Simply stated, **texture** is the appearance of a plant in terms of coarseness or fineness, roughness or smoothness, heaviness or lightness, denseness or thinness. Coarse-textured plants have a higher visual energy than

6-12. The texture of a plant is based largely on the leaves. (Pictured is an ornamental grass.)

6-11. Texture is the appearance of a plant in terms of coarseness or fineness, roughness or smoothness, heaviness or lightness, denseness or thinness.

TIP: Select plant materials that give a smooth transition from finer textured plants to coarser textured plants.

fine-textured plants. Coarse-textured plants appear closer to the viewer than they really are, while fine-textured plants appear more distant.

Both leaves and branches determine a plant's texture. Coarse textures result from large leaves and twigs, dull leaf surfaces, short petioles, and entire leaves (entire leaves lack serrations or sinuses). Smaller leaves and twigs, glossy leaf surfaces, long petioles, and cut leaves contribute to fine-textured plants.

There are some rules of design to keep in mind as you consider the texture of plants. Monotony results if all the plants in the landscape have similar textures. Therefore, use some variation to add interest. It is most pleasing to the eye if changes in texture take place gradually. A smooth transition from finer textured plants

6-13. Coarse texture results from large leaves, short petioles, and a dull leaf surface as in this Elm, *Ulmus species.*

6-14. The textures of the iris and the hosta in this landscape are in sharp contrast with one another. (Courtesy, Midwest Groundcovers)

to coarser textured plants is preferred. Never place an extremely fine-textured plant next to a coarse-textured plant.

The designer can also create a different feel in the landscape by selecting plants based on plant textures. Because coarse-textured plants have high visual energy and appear closer to the viewer, they should be used in larger settings. If coarse-textured plants were used in a small setting, such as a courtyard, they would make the courtyard appear even smaller. Use finer textured plants in small landscape settings or when the viewer is close to the planting, as in a patio seating area.

6-15. The feathery leaves of this Baldcypress, *Taxodium distichum* give it a fine texture.

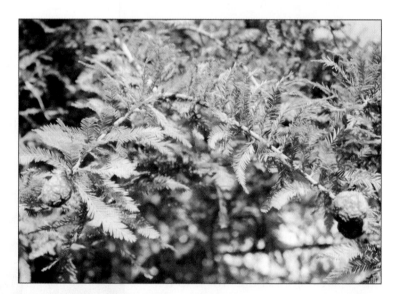

COLOR

TIP: Use at least nine green plants for every one plant that has visually active, warm leaf colors.

Color is the final design quality of plants to consider. It has the greatest appeal or visual impact of all the design qualities. The primary concern when considering plant color is the leaves.

The source of **color** is light. Sunlight contains wavelengths of different lengths including x-rays, gamma rays,

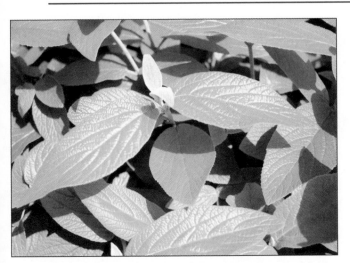

6-16. The primary concern when considering plant color is the leaves. (Shown is Lantanaphyllum Viburnum, *Viburnum x rhytidophylloides*.)

microwaves, ultraviolet waves, and visible light. Visible light has all the colors to which we are familiar. When visible light hits an object, light waves are either absorbed by that object or reflected. When light hits a green leaf, all the wavelengths are absorbed except green light wavelengths. The green wavelengths are reflected into the viewer's eye.

The colors of visible light are divided into two major groups—warm colors and cool colors. Warm colors include yellow, orange, and red. People find warm colors to be striking, stimulating, and cheerful. They have high visual energy. Cool colors have lower visual energy. They include violet, blue, and green. Cool colors invoke a feeling of restfulness and

6-17. Color has greater visual impact than other design qualities. (Courtesy, Church Landscape)

Table 6-1. Colors

	Warm Colors	Cool Colors
Colors	yellow, orange, red	blue, green, violet
Energy	high visual energy	low visual energy
Human response	striking, cheerful, stimulating, appear to advance toward the viewer	restful, peaceful, relaxing, appear more distant to the viewer

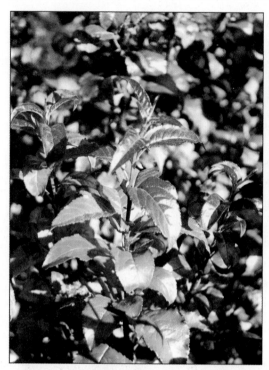

6-18. Foliage with warm colors has high visual energy and appears closer to the viewer.

6-19. Plants with blue-green or green foliage have lower visual energy and appear more distant. (Shown is Juddi Viburnum, *Viburnum "Juddi."*)

peacefulness. As with the other design qualities, the designer can select plants to create a desired effect. Plants with red-green, yellow-green or black-green foliage have high visual energy and appear closer to the viewer. Those plants with blue-green or green foliage have lower visual energy and appear more distant.

The main purpose of using plants in the landscape is to provide a natural, green setting that creates an atmosphere of restfulness. Therefore, design the landscape plan using mostly green-leafed plants. For variety and interest, plants with warmer leaf colors can be used. However, be careful in using plants with yellow, maroon, bronze, or variegated leaves. They can easily dominate a landscape. In the public area, they draw attention from the most important feature of the landscape—the house. A good rule to follow is to use at least nine green plants for every one plant that has the visually active, warm leaf colors.

6-20. Design the landscape plan using mostly green-leafed plants, which provide an atmosphere of restfulness. (Courtesy, Illinois Landscape Contractors Association)

PRINCIPLES OF DESIGN

UNITY

A well-designed home landscape has a look of oneness or a sense of **unity**. Elements of the design flow together and create a unified view. The plants neither stand out as individuals, nor does an individual plant "scream for attention." Overall, the aim of a well-designed landscape is to attract and hold the attention of the viewers. The design appears organized, and the various parts flow together.

How do you achieve a unified landscape design? Unity in the landscape is accomplished by applying principles of design to the design qualities: line, form, color, and texture. In other words, the designer can create unity by selecting plants based on their qualities of line, form, texture, and color. Careful planning and selection of landscape elements creates a whole picture that appears harmonious.

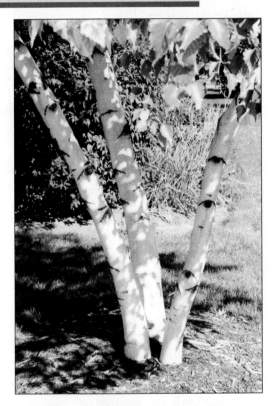

6-21. The unity of three is reflected in this image of a multi-stem European White Birch, *Betula pendula*.

Unity of Three

An interesting concept called the unity of three can be used to unify the landscape. The **unity of three** principle involves the use of anything in multiples of three. An example is three shrubs of the same species and size. Another example is a multi-stem tree having three trunks. Items in multiples of three create oneness and appear as a unit. The human mind easily accepts threes as a unit. Even num-

TIP: Keep a design simple by using a limited number of different plant species.

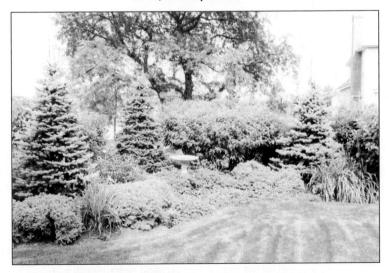

6-22. The designer of this planting used three Blue Colorado Spruce, *Picea pungeons* 'Glauca' to create interest and unity.

6-23. A unified landscape planting is accomplished by manipulating line, form, texture, and color and by applying principles of design. (Courtesy, University of Illinois Cooperative Extension Service)

6-24. Repetition is accomplished by repeating the lines, forms, textures, and colors of the plants throughout the design.

bers of two and four create contrast and duplication. Numbers larger than three, such as, five, six, seven or more progressively lose their sense of unit as the numbers grow larger. Three has that special property of unity not found with other numbers.

Unity is achieved by following the principles of design. The principles of design are used in many forms of art. The principles referred to in this book include repetition, variety, balance, emphasis, sequence, and scale.

Repetition—Simplicity is another way to express this concept. Keep the plantings simple by repeating forms, textures, and colors of the plants throughout the design. The repetition of the design qualities of plants contributes to unity in the landscape. A design can be kept simple by using a limited number of different plant species. Also, design groupings of 3, 5, or 7 plants of the same species.

Variety—If every plant in the design was the same or if all the plants shared the same line, form, texture, and color the view would be boring. Therefore, provide variety or contrast in the design by selecting some plants with different qualities from the mass of plants. The contrast can be achieved by varying colors, textures, and forms of the plants used. Variety in the plantings contributes interest to the design.

Balance—Balance implies equilibrium. Objects in the landscape carry visual weight based on line, form, texture, color, and size. Extreme forms, coarse-textured

6-25. Provide variety in the design by selecting some plants with different qualities of line form, texture, or color from the mass of plants.

Formal or symmetrical

Informal or asymmetrical

6-26. Balance is an equilibrium of landscape elements, which provides a sense of stability.

6-27. The designer elected to use the same plants on each side of the door complimenting the formal look of this house.

plants, and plants with dark or colored leaves appear heavy. Whereas those that are rounded forms, fine-textured and light colored appear lighter. The goal of the designer is to create visual balance on each side of a view.

There are two types of balance used in art. **Formal balance**, or symmetrical balance, consists of the same plantings on each side of a view. Designs with formal balance give a feeling of stability. **Informal balance**, or asymmetrical balance, has different plants and plants of varied sizes on each side of a view. Although the plantings differ, the visual weights of these plants balance one another. Informal balance has a more dynamic appearance than formal balance.

6-28. The landscape for this house has a formal design with the same plantings on each side.

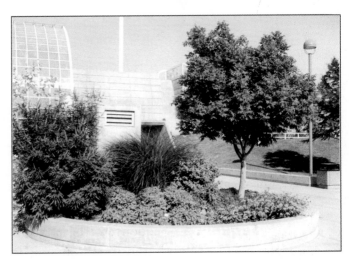

6-29. This small planting shows informal balance.

The architectural style of the house dictates whether the landscape in the public area should be formal or informal. Design plantings to be the same on either side of the entrance of houses with formal architecture. With houses having informal architecture, use different plantings on each side of the entrance.

Emphasis—Emphasis indicates dominance of some elements of the design over others. Designs should have a point or points that draw and hold the attention of the viewer. These points of interest can be established by selecting some plants with visually active qualities (extreme lines, forms, coarser textures, warm colors) to serve as accents in certain areas of the design. The visually active characteristics of these plants give them dominance over surrounding plants.

> **TIP:** Establish a point of emphasis to draw and hold the attention of the viewer by selecting some plants with visually active qualities to serve as accents.

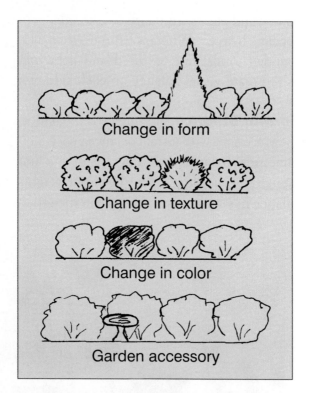

6-30. Emphasis is achieved with changes in form, texture, color, or with garden accessories.

6-31. The visually active qualities of this European White Birch, *Betula pendula*, provide emphasis to the design.

Sequence—Sequence is the uniformity of change from one item in the landscape to the next. A smooth transition from one design element to the next is desired. Change of at least one quality of form, texture, or color from one area of the planting to another gives

6-32. Sequence is gained through the uniformity of change of form, texture, or color from one item in the landscape to the next.

This house appears larger than it is

This house appears smaller than it is

6-33. Scale is the proportion of one object to another.

transition. The gradual sequence of change creates visual motion as the viewer's eye progresses from one element to the next.

Scale—Scale is the proportion of one object to another. It sometimes means the relationship of an object with a designated standard, such as a building or a person. It can also apply to the size of one object in relation to another in a planting. Use landscape elements to which people can relate. For example, it is difficult to relate to the size of a giant redwood and feel comfortable, whereas, a smaller tree with limbs closer to the person creates a comfortable feeling.

Often scale is defined as being "in scale" or being "out of scale." The meaning of in scale is that the appearance is pleasing or comfortable. Out of scale means the view or feeling is awkward or it does not relate to human size.

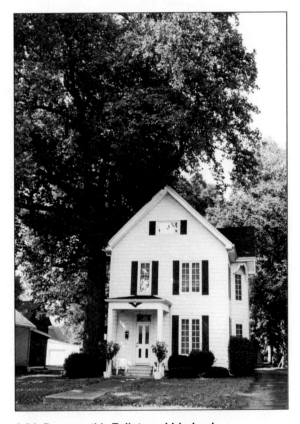

6-34. Because this Tuliptree, *Liriodendron tulipifera*, dwarfs the house, it is out of scale.

REVIEWING

MAIN IDEAS

Landscaping involves the principles of art and the science of growing plants. The landscape designer must therefore be knowledgeable in both areas. Selecting plants based on their design qualities and their ability to survive is often the most time-consuming step in the landscape design process.

Landscape design is a visual art. The principles of design applied to the landscape are the same as those applied to other forms of visual art. The major qualities of design are line, form, texture, and color. Line is the outline of the elements in the landscape. The eye follows the lines of landscape elements. Vertical lines are severe, while horizontal lines are restful. Form is the three-dimensional shape of a landscape element. The more extreme the form, the more visually active it appears. Texture is the appearance of a plant in terms of coarseness or fineness, roughness or smoothness, heaviness or lightness, denseness or thinness. Coarse-textured plants have high visual energy and appear closer to the viewer. Fine-textured plants have low visual energy making them ideal for small landscape settings. Color is the design quality that gains the most appeal. Warm colors, red, orange, and yellow are stimulating and cheerful. They have high visual energy. Cool colors consisting of blue, violet, and green have lower visual energy and are restful.

The application of the principles of design to the design qualities results in unity. The designer can select plants and artificial design elements based on their qualities while following principles of design. Repetition is accomplished by repeating lines, forms, textures, and colors of the plants throughout the design. Variety is provided in the design by selecting some plants with different qualities of line, form, texture, or color from the mass of plants. Some areas of the design can be emphasized by selecting plants more visually dominant over other plants. Sequence is the uniformity of change from one item in the landscape to the next. Scale is the proportion of one object to another.

QUESTIONS

Answer the following questions using correct spelling and complete sentences.

1. How is landscaping both an art and a science?
2. What is line?
3. What is form?
4. How do plant characteristics affect the quality of coarseness or fineness?
5. How do warm and cool colors influence the viewer of a landscape design?
6. How is unity in the landscape accomplished?
7. What are the principles of design? Define each.
8. What are the major design qualities to consider in plants and artificial design elements?

CHAPTER SELF-CHECK

Match the term with the correct definition. Write the letter by the term in the blank provided.

a. color   d. variety   g. repetition
b. scale   e. sequence   h. form
c. texture   f. line

_____ 1. Accomplished by repeating lines, forms, textures, and colors of the plants throughout the design

_____ 2. The greatest appeal or visual impact of all the design qualities

_____ 3. The appearance of a plant in terms of coarseness or fineness, roughness or smoothness, heaviness or lightness, denseness or thinness

_____ 4. The three-dimensional shape of the plant

_____ 5. Gives the viewer's eye direction and movement

_____ 6. Contrast in the design achieved by selecting some plants with different qualities from the mass of plants

_____ 7. The proportion of one object to another

_____ 8. The uniformity of change from one item in the landscape to the next

EXPLORING

1. Take a walk around your neighborhood or school and try to identify features in plants that contribute to the plant's texture, form, and color. Why do some plants grab your attention before others?

2. Developing a critical eye is an important step in understanding principles of art. For a day, keep notes of your observations and surroundings. Study and note textures, colors, and line. Note aspects such as the texture of the carpet, the color of the wood trim, and the line of the furniture. Make similar notes in the school classroom.

3. Look at paintings at home or at school for the principles of art described in this chapter.

4. Use Figure 6-35 and assess the landscape at the front of the house on Mackinaw Island. How do you feel it follows principles of art? What would you do to improve the landscape? Prepare a short written report on your findings.

6-35. The entrance landscape to a stately home. (Courtesy, Education Images, Inc.)

Selecting Plants for the Design

CHAPTER 7

OBJECTIVES

1 Identify the types of plant materials used in landscaping.

2 Describe plant nomenclature and its importance.

3 Identify qualities to consider in selecting trees for the landscape.

4 Explain how to select shrubs for the landscape.

5 Describe how to best use flowers in the landscape.

6 Explain how to locate and draw plants on the landscape plan.

7 Describe how a plan is labeled.

TERMS

accent
annual
biennial
border garden bed
bulb
color rendering
color rotation
cultivar
foundation plant
genus

ground cover
group planting
hardiness
hedge
herbaceous perennial
island bed
ornamental grass
ornamental tree
perennial
plant nomenclature

screen
shade tree
shrub
shrub border
species
specimen plant
title block
tree
variety
vine

7-1. Plants are the major building blocks of residential landscapes.

IMAGINE baking a homemade apple pie from scratch without any knowledge of ingredients. You cannot identify flour, sugar, eggs, lard, apples or other food products in the kitchen. Even if you could identify them, you would not know the amounts to use. Would you use wheat flour, soy flour, rye flour? In addition, you would need to know the reason for adding specific ingredients. Would you use lard for the crust or the filling? It is safe to say that without knowledge of the materials your pie would be a disaster.

The major ingredients in the landscape are plants. Instead of baking a pie, the landscaper is creating an attractive and functional landscape. Knowing the materials with which to work and the reason for using certain plants for certain situations has an immense impact on the final product.

PLANTS—BUILDING BLOCKS OF THE LANDSCAPE

The residential landscape is made of two different elements. There are the plant materials and physical structures. Of the two, plants are the most important. Plants are considered the major building blocks for a landscape. Physical structures in the landscape, such as patios, walls, and fences, are often needed to serve specific landscape functions. When they are well built, they are attractive. It is up to the landscape designer to determine the best selection and use of plants and physical structures.

7-2. Thousands of plants are available for use in the landscape. The designer of this landscape has used a variety of trees, shrubs, annuals, ground covers, and perennials.

In the design process explained in this book, the actual selection of the plant species, varieties, and cultivars is one of the last steps. A landscape designer has literally thousands of plants from which to choose for use in the landscape. How does the designer go about determining which plants to use? First, the designer must decide what function a plant has in the landscape. Is it to be a tree or a shrub? How large should the plant be? Is the plant to blend in with others or is it to be of high interest to attract attention? Also, plants are living organisms. How is the selection of plants influenced by the conditions a plant must have to live and be healthy? These are some questions a designer must answer before selecting specific plants to serve specific functions.

PLANT TYPES

It helps to know a little about the plants used for landscape purposes. Plants are available in thousands of different shapes and sizes for landscape use. Each type of plant serves a different purpose in the landscape.

Tree—A tree can be defined as a single-stem, woody, perennial plant reaching the height of 12 feet or more. An exception to this rule involves some trees, such as birches and alders, which are often grown with multiple stems that increase their ornamental value. Some trees are grown with limbs to the ground, such as beeches, firs, pines, and red maples. Also, trees may be deciduous or evergreen.

Shrub—Shrubs are multi-stem, woody plants that do not exceed 20 feet in height. In general, shrubs are about as tall as they are wide. They may be deciduous or evergreen. There are many types of shrubs from which to choose, including viburnums, honeysuckles, spireas, hollies, junipers, and yews.

7-3. Trees are single-stem, woody, perennial plants reaching the height of 12 feet or more. Shown is a Red Maple, *Acer rubrum*, in fall color.

7-4. Shrubs are multi-stem, woody plants that do not exceed 20 feet in height. Pictured is bottlebrush buckeye, *Aesculus parviflora*.

7-5. Ground covers are woody or herbaceous plants that form a mat less than one foot high covering the ground. Pictured is Japanese spurge, *Pachysandra terminalis*. (Courtesy, Midwest Groundcovers)

Ground cover—Ground cover may be woody or herbaceous. It forms a mat less than 1 foot high covering the ground. Grass is the most common plant used as a ground cover. Other common ground covers include English ivy, periwinkle (vinca), euonymus, and Japanese spurge (pachysandra).

Vines—A vine is a woody or herbaceous (soft stemmed) plant that requires some type of support. It may climb on objects or creep along the ground. Some ornamental vines include Boston ivy, wisteria, and clematis.

7-6. Vines are woody or herbaceous (soft stemmed) plants that require some type of support. Shown is Boston ivy, *Parthenocissus tricuspidata*.

Annuals—An annual is a herbaceous plan that lives for one growing season and is valued for the color its flowers or ornamental foliage add to the landscape. Common annuals are impatiens, marigolds, petunias, coleus, and zinnias.

Biennial—A plant that normally requires two growing seasons to produce flowers and seed before dying is known as a biennial. It grows foliage the first year and blooms the second year. There are relatively few biennials used in flower gardens. A few examples of biennial plants are foxglove, hollyhock, and blackberry lily.

7-7. Annuals are herbaceous plants valued for the color their flowers or ornamental foliage adds to the landscape.

7-8. In the landscape industry, perennial refers to herbaceous plants with life cycles of more than two years grown for their display of flowers or foliage. Pictured is the yellow *Coreopsis verticillata* 'Moonbeam' and the orange Poppy, *Papaver species.* (Courtesy, Midwest Groundcovers)

Perennial—Technically, a perennial is a plant that has a life cycle of more than two growing seasons. They may be woody as with trees and shrubs or herbaceous. ***Herbaceous Perennials*** have soft tissue and die back to the ground each winter. In the landscape industry, the term perennial refers to herbaceous plants with life cycles of more than two years grown for their display of flowers or foliage. Some popular perennials are daylilies, peonies, lilies, and iris.

Bulb—A special type of perennial is a bulb. In the horticulture industry, plants that have bulbs, corms, tubers, or rhizomes are often clumped together and called bulbs. Technically, a ***bulb*** is a short, flattened stem that bears fleshy, food-storage leaves. Most bulbs are planted in the fall and they flower the following spring, like tulips and daffodils. There are a few bulbs like gladiolas and tuberous begonia that are planted in the spring and flower in the summer.

Ornamental grasses—An ornamental grass is valued for its textures and colors which add interest to the landscape. Some ornamental grasses are annuals, while others are perennials. Some grow

7-9. Variegated Chinese Silver Grass, *Miscanthus sinensis* 'Variegatus,' is a warm season grass grown for its ornamental value. (Courtesy, University of Illinois Cooperative Extension Service)

best in warm climates, while others prefer cool climates. Use of ornamental grasses has grown in popularity in recent years.

PLANT NOMENCLATURE

There are so many trees, shrubs, ground covers, vines, annuals, and perennials, how does one begin to learn how to tell one plant from another? A good place to start is with plant nomenclature. **Plant nomenclature** is the naming of plants. Horticultural plants have two types of names, common names and botanical names. Plants often have more than one common name. For instance, the tuliptree may also be known as yellow poplar, tulip magnolia, tulip poplar, and whitewood depending on where you are in the United States. The number of common names can lead to confusion when people from different regions refer to the same plant by different names.

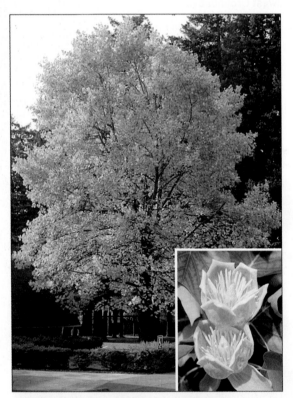

7-10. *Liriodendron tulipifera* **is known by many common names including yellow poplar, tuliptree, tulip magnolia, tulip poplar, blue poplar, whitewood, and yellowwood, but has only one Latin name. (Courtesy, J. Frank Schmidt & Son, Co., Boring, Oregon)**

In 1753, Carl von Linne (Linnaeus) of Sweden ushered in the beginning of the binomial system of naming plants. The binomial system of naming plants reduces confusion. All plants today, including landscape plant materials, are given a binomial name. This means each plant has two Latin names. The first of the two names is the genus, and the other is the specific epithet. So, the tuliptree, known by many different common names, can be clearly identified by its Latin name, *Liriodendron tulipifera*. The advantage to the binomial system is it is recognized and used by horticulturists around the world.

Most landscape customers know plants by their common names. In communicating effectively with the customer, the landscaper must know the common names of plants. However, it is equally important for the landscaper to be able to identify plants by their botanical name. This is especially true when ordering plants from nurseries, when reading professional literature, or when talking to people in the landscape industry from other regions of the country.

The **genus** is a closely related group of plants comprised of one or more species. Plants with the same genus are more similar to one another than with plants of other genera. Classification is based largely

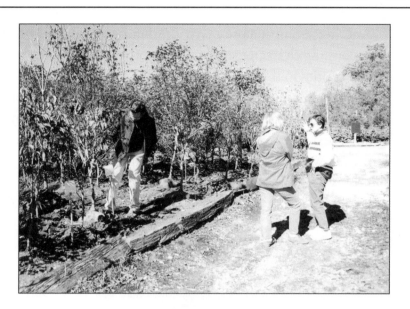

7-11. In communicating effectively with the customer, the landscaper must know the common names of plants.

on the structure of flowers and fruit and to some extent leaves, buds, roots, and stems. The generic name is written with a capital letter and underlined or italicized. For example, sugar maple, silver maple and other maples are more similar to one another than they are to plants of other genera. Therefore, they share a generic name. It is *Acer*.

The **species** is composed of plants that show characteristics that distinguish them from other groups in the genus. The species can pass distinct characteristics from one generation to the next. The specific epithet is written in lower case and underlined or italicized. There are many maples in the genus *Acer*. Some of these are distinct from the others. Although all the maples carry the *Acer* genus, the specific epithets differ. For instance, the specific epi-thet for the red maple is *rubrum* and the specific epithet for the Japanese maple is *palmatum*.

A group of plants within a species that show a significant difference from other plants in the species is termed a variety. The difference is inherited from the previous genera-tion through sexual reproduction. The variety follows the specific epi-thet and is written in lower case and underlined or italicized. A thornless variety of honey locust is written as follows: *Gledtisia triacanthos* var. *inermis* or *Gledtisia triacanthos inermis*

7-12. Obtain plants from nurseries where care is used to produce a quality product. (Courtesy, Education Images, Inc.)

Another group important to the landscape industry is **cultivar**. Some plants have distinguishing characteristics from the other plants in the species but do not transfer those characteristics to their offspring through sexual reproduction. Instead, they must be propagated asexually, possibly through grafting or cuttings. For example, the Crimson King Norway Maple with maroon leaf color is distinct, but cannot pass on the unique feature through sexual reproduction. Because it is technically different from a variety, it is written with each word of the cultivar name capitalized and with single quotations. The correct name is written as *Acer platanoides* 'Crimson King.'

7-13. Autumn Purple White Ash, *Fraxinus americana* **'Autumn Purple', is a cultivar selected for outstanding fall color.**

SELECTING TREES

One of the first things to consider in the selection of trees for the landscape is the appearance of the plant. Quality trees are said to have a four-season value. That means the tree has attractive qualities at any time of the year. This includes showy and possibly fragrant flowers, good-looking appearance, healthy foliage in the summer, beautiful fall color and fruit effects, and winter interest created by the branching structure or bark color. Quality trees also have a symmetrical form or shape. However, trees should not be selected on their appearance alone. Other factors need to be considered.

7-14. Landscape plants are valued for various ornamental features including; (a) flowers, *Malus* species (b) fruit, *Malus* species (c) foliage, *Nyssa sylvatica* and (d) bark, *Betula nigra*.

Trees are the largest and most permanent plant material used in the landscape. Some shade trees may grow 100 feet tall and some may live for hundreds of years. Because of their size, fewer trees are used in the landscape than shrubs or ground cover plants. A large residential landscape may only have 5 to 10 trees. The same landscape may have 50 or more shrubs and hundreds of ground cover plants. Proper selection of trees for the landscape involves the line, form, texture, and color, (discussed in Chapter 5) that contribute to an aesthetically pleasing landscape. Proper selection is also important in terms of the future health and vigor of the tree. Selecting trees tolerant of the growing environment results in an attractive landscape many years after the trees have been installed.

7-15. This Pagoda dogwood, *Cornus alternifolia*, has declined over 10 years due to the heavy clay soil in which it was planted. The plant selection was poor for the location.

7-16. Shade trees are described as large trees, with spreading canopies, such as this Silver Maple, *Acer saccharinum*.

7-17. Smaller trees with high ornamental value, such as this flowering crabapple (*Malus sp.*), are often called ornamental trees.

FUNCTION

When selecting a tree, consider the function it is intended to serve. Some trees lend themselves well to specific uses. Large trees, with spreading canopies, such as sugar maples, red oaks, and tuliptrees, make good **shade trees**. Shade trees are preferred for use in residential lawns, parks, and along streets. Trees that are smaller and have high ornamental value are often called **ornamental trees**. Some ornamental trees include flowering dogwood, flowering crabapples, redbud, crape myrtle, and Japanese maple. Ornamental trees are suggested for smaller areas and when high visual interest, such as a display of flowers in spring, is desired.

During the design process, allow for the mature size of the tree. Avoid placing a large tree too close to the house. The view of the house may be blocked as the tree grows or structural damage may be caused. Also, avoid planting large trees below power lines and telephone wires. The lines and wires can be damaged as the tree grows. Trees beneath power lines are frequently pruned severely by utility companies to protect the wires.

Decide if the trees are to stand alone or if they are to form a group. If grouping is desired, place the trees closer to one another. Grouping of visually active, upright evergreens including spruce and fir is often desired to soften the visual effect of an individual tree.

7-18. Group visually active, upright evergreens to soften the visual effect of an individual tree. Notice how the evergreens provide a backdrop for the Burning bush, *Euonymus alatus,* in fall color.

HARDINESS

Select trees that are hardy. **Hardiness** refers to the ability of a tree to withstand cold temperatures. Trees have differing abilities to survive in areas in the United States. Southern magnolia, *Magnolia grandiflora*, can survive in the warm southern states, but is not tolerant of the cold winter temperatures of the northern states. Hardiness zones in the United States have been established. The U. S. Department of Agriculture Plant Hardiness Zone Map is useful in deciding what trees will survive in your region.

To benefit from the plant hardiness zone map, begin by identifying what zone the landscape is

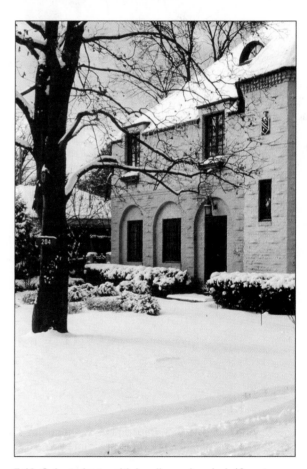

7-19. Select plants with hardiness in mind. (Courtesy, Church Landscaping)

within. For example, Champaign, Illinois is in zone 5 where the average minimum winter temperature is between –20 and –10 degrees Fahrenheit. Then, read the literature that states what zone the trees you are considering can survive. If they match, the tree is tolerant to the average minimum temperature in that zone. Usually, trees survive over several zones. For instance, Southern magnolia grows in zone 6 with average minimum temperatures of –10 to 0 degrees Fahrenheit and in warmer zones. It would not be a good choice for the zone 5 Champaign, Illinois landscape that gets below –10 degrees.

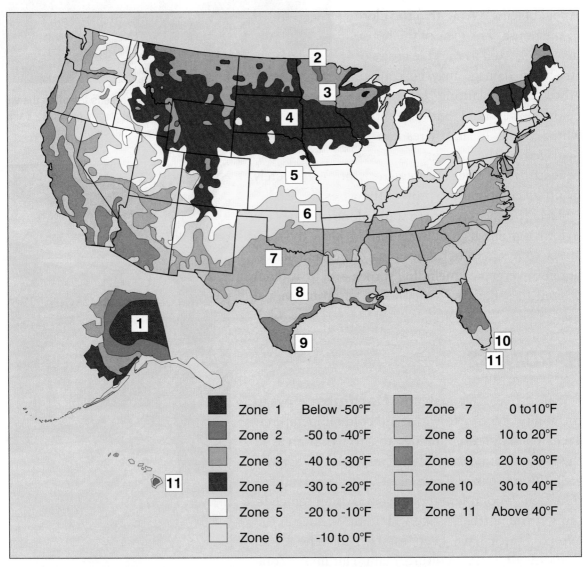

▪	Zone 1	Below -50°F	▪	Zone 7	0 to10°F
▪	Zone 2	-50 to -40°F	▫	Zone 8	10 to 20°F
▪	Zone 3	-40 to -30°F	▪	Zone 9	20 to 30°F
▪	Zone 4	-30 to -20°F	▫	Zone 10	30 to 40°F
▫	Zone 5	-20 to -10°F	▪	Zone 11	Above 40°F
▫	Zone 6	-10 to 0°F			

7-20. The U. S. Department of Agriculture Hardiness Zone Map is useful in selecting landscape plants based on tolerance to cold temperatures. The map shows the average annual minimum temperatures of 11 zones.

Hardiness of trees is more important than just survival. Some trees valued for outstanding spring floral displays, such as flowering dogwood and magnolia, may grow in cold climates. Unfortunately, the flower buds are not as hardy as the tree. In cold winters, the flower buds are sometimes the only parts of the tree damaged.

TIP: Consult the hardiness zone and heat-zone maps when selecting plant materials.

7-21. Newly establish palm trees are in a parking lot. Such plants are adapted to warm climates. (Courtesy, Education Images, Inc.)

HEAT TOLERANCE

Heat also plays a role in the performance of plant species. Some plants are more sensitive to heat than others. The plant heat-zone map has been developed by the American Horticultural Society to help identify areas in which landscape plants can flourish. The map shows 12 zones. Each zone reflects a rating of summer heat based on the average number of days above 86°F. Eighty-six degrees is a temperature at which plants are unable to process water fast enough to maintain normal functions. Plants also experience damage to cellular proteins.

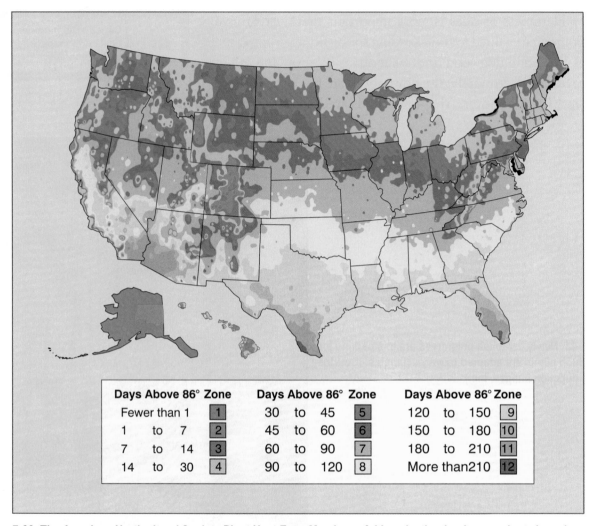

Days Above 86°		Zone	Days Above 86°		Zone	Days Above 86°		Zone
Fewer than 1		1	30	to 45	5	120	to 150	9
1	to 7	2	45	to 60	6	150	to 180	10
7	to 14	3	60	to 90	7	180	to 210	11
14	to 30	4	90	to 120	8	More than 210		12

7-22. The American Horticultural Society Plant Heat-Zone Map is useful in selecting landscape plants based on tolerance to hot temperatures. The map shows the average number of days that exceed 86°F.

Southern landscapers have found the plant heat-zone map very useful. Consult the hardiness zone and heat-zone maps when selecting plant materials. Plant labels often provide information as to the hardiness zones and heat-zones for which the plants are adapted.

MESSINESS

Avoid using trees that are known to be messy. Messiness may be in the form of fruit, peeling bark, and easily broken twigs that litter the landscape. Some varieties of crabapples, honeylocust, and sweetgum produce large numbers of fruit that require cleaning. Sycamores and hickories have peeling bark that forms debris below the tree. Siberian elms have brittle twigs that break easily in winds and fall to the ground. Messy trees increase the labor needed to maintain the appearance of the landscape.

LIFE EXPECTANCY AND GROWTH RATE

Another consideration is the life expectancy of trees. Some trees, like oak, beech, and Douglasfir, can be expected to live hundreds of years. Others, including some types of poplars, elms, maples, and cherries, are short lived. Some of these trees may show signs of decline after only 15 to 20 years in the landscape. Short-lived trees tend to be fast growing. While fast growth is desirable to someone in a new landscape, it does have drawbacks. Fast growing trees have weaker wood and are more likely to suffer storm damage.

7-23. Although ornamental, the fruits of some trees are known to be messy.

PEST RESISTANCE

Choose trees resistant to disease and insect problems. If a tree has beautiful characteristics, but is susceptible to insect infestations and diseases, its value is reduced. Some trees are vulnerable to certain problems, while others are not. American sycamores suffer from a fungal disease called **anthracnose**. A tree similar in appearance, the London planetree, is resistant to anthracnose. Selecting the London planetree over the American sycamore will reduce problems later. Some crabapple cultivars are terribly susceptible to apple scab, which can defoliate a tree. Other cultivars are resistant to apple scab. The smart designer selects trees known to be relatively disease free. The paper birch has been decimated in some parts of the country by an insect known as the bronze birch borer. If a birch must be included in the design, use birches resistant to the insect attacks, such as the river birch.

7-24. In some climates Lombardy Black Poplars, *Populus nigra* 'Italica', are short-lived trees.

7-25. The American Sycamore, *Platanus occidentalis*, at the center of this photograph is slow to leaf out due to anthracnose.

7-26. This Pin Oak, *Quercus palustris*, shows signs of nutrient deficiency due to high soil pH.

PHYSIOLOGICAL FACTORS

Trees may suffer physiological disease. A common problem involves the pH of the soil. pH is a measure of acidity or alkalinity of a soil. The pH scale ranges from an extremely acid reading of 1 to an extremely alkaline reading of 14. A neutral reading is seven. Most plants prefer a soil pH between 5.5 and 7.0. If the pH is outside that range, nutrients become unavailable to the plant. Without the ability to absorb certain nutrients, the plant sickens, the leaves show symptoms of discoloration (often yellowing), and the tree may die. It is much wiser to select trees that tolerate the soil pH found on the site than to change the pH of the soil to accommodate the tree.

Select trees that tolerate the moisture level in the soil. Most trees prefer loose, well-drained soils. If you have a situation where the soil is wet and the conditions cannot be easily corrected, select trees that will tolerate those conditions, such as baldcypress, red maple, and river birch. In other cases, the soil may be sandy and prone to dry quickly. Use trees tolerant to dry soils, such as hackberry, honeylocust, and pines.

OTHER CONSIDERATIONS

There are other considerations when selecting trees. Avoid using trees with thorns that could present safety hazards in certain settings. Native honeylocusts and some hawthorns have dangerously sharp thorns. Con-

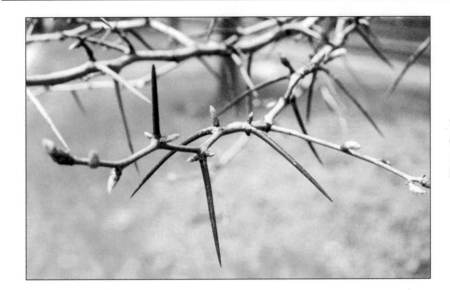

7-27. The thorns on this Cockspur Hawthorn, *Crataegus crusgalli*, could be dangerous.

sider the rooting habits of the trees. The roots of Norway maples grow at the surface of the ground. This makes it difficult to grow grass or other plants beneath the tree. Also, consider the density of the shade cast by the tree. Honeylocusts are open, allowing sunlight to reach the ground and permitting grass growth. On the other hand, Norway maples, American elms, and other trees create dense shade making it difficult to grow grass or other plants underneath. Some plants can also be selected to attract wildlife to the landscape. Birds in particular are attracted to the edible fruit of some trees and shrubs.

A final consideration involves the harsh growing conditions found in many urban centers. A consideration for plant selection in these areas is the tree's tolerance to pollution and salt. Ginkgo, red oak, and littleleaf linden are examples of trees tolerant of pollution. Honeylocust, goldenraintree, and green ash are three trees with salt tolerance. They would be appropriate where de-icing salts are used.

7-28. The shade of this Norway Maple, *Acer platanoides*, is dense and prevents grass growth below.

SELECTING SHRUBS

Shrubs have multiple functions in the landscape. They can be used as specimen plants, group plantings, hedges, screens, foundation plants, or shrub borders. Select shrubs based on their intended use. Also, consider their flowers, foliage, branching habits, and suitability to the growing conditions. Many considerations discussed in the selection of trees apply to the selection of shrubs. A definition for different uses of shrubs follows:

Specimen plants—A specimen plant displays outstanding form, texture, and color. Because of its qualities, it can stand alone. When placed with other plants in a grouping, it should be planted so it can be seen and enjoyed as an individual plant.

Group plantings—Group plantings consist of several different species of shrubs. The importance of each individual plant is lower within group plantings than it is with a specimen plant. The individuals of each species are located so they will overlap slightly with each other to form a mass or there may be some space left between the plants.

Interest in the design can be raised by the numbers of materials used. Use odd numbers of materials to create interest for the viewer. Design the plan using three, five, and seven shrubs grouped together.

7-29. This Ginkgo, *Ginkgo biloba*, shown in fall color is very resistant to pollution damage making it a good tree for city streets.

7-30. This Rhododendron displays outstanding characteristics and could be used as a specimen plant. (Courtesy, Midwest Groundcovers)

Hedges—Hedges consist of all one type of shrub. They define space, they tie other landscape elements together, and they may screen views. Some hedges are 20 feet tall while others may be only 1 foot in height. Hedges can be clipped for a formal appearance or they can be unclipped for an informal, natural look.

Screens—A screen is a solid mass of one type of shrub. It serves as a living wall that effectively blocks views. The ideal shrubs for use as screens are tall, narrow, upright plants.

Foundation plants—Foundation plants are shrubs placed around the foundation of the house. They help tie the house to the landscape by softening the corners, and they block the view of the foundation. It is best to use shrubs that do not get very large.

Shrub borders—A mass of many shrubs on the border of the property is called a shrub border. Shrub borders help to create the outdoor living room, screen views, and serve as a backdrop for annual and perennial flowers. Unlike the group planting, draw all the shrubs in the shrub border to touch or overlap one another to form a single mass.

7-31. Group plantings consist of several different species of shrubs and trees. (Courtesy, Midwest Groundcovers)

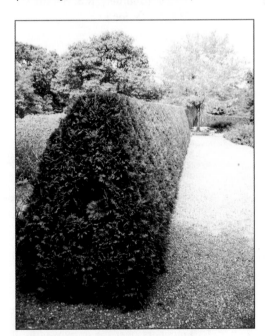

7-32. This clipped Eastern Arborvitae, *Thuja occidentalis*, hedge defines space, ties other landscape elements together, and screens views.

7-33. This row of rose shrubs serves as an effective screen. (Courtesy, Midwest Groundcovers)

7-34. Foundation plants are shrubs placed around the foundation of the house.

7-35. A mass of many shrubs on the border of the property is called a shrub border. (Courtesy, R.S. Hursthouse & Associates, Inc.)

SELECTING FLOWERS

Annuals and perennials have many uses in the landscape. When placed in the proper environment and given periodic maintenance, these flowering plants can become an asset to any well-designed landscape.

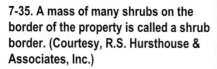

TIP: Limit your use of flowers to the outdoor living area or in small numbers near the entry way in the public area.

Annual and perennial flowers provide an accent of color to the landscape. *Accent* is special emphasis provided by striking or prominent features of the landscape plants or structures. The bright flower and foliage colors are visually appealing. However, because the colors attract the attention of the viewer, they must be used with caution.

Limit your use of flowers in the public area. Remember, the house is the most important feature of the landscape. Bright-colored flowers can easily attract the attention of the viewer, which should be directed to the house. Flowers placed between foundation plants, lining driveways, and in island beds in the front lawn divert attention from the house and are considered poor design. A few flowers placed by the front door are acceptable as the flowers help to call attention to the door.

The best place for extensive use of flowers is in the outdoor living area. In the outdoor living area, plant flowers in full view of the patio, deck, or interior rooms. Here, flowers can be enjoyed without detracting from the house. Again, be careful not to overwhelm the viewer with color. Use the flowers to create high interest areas within the design. Overuse of flowers disrupts the relaxing effect of the landscape achieved through the use of green plants.

Select annuals and perennials adapted for the growing conditions in the landscape. Two of the most critical environmental fac-

7-36. Select flowering annual plants that are healthy and growing. (Courtesy, Education Images, Inc.)

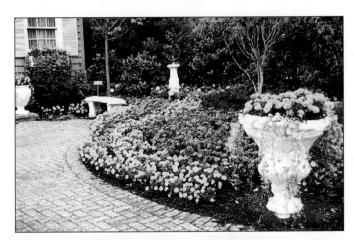

7-37. Flowers have high visual energy and can dominate the residential landscape if not used with caution.

7-38. A few flowers placed by the front door help to call attention to the door.

7-39. Plant flowers in full view of the patio, deck, or interior rooms. (Courtesy, R.S. Hursthouse & Associates, Inc.)

tors for growing flowers are the amount of sunlight and the amount of moisture. Be sure to check a reference book to find out which plants prefer sun, shade, dry soils, or moist soils. It is very important that the soil is in the right condition for perennials because these plants will stay in the garden for many years.

DESIGNING A FLOWER BORDER

The most important thing to do before actually planting a flower garden is to place the garden design on paper. Decisions should be made on the purpose of the garden and the location of the garden. The growing conditions should be evaluated. Then, plants can be selected to fit the design needs. Advanced planning is necessary to purchase the correct type and number of flowers and avoid having to make changes to the garden later.

Two types of flower gardens are the border garden and the island bed. A **border garden** is placed along a fence or a wall in the yard. It is usually viewed from only one side. An **island bed** is placed in the center of a yard with the tall plants in the center of the garden and the shorter plants toward the outer edges.

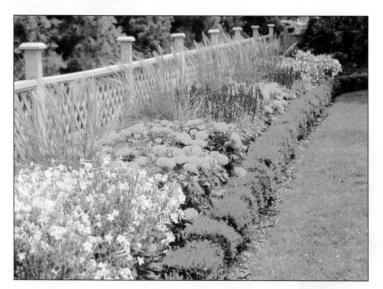

7-40. This design has the flower border planted in front of a fence. (Courtesy, University of Illinois Cooperative Extension Service)

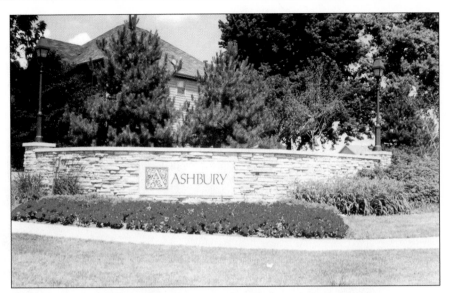

7-41. Plant flowers in drifts of the same varieties.

The best designs for a border garden are angled or incurved flower beds. The angled or incurved bed pattern itself creates interest. With flower borders it is important to design the bed so that it is no more than five feet in depth. This allows for easy maintenance, and view of all the flowering plants. Taller plants should be placed in the back of the garden with the shorter plants up front. The designer should also avoid a stair step look when viewed from the side of the garden. This can be accomplished by staggering the location of the various heights of plants.

It is best to use flowers in combination with woody plants. Effective flower border designs have flowers located in front of woody plant materials or physical structures, such as fences and walls. Woody plants with green foliage provide an excellent backdrop for the flowers.

Warm color flowers are powerful and should be used sparingly in small landscapes as they tend to close in on the viewer. Follow the principle of design of sequence, and select flowers with colors that provide a smooth transition from one drift to the next. Place coarse-textured flower-

1. Peony
2. Salvia (annual)
3. Oriental Poppy
4. Geranium
5. Lily Bulbs
6. Iris
7. Purple Coneflower
8. Pennisetum (ornamental grass)
9. Dianthus
10. Daylily
11. Achillea
12. Petunia (annual)
13. Chrysanthemum
14. Dahlia (annual)

7-42. Angled or incurved flower beds work best for designing a flower border.

ing plants at the ends to provide strength and to frame the flowers in the incurve.

Plant the flowers in drifts of the same varieties. Drifts of color are bold in appearance and striking. Avoid mixing individual flower varieties and colors within a flower bed. The spattering of different colors in a flower bed has a busy appearance and is difficult for the viewer to process.

7-43. River rock has been used to provide an outline and border for planting an annual bed with a small tree in the upper circle. (Courtesy, Education Images, Inc.)

COLOR ROTATION

Flowers provide seasonal displays of color. Sometimes only a few months of color can be expected from a type of plant. Mix groups of annual flowers with groups of perennials to extend and enrich the floral display. The length of time a flower bed shows color can be extended by applying a color rotation strategy. Color rotation involves the cycle of several floral displays in one growing season. In spring, the flower bed may display flowers of spring flowering bulbs, such as tulips, narcissus, and hyacinths. When the bulbs finish flowering, they are replaced with annuals including petunias, marigolds, and impatiens. A third planting occurs as temperatures drop in the fall. The fall bed might display chrysanthemums or ornamental cabbage.

Perennial flower gardens have increased in popularity. There are some very good reasons for this. Perennial gardens provide a natural appearance to landscape. Perennial plants are not planted every year the way annual plants are, and they require somewhat less maintenance. Perennial gardens can be designed to have showy displays at different times of the year, giving a look that changes. Many unusual and interesting plants are available for use in the perennial garden.

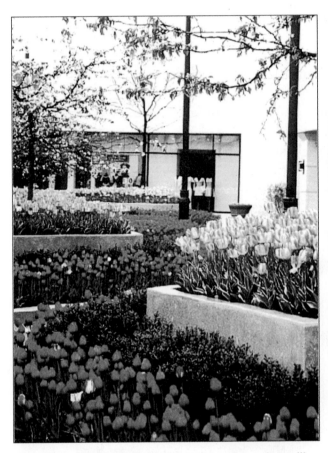

7-44. These tulips, which provide color in the spring, will be followed by annuals for summer color, which in turn will be replaced by chrysanthemums for fall color. (Courtesy, Church Landscape)

7-45. In some parts of the country, perennial gardens consist of native plants for a natural prairie look. (Courtesy, Church Landscaping)

DRAWING PLANTS INTO YOUR PLAN

Now that you have a greater understanding of the materials used in landscaping and their functions, you can begin design work with plants. Plant size is the next consideration in the design process. Basic steps to placing plants on the plan include:

1. Locating trees on the plan
2. Drawn at mature size using simple circles, locate shrubs within planting beds
3. Assign desired textures and colors to the plant symbols
4. Select plants that meet size, texture, and colors determined in the previous steps
5. Trace the plan onto quality vellum using plant symbols

It is advisable to begin by drawing a rough draft of the landscape plan. Bed patterns have been established in previous design steps. Locate all of the plants within the planting beds, except those trees placed in the lawn. On the first draft of the landscape plan or on an overlay of trash paper, draw light circles that represent the different trees and shrubs. Detailed plant symbols can be drawn as the final plan is completed. A rough draft of the plan allows for erasures and some messiness as you try different solutions to the plan.

LOCATE TREES

Draw simple circles to represent the trees. Refer to the discussion in Chapter 5 on locating trees. Some trees are extremely large at maturity. It is acceptable to use symbols smaller than the mature size of the larger trees to provide an easy-to-read plan.

TIP: Locate all of the plants within the planting beds, except those trees placed in the lawn.

7-46. Draw circles that represent the different trees and shrubs at their mature size in the planting beds.

LOCATE SHRUBS

Draw the shrubs at their mature size in the planting beds. For instance, if you want a grouping of 6- foot shrubs, draw 3/4 inch (the same as 6/8 at 1/8 inch scale) circles using the circle template. Careful measurements obtained during the site analysis are very helpful in determining the size of foundation plantings. Too often, people place shrubs in the landscape while they are small without knowing that the plant has a natural tendency to get quite large.

> **TIP:** Draw the shrubs at their mature size in the planting beds.

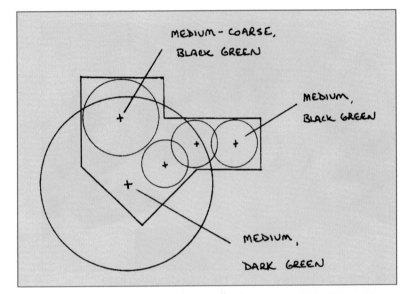

7-47. Assign each plant or grouping of one species a desired texture and color.

Locate plants in the planting bed by placing the larger shrubs toward the back of the bed. Smaller plants should be placed in front of these. The smallest plant material should be to the front of the planting. Also, group plants of the same species by slightly overlapping your symbols. Shrubs that are planted close enough to one another to form a massing create a more attractive view than individual shrubs scattered throughout the planting bed.

DETERMINE TEXTURES AND COLORS

Once the size of the plants has been decided, determine if the plants are to be evergreen, deciduous, or broadleaf evergreen. Then, assign each plant or grouping of one species a desired texture and color. Abbreviations for textures include: C – coarse, MC – medium coarse, M – medium, MF – medium fine, and F – fine. Abbreviations for colors include: G – emerald green, BLG – blue-green, YG – yellow-green, RG – red-green, GG – gray-green, and BG – black-green. As you choose these plant characteristics, keep the principles of design in mind.

SELECT PLANT NAMES

The next step is to select the plants that fulfill the description you have established in the previous steps. Refer to reference books that describe woody plant materials. For example, you may have decided that the plan calls for a grouping of 6- foot shrubs that are of medium texture and emerald green. Looking at the reference materials, you find that the compact American cranberrybush viburnum (*Viburnum trilobum compactum*) and dwarf winged euonymus (*Euonymus alatus compactus*) are two plants with these characteristics. Consider other factors, such as hardiness, shade requirements, fall color, etc. before making your final choice.

DRAW PLANT SYMBOLS

Up to now, all of your work has been rough and your plan is probably a bit messy. At this point, tape a piece of quality vellum over your rough plan. Take care to center the drawing. Trace the house walls and paved areas onto the clean, vellum paper. Now, trace the bed patterns. Slight changes may be necessary at this point to make a more functional and attractive design. The last items to trace are the plant symbols.

It is helpful to use symbols in your design work that represent the different types of plants. The symbol styles used vary from one designer to the next. Most designers have developed their own symbols over the years. The style you adopt is not as important as whether the plan is easy to read and attractive. Keep in mind that many plans sell primarily because the customers find them attractive.

Use different symbols for the various types of plants in the plan. Draw evergreen plants, deciduous plants, broadleaf evergreens, ground covers, and vines with their own symbols. Be sure to indi-

7-48. Select the plants that fulfill the description you have established in the previous steps.

7-49. Use symbols to represent different types of plants on the final plan. (Courtesy, University of Illinois Cooperative Extension Service)

cate the center of all trees and shrubs with a dot or a + sign. The center point tells the installation crews where to locate the plants.

7-50. Examples of plant symbols.

Deciduous Trees

Evergreen Trees

Broadleaf Evergreen Trees

Deciduous Shrubs

Evergreen Shrubs

Deciduous Hedge

Evergreen Hedge

Broadleaf Evergreen Hedge

Ground Cover

Gravel

Cobbles

The plan can also be easier to read if the larger trees are drawn with a darker line than the smaller plants. The darker line gives the appearance of the tree providing a canopy over the other plants. Draw the darkest lines last to reduce smudging of the plan. Keep the tree symbols simple if there are plantings beneath them.

TIP: Draw tree symbols darker than the smaller plants in order to make the plan easier to read.

COLOR RENDERING

It is important for the landscape designer to present his or her plan to the client in an attractive way. Color also can make the plan easier to read. Giving symbols and hardscape features different colors allows the viewer to easily distinguish between the different materials. One way to enhance a landscape design is to add color to the plan using markers or colored pencils. The process by which the designer adds color to a landscape plan is called *color rendering*. Plant material and physical features like a pool or driveway are colored. Different shades of color are used to create the appearance of depth and shadows within the

7-51. At work on a plan. (Courtesy, Eddie Seagle, Abraham Baldwin Agricultural College)

7-52. A plan drawn with final plant symbols. Notice how the color enhances the appearance. (Courtesy, R.S. Hursthouse & Associates, Inc.)

plan. Start by coloring the entire plant with a light color. With a medium shade, color about half of the plant, and then, with a darker color, color half of that. Try to blend the colors together.

When a plan has a tree with a lot of underplantings, the designer can choose to color the tree or the shrubs under the tree. If the designer colors the shrubs, the tree is usually just outlined in color.

An effective rendering technique provides shadows that create a 3-D appearance. All the plants are colored as if the sun were shining on them from one direction. The shadows are drawn on the side opposite the light source.

LABELING

On the final plan, it is important to provide information that will make the plan easier to read. This is achieved through labeling. Plants, hardscape materials, a title block, and directional information are labeling items. The design should be labeled in such a way that the average person can read what is being presented.

There are a number of practices that if followed can result in understandable labeling. Try to keep the plan neat while labeling. Print clearly, using upper case letters. Hand printing gives a personal touch to the plan. Labeling with computerized programs has benefits as well; the plan is often easier to read. Also, label the plan in an organized manner. The logical way to label is to begin at one point of the plan and move in a clockwise fashion.

The plant list is a catalog of plants that are called for in the landscape plan. Plant lists include both the Latin name of the plant and the common name. The plants are labeled by using numbers or letters. This can be done by drawing a line to the center of a plant symbol. Then, a ¼ inch circle can be placed at the end of the line in which a labeling number or letter is placed. The number or letter assigned to each plant corresponds with that number or letter in the plant list. Some designers use alternative labeling methods. One involves drawing a line to the center of the plant symbol extending to an open area. At the end of the line the plant name is written.

Notes are labeled in a fashion similar to the plant list. This second list includes information regarding hardscape features, soil preparation, mulch, edging material, etc.

7-53. A style of letters and numbers that can be used for labeling.

7-54. This design shows plants labeled with numbers and hardscape features with letters.

THE TITLE BLOCK

The **title block** provides the reader with essential information. The client's name for whom the design is prepared should appear in a title block. The client's name might be used as the drawing title. For example, the most prominent line in the title block might say "The Thomas Residence." Record the scale at which the design is drawn (for example, scale: 1/8 inch

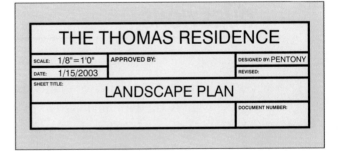

7-55. An example of the title box for a plan.

= 1'0"). Also, date the plan and include the designer's name. In an open area on the plan, indicate which direction is north in relation to the site. Any number of arrow symbols can be used to indicate north.

REVIEWING

MAIN IDEAS

Plants are the major building blocks of the landscape. The plants used include trees, shrubs, ground covers, vines, annuals, and perennials. All plants have been given a Latin name. The two-part Latin name consisting of the genus and the specific epithet eliminates confusion that occurs with common names. The genus and species names are given based on the similarity of flowers, leaves, stems, and fruit.

Trees are the largest element of the landscape. Trees are placed on the landscape plan before other plants. A number of considerations go into the selection of specific trees. Consider the principles of design (line, form, texture, and color), the mature size, hardiness, and life expectancy. Consider the messiness, growth rate, insect and disease resistance, and pollution and salt tolerance of the tree. Also, consider soil conditions, safety factors, such as thorns, and shade effect.

Shrubs are used in greater numbers than trees. They also have many purposes. Specimen shrubs are those that are outstanding in their qualities of form, texture, and color. Group plantings consist of several different species of shrubs. A hedge is a row of shrubs that define space and may be clipped or unclipped. Shrubs of all one species that block a view are screens. Foundation plants are those planted in front of the house foundation. Shrub borders consist of many species of shrubs that have similar form, texture, and color creating the look of oneness.

Flowers add color to the landscape. Because of their bright colors, they need to be used with caution to avoid dominating the landscape. Avoid placing flowers in the public area as they divert attention away from the house. In the outdoor living area, place flowers in drifts within the shrub border. The shrubs provide a backdrop for the flowers.

Begin placing landscape plant materials on the rough draft of the plan using circles to represent the plants. Draw the circles to scale to establish the size of plants needed. Next, assign qualities of design including texture and color to each plant or plant group. Once the plant characteristics have been established, use reference materials to select specific plants. On the final plan, draw the plant materials with symbols that help to differentiate the plant types.

QUESTIONS

Answer the following questions using correct spelling and complete sentences.

1. What are the types of plants used in the landscape? Describe each.
2. Why is the binomial system of plant nomenclature important?
3. How do varieties and cultivars differ?
4. What factors must be considered in selecting trees?
5. What are the major uses of shrubs in the landscape? Explain each.
6. Why is it difficult to use flowers in the public area?
7. Why is it important to draw plants at their mature size on the landscape plan?
8. What are the steps for selecting plants for the design beginning with the drawing of circles to choosing plant names?
9. Why are symbols used to represent different plant types?

CHAPTER SELF-CHECK

Match the term with the correct definition. Write the letter by the term in the blank provided.

a. hardiness   e. hedges   h. shade trees
b. genus   f. cultivar   i. annuals
c. shrubs   g. tree   j. ground cover
d. foundation plants

_____1. Refers to the ability of a plant to withstand cold temperatures

_____2. Plants that have distinguishing characteristics from the other plants in the species, but do not transfer those characteristics to their offspring through sexual reproduction

_____3. Multi-stem, woody plants that do not exceed 20 feet in height

_____4. A single-stem, woody, perennial plant reaching the height of 12 feet

_____5. Large trees, with spreading canopies, such as sugar maples, red oaks, and tuliptrees

_____6. Shrubs placed around the foundation of the house

_____7. All of one type of plant that can be clipped for a formal appearance or left unclipped for an informal, natural look

_____8. Herbaceous plants that live for one growing season and are valued for the color their flowers or ornamental foliage adds to the landscape

_____9. A closely related group of plants comprised of one or more species

_____10. Woody or herbaceous plants that form a mat less than 1 foot high covering the ground

EXPLORING

1. Locate plants on your rough landscape plan. Draw circles to scale to represent the trees and shrubs.

2. Determine if the plants are to be evergreen, deciduous, or broadleaf evergreens. Then, decide what texture and leaf color each type of plant should have.

3. Based on the sizes, textures, and colors established in the previous steps, choose plants to fill the needs of your design. Use reference books to help you with the plant selection. Also, minor changes, such as adjusting size, texture, and color requirements, are permitted as you follow this process.

4. Place a piece of good quality vellum paper over your rough draft. Trace the design including the house, walks, driveway, patio, bed patterns, and plants. As you trace the plants, use symbols that represent the different plant types.

CHAPTER 8

Pricing the Plan

OBJECTIVES

1 Define landscape estimates and bids.

2 Describe landscape specifications.

3 Explain how to prepare an estimate for landscape work.

TERMS

area measurements
bid
contingency costs
cost summation

estimate
estimate sheet
linear measurements
overhead costs

Planimeter/Digitizer
profit
specifications
volume measurements

8-1. Landscaping is a business.

S money important to you? It probably is to landscape customers. Money, often hard earned, gives people an opportunity to have landscape work performed on their property. Naturally, customers would like the best materials available, quality service, and timely results for their money. Most customers will approach several landscape companies in search of the best price for landscape work.

Money is definitely important to the landscaper as pay for services performed. Money received pays for salaries and other business expenses. Money allows the landscaper to stay in business. But what if the landscaper consistently prices the work too high? Work may be lost to competitors. This chapter centers on pricing landscape construction work.

LANDSCAPE ESTIMATES AND BIDS

Work for the designer is not limited to the design of the landscape plan. The landscape designer is also involved in determining the price of landscape work. Pricing of landscape work involves two common business procedures. The two terms used for these procedures are the estimate and the bid.

THE LANDSCAPE ESTIMATE

An **estimate** is an approximate price for the work to be done. The estimate includes the cost for materials and labor. The materials needed for the project must be counted. The number of workers required and the time it takes them to complete the project are also calculated. Experience in the industry is of great help to the designer in determining an estimate, because the designer must anticipate the costs for the entire project. Depending on the importance or the size of the project, the designer may spend anywhere from minutes to hours to complete an estimate.

TIP: An estimate is an approximate price for the work to be done.

8-2. Shown are the designer and the owner of a landscape company discussing the price of a landscape project.

The estimate is presented to the customer as a proposal as discussed in Chapter 2. The price quoted in an estimate is flexible. The final cost to the customer may change as actual costs are learned. Sometimes, the landscape installation takes longer than expected or additional materials are needed that alter the cost of the project. It is important for the customer to understand that the price may change because of these unanticipated costs. The advantage of the estimate is it gives the customer an idea as to the cost of the landscape project.

THE LANDSCAPE BID

A **bid** is a fixed price placed on the landscape work to be done. A bid differs from an estimate in that the bid price cannot be changed once it is accepted without the agreement of the customer. Bids are common when more than one company is competing for a particular project. Each company may prepare and submit a bid based on their estimated costs. Usually the low bid wins the customer's business.

> **TIP:** A bid differs from an estimate in that the bid price cannot be changed once it has been accepted without the agreement of the customer.

Because bidding is competitive, there is a tendency to want to present as low of a price as possible. However, landscapers must take care not to lower their offer so much that they lose money. Over the long term, landscape companies that lose money through low bids lower the value of the landscape industry. If it happens often enough, the companies go out of business. Therefore, landscapers must take great care to perform accurate calculations to ensure a fair profit.

LANDSCAPE SPECIFICATIONS

To establish the accurate pricing of a job, the designer must first specify what the project includes. **Specifications** are written descriptions of landscape materials, work, and time schedules for a project. Specifications include the details of the project. Some examples are the size of each plant, the number of plants, the depth of the mulch, instructions for soil amendments, and the installation techniques for the patio.

The quality of landscape materials can vary widely. Individual plant species of the same size may command different prices. A 3-inch Sugar Maple, *Acer saccharum*, is less expensive than a patented cultivar, such as the Green Mountain Sugar Maple. Of course, the Green Mountain Sugar Maple has been selected for outstanding characteristics. The price of the tree also hinges on the care it received while it was being grown. A high-quality Green Mountain Sugar Maple pruned properly during its develop-

8-3. The value of plant material depends on the variety selected as well as the manner in which it was grown.

8-4. Good quality container-grown landscape trees. (Courtesy, Education Images, Inc.)

ment will have an attractive and sound branching structure. The same type of maple not given equal attention could have a poor branching structure making it less valuable.

The quality of landscape materials extends to the hardscape materials. Wood and stone used in the landscape are available in different grades of quality. The highest grades hold the highest prices. Similarly, highly skilled laborers can demand higher prices based on the superior quality of their work.

Although specifications are in writing, it is usually necessary to verbally express these to the customer. The additional explanations clear up specifications that may be unclear to the customer. It also gives the landscaper the opportunity to explain the differences in quality of materials and work.

PREPARING A LANDSCAPE ESTIMATE

The preparation of an estimate can be made easier with a landscape construction **estimate sheet**. An estimate sheet is a form for calculating prices. It helps if the same form is used for each project. Many landscapers use computer spreadsheets to speed the preparation of estimates. On the estimate sheet, the designer can record material descriptions, quantities, material costs, labor costs, cost for site preparation, and total costs. Table 8-1 shows a sample estimate sheet. Consider the wide range of material costs and prices as you study the sample estimate sheet.

8-5. Mathematics calculations must be accurate and precise. (Courtesy, Education Images, Inc.)

CALCULATING COSTS

A number of factors need to be taken into account in calculating installation costs. They include labor costs, material costs, overhead costs, contingency costs, and profit.

1. The anticipated cost for both labor and materials should be listed in detail. Use the actual wages the employees will be paid and the cost of the materials purchased wholesale.

2. **Overhead costs** are the general costs in running a business. Examples include: mortgage or lease payments, legal fees, utilities, insurance, office expenses, and maintenance of equipment. To obtain the overhead, multiply the total for labor and materials by 20 percent.

3. **Contingency costs** should be figured into all jobs. This accounts for theft of materials on the work site, mechanical breakdowns, rainouts, etc. The contingency charge may vary from job to job. An acceptable charge is to multiply the overhead plus labor and materials by 10 percent.

8-6. All costs must be considered in a landscape plan including buying, hauling, and placing pine needle mulch. (Courtesy, Eddie Seagle, Abraham Baldwin Agricultural College)

4. Add the labor, materials, overhead, and contingency charges to obtain a **cost summation**.

5. **Profit** is the amount of money the landscaper receives after deducting all costs of the project. The markup for profit is included on the estimate sheet. A fair markup for profit is 20 percent. Multiply the cost summation by 20 percent to determine the profit.

6. Total cost for the project is the addition of the summation costs and the profit.

Table 8-1. A Sample Estimate Sheet

LANDSCAPE CONSTRUCTION ESTIMATE SHEET					
JOB NAME				**DATE**	
JOB LOCATION				**DESIGNER**	
JOB DESCRIPTION					
Description	**Quantity**	**Material Unit Cost**	**Total Material Cost**	**Total Labor Cost ($15.00/hr)**	**Total Labor and Material Costs**
Plant List					
Acer saccharum 'Green Mountain,' 3" B&B	3	275.00	825.00	90.00	915.00
Fothergilla gardenii, 3 gallon container	12	16.00	192.00	60.00	252.00
Sod	235 yds	2.10	493.50	180.00 (12 hours)	673.50
Hedera helix 'Thorndale,' 3" pot	300	0.58	174.00	45.00	219.00
Construction Materials					
Finish grading of site				525.00	525.00
Brick pavers, 6 cm	1230	1.61	1,980.30		1,980.30
Sand, construction grade, 2" deep	3 tons	5.00	15.00		15.00
Gravel, grade 8, 3" deep	4 tons	6.00	24.00		24.00
Landscape fabric, 3' H 50' roll	3 rolls	9.95	29.85		29.85
Patio installation	300 sq. ft.			900.00 ($3/sq. ft.)	900.00
Florida cypress mulch, 4" deep	10 yds	36.95	369.50	90.00	459.50
Subtotal Costs (total materials and labor costs)			$4,103.15	$1,890.00	$ 5,993.15

Overhead Costs (subtotal material and labor costs × 20%)	$ 1,198.63
Contingency Costs (overhead + subtotal materials and labor × 10%)	$ 719.18
Cost Summation (subtotal material and labor costs + overhead + contingency)	$ 7,910.96
Profit (cost summation × 20%)	$ 1,582.19
TOTAL (cost summation + profit)	$ 9,493.15

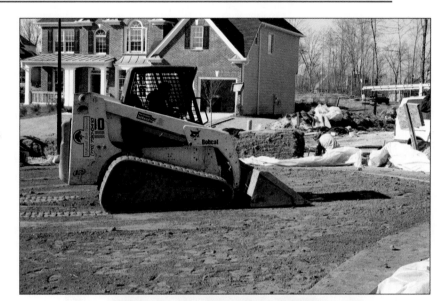

8-7. Equipment fixed and variable costs for preparing sites must be considered in the price. (Courtesy, Education Images, Inc.)

LABOR REQUIREMENTS

The landscaper calculates the amount of time required to complete a job. The unit of measurement for time is hours. Labor requirements are calculated on how many hours are required to do a specific function, whether it is by an individual or a crew. This calculation is applied to all phases of the planting plan in order to estimate the amount of time the job will take to complete. The size and capability of the landscape crew largely determines the amount of time required.

An example for calculating a sod job follows. Each landscape crew member installs 75 sq. yd. of sod per hour. Divide the total number of yards of sod needed for the landscape job by 75 sq. yd. per worker hour. The total number of hours required to install the sod is calculated with a simple formula.

8-8. Labor will be required to set plant materials. (Courtesy, Education Images, Inc.)

$$\frac{\text{sq. yd. of sod needed}}{75 \text{ sq. yd. per worker hour}} = \underline{\hspace{2cm}} \text{ total worker hours to install sod}$$

How many worker hours will be needed to install 1,500 square yards of sod?

$$\frac{1,500 \text{ sq. yd. of sod needed}}{75 \text{ sq. yd./per worker hour}} = 20 \text{ total worker hours to install sod}$$

Similar labor calculations would be made for grading soil, planting trees and shrubs, installing brick patios, and other construction tasks. Estimating landscape costs requires basic mathematical skills. Besides counting the total number of plants to be installed, the designer needs to be able to determine accurate measurements for hardscape materials. This involves linear, area, and volume measurements.

8-9. The edging for this patio and planting bed is measured in linear feet. The paving is measured in area, the stone wall in weight, and the wood fence in linear feet. (Courtesy, Illinois Landscape Contractors Association)

8-10. Sod is measured by the square yard or yard. (This sod is harvested and installed in roles.)

LINEAR MEASUREMENTS

Linear measurements are the measurements made of a line. Linear measurements are one-dimensional. Most linear measurements are made in feet, referred to as linear feet. A common linear measurement in the landscape involves edging for the planting beds. The total length of the bed outline needs to be learned before edging materials can be purchased or a cost estimated.

Measurement of linear feet on a design is done with a scale. It usually involves making a series of measurements and adding them to get a total. On plans with curving lines, a nylon string is some-

8-11. Pallets of sod have been harvested and delivered to the construction site. (Courtesy, Education Images, Inc.)

times used. The string is laid over the curving lines, straightened, and measured with a scale.

AREA MEASUREMENTS

Area measurements are those made of the surface. They are two-dimensional. The common units of area measure are square feet and square yards. An example of the use of area involves the number of square yards (yards for short) of sod required for a lawn. Other examples include the number of square feet in a brick patio and the number of square feet to be planted with ground covers.

Area measurements require the use of a scale and some basic geometry. Some examples follow:

1. Areas of rectangles and squares are equal to the length times the width.

L × W = Area
10' × 5' = 50 square feet

2. Areas of triangles are equal to ½ the base times the height.

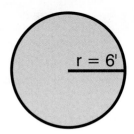

½ × (base × height) = Area
½ × (14 × 5) = 35 square feet

3. Areas of circles are equal to the radius squared times pi. The radius (r) is half the diameter of the circle, and pi is a constant at 3.14.

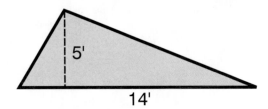

r^2 × pi = Area
r^2 = 6 × 6 = 36
36 × 3.14 = 113.04 square feet

VOLUME MEASUREMENTS

Volume measurements are the measure of size or amount in three-dimensions. The units of measure for volume in landscape applications are cubic feet or cubic yards (yards for short). Some materials measured by volume include soil, sand, gravel, and mulch. A common problem is determining the number of cubic yards of mulch needed to cover the planting beds. This type of problem requires some computations. Mulch is usually spread 3 to 4 inches deep, but is sold by the cubic yard.

The space that is measured is most often contained in a rectangle. The volume of a rectangle is learned by multiplying the length × the width × the height.

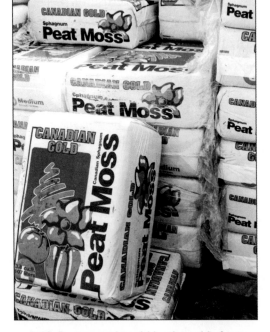

8-12. Peat moss is sold by the cubic foot.

Length × width × height = volume
8' × 4' × 3' = 96 cubic feet

Planimeter/Digitizer

Some landscape companies use a computer device called a ***Planimeter/Digitizer*** to accurately and quickly calculate linear feet, area, and volume. The device saves a great deal of labor by reducing hand measurements. By moving the arm of the Planimeter/Digitizer from various points on the design, linear feet, area, and volume are calculated. Because of the expense of the device, it is used primarily with large landscape plans.

8-13. This person is using a Planimeter/Digitizer to cost out a plan.

REVIEWING

MAIN IDEAS

Landscaping is a business in which money is exchanged for landscaping services. The designer of the landscape plans is usually the one with the task of pricing a project. An approximate price for the project can be given to the customer as an estimate. The final price may change from the original estimate if unforeseen costs arise. A bid, on the other hand, is a fixed price that cannot be changed without the consent of the customer. Bids are used when more than one landscaper is competing for a particular job.

The landscaper must specify what is involved in the landscape project. Specifications include written descriptions of landscape materials, work, and time schedules for a project. Some details of the project to be listed as specifications are the size of each plant, the number of plants, the depth of the mulch, instructions for soil amendments, and the installation techniques for the patio. Specifications can be placed on an estimate sheet. Overhead and profit are included on the estimate sheet along with material totals and costs.

In determining landscape costs, the landscaper must be able to use basic mathematical computations. Three common measurements are linear, area, and volume. Linear measurements are one-dimensional. Area measurements are two-dimensional and units used are square foot and square yard. Volume is the measure of space in three-dimensions. Units of measure associated with volume are cubic foot and cubic yard. A computer device called a Planimeter/Digitizer is used to measure linear feet, area, and volume.

QUESTIONS

Answer the following questions using correct spelling and complete sentences.

1. What is the difference between an estimate and a bid?

2. How do specifications relate to estimates and bids?

3. Why is it important to add overhead costs to the price of the project?

4. What is considered a fair profit?

5. Why are mathematical calculations important in preparing a landscape project estimate?

6. What are linear measurements?

7. What are area measurements?

8. What are volume measurements?

9. What is a Planimeter/Digitizer?

CHAPTER SELF-CHECK

Match the term with the correct definition. Write the letter by the term in the blank provided.

a. volume measurements   e. profit   h. Planimeter/Digitizer
b. bid   f. estimate   i. overhead
c. estimate sheet   g. specifications   j. area measurements
d. linear measurements

_____1. Measurements made of the surface that are two-dimensional

_____2. A form used for calculating prices for each project

_____3. The general costs in running a business

_____4. An approximate price for the work to be done

_____5. One-dimensional measurement of a line

_____6. The amount of money the landscaper receives after deducting all costs of the project

_____7. A fixed price placed on the landscape work to be done

_____8. Computer device used to accurately and quickly calculate linear feet, area, and volume

_____9. Written descriptions of landscape materials, work, and time schedules for a project

_____10. The measure of size or amount in three-dimensions

EXPLORING

1. Develop your own estimate sheet and price your landscape plan. Practice your skills in measuring linear feet, area, and volume. Use landscape supply company catalogs and nursery catalogs to obtain material prices. Your instructor can help you with pricing for labor. Do not forget to add overhead costs and a profit to your total. Are you surprised with your results?

2. Visit with local landscapers. Ask them how they go about preparing bids and estimates. What techniques do they use to ensure that their overhead costs, contingency costs, and profit are covered?

PART TWO

Landscape Construction

Preparing the Site for Planting

1 Interpret specifications of a planting plan.

2 Identify landscape construction tools and equipment.

3 Measure and calculate the slope of a hillside.

4 Establish proper elevations and grade a landscape site.

5 Locate existing utilities.

6 Determine the need for soil cut and fill.

7 Describe staking the landscape site.

8 Determine the texture and percolation characteristics of the soil.

9 Describe proper landscape bed preparation.

10 Discuss the elements necessary for good plant growth.

TERMS

acidic	hygroscopic water	pore space
alkaline	infiltration	rough grade
berm	landscape construction	soil
capillary water	leaching	soil amendment
contour line	nursery	soil structure
cut	nutrient	soil texture
fill	percolation	stake the site
final grade	permeable	terrain
grading	pH scale	topography
gravitational water	planting bed	
hardscaping	planting plan	

9-1 Establishing landscapes includes land forms, pavements, constructed features, water, and plantings.

ONCE planned, proper installation of a landscape is needed. The planting plan must be carried out. A landscape often includes more than plants. Fences, paved areas, walls, lighting, and other features may be used to enhance a landscape. Proper installation of these features makes a landscape attractive, long lasting, and functional for the home-owners.

What tools and equipment are going to be needed? Where are the trees and shrubs to be planted? Where are existing utility lines located? Will grading be required? What is the condition of the soil? These are some of the questions that need to be answered when preparing the site for planting.

LANDSCAPE PLANNING AND CONSTRUCTION

Landscape plans for newly constructed homes may call for grass, trees, shrubs, fences, and patios. The landscape contractor, not the home contractor, performs construction work outside the house. The same general design and construction steps apply in landscaping the yard as in building a new house. Developing a house plan starts the house construction process. After developing a planting plan, the outdoor phase of landscape construction is ready to begin. **Landscape construction** is the execution of the planting plan and installation of hardscape features.

9-2. A tree spade may be needed to install large trees.

Landscape contractors do many more tasks besides planting trees and shrubs. Today, they must also construct and install a variety of hard goods, such as patios, decks, walks, fences, walls, and fountains. The term **hardscaping**, first used during the 1970s, describes installing non-plant landscape features, such as fences, patios, walks, pools, and walls. Some landscape contractors may specialize in only one or two types of landscape installation. However, most landscape contractors plant trees and shrubs, install patios, and build fences.

THE PLANTING PLAN

The landscape designer talks with the homeowners about their specific outdoor needs, desires, and problems. The landscape designer, through the design process, can then develop a **planting plan** that shows the exact location for plant materials, includes a plant materials list, and also shows the location for any hardscape features. Contours and spot elevations may also be shown on the planting plan. **Contour lines** show how the terrain changes elevation, the vertical rise of fall of the land. Solid contour lines indicate changes from the original land elevations. Landscape contractors use the planting plan to install the hardscape features and plant the trees, shrubs, and flowers as designed.

PLANT LIST

1. COMPACT KOREANSPICE VIBURNUM   VIBURNUM CARLESII 'COMPACTA'
2. FLOWERING ANNUALS
3. JAPANESE SPURGE   PACHYSANDRA TERMINALIS
4. CARPET BUGLE   AJUGA REPTANS 'METALLICA CRISPA'
5. COMPACT AMERICAN CRANBERRYBUSH VIBURNUM   VIBURNUM TRILOBUM 'COMPACTUM'
6. CANADIAN PURPLELEAF PLUM
7. DENSE YEW   TAXUS MEDIA 'DENSIFORMIS'
8. ONEIDA LINDEN VIBURNUM   VIBURNUM DILATATUM 'ONEIDA'
9. BOTTLEBRUSH BUCKEYE   AESCULUS PARVIFLORA
10. YOUNGSTOWN ANDORRA JUNIPER   JUNIPERUS HORIZONTALIS 'PLUMOSA COMPACTA YOUNGSTOWN'
11. DAYLILY 'MARY TODD'   (26" EM)
12. DAYLILY 'RED SIREN' OR 'TURNED ON' (34" M)
13. DAYLILY 'GOLDEN PRIZE' OR 'TICK TOCK' (26" L)
14. BIGLEAF WINTERCREEPER EUONYMUS   EUONYMUS FORTUNEI 'VEGETUS'
15. RED OAK   QUERCUS RUBRA
16. CONTORTED EUROPEAN HAZEL   CORYLUS AVELLANA 'CONTORTA'
17. EASTERN HEMLOCK   TSUGA CANADENSIS
18. SNOWDRIFT CRABAPPLE   MALUS 'SNOWDRIFT'
19. BARREN-STRAWBERRY   WALDSTEINIA TERNATA
20. CRANBERRY COTONEASTER   COTONEASTER APICULATA
21. CANBY PACHISTIMA   PACHISTIMA CANBYI
22. RHODODENDRON PJM

NOTES

A. FLAGSTONE EDGING
B. WOODCHIP MULCH ALL PLANTING BEDS
C. FLAGSTONE WALK
D. WOOD DECK
E. VEGETABLE GARDEN
F. PROVIDE A LOOSE, ACID SOIL FOR PLANTS 9, 17, 21, AND 22

9-3. Planting plan for a residence.

A **nursery** is a type of farm or horticulture business that grows many different varieties of trees, shrubs, and bedding plants used by the landscape contractor and do-it-yourself homeowner. In the past, most landscape companies grew the plant materials, drew the plans, and installed the plants. Today, many landscape companies specialize in only one phase of the landscape business.

LANDSCAPE TOOLS AND EQUIPMENT

Landscape contractors need a wide variety of tools and equipment to prepare the site for planting and to install plant materials. Proper preparation and installation techniques are essential in executing the planting plan. If the landscape contractor does not have a particular tool or piece of equipment, it may have to be rented or that portion of the job subcontracted.

9-4. Select durable and economical tools that are comfortable to use. (Courtesy, Education Images, Inc.)

When using tools or operating equipment, safe practices should be followed. Follow manufacturers' guidelines for operating equipment and power tools. Tools and equipment must be maintained and kept clean if they are to save time and function properly. Some good tool and machine operation tips include:

- Read and follow owner's manual recommendations.
- Perform daily maintenance procedures.
- Check the condition of the tool or equipment before starting.

- Warm up the engine before operating.
- Operate at safe speeds.
- Check instrument readings while in operation.
- Select the proper tool or machine for each job.

Properly storing hand and power tools used in landscaping helps ensure efficient and safe use. Always store tools in a safe, dry place such as a shed or cabinet. Hand tools and cutting edges should be cleaned free of dirt, rust, and moisture before storage. Most cutting edges need to be lightly oiled. Tools that are dull and rusty will not work satisfactorily. A storage area should be organized so that it is easy to find tools when you need them. Tools should be stored so that cutting edges are not dulled by bumping together or pose safety hazards to people who use them.

Use tools properly. Misusing tools can result in injury to the person using it or a broken tool. For example, shovels are not meant to pry rocks from the soil. Exerting too much pressure on the handle can result in the handle breaking or the shovel itself bending. It is also a good idea to wear gloves when using most landscape tools.

SITE CHARACTERISTICS AND THE PLANTING PLAN

Implementing the planting plan, while dealing with the unique characteristics of a site, is the responsibility of the landscape contractor. The landscape designer worked within the boundaries of nature when altering the land forms. Usually, there will be some alteration needed at the site.

TERRAIN

The landscape site is seldom flat. Areas that appear to be level usually do slope in one direction or the other. **Terrain** describes the rise and fall of land (hills and valleys). **Topography** is a record of an area's terrain. Some slope is necessary to allow excess surface water from rain and snow to drain. Medium to large hills allow the landscape designer many opportunities to create unusual landscapes. Many outdoor activities need flat surfaces, while slopes can provide interesting visual experiences in the landscape.

Measuring Horizontal Distances

Landscapers typically need to know the dimensions of the area that is to be landscaped. Distances along buildings, driveways, streets, and other features are needed to determine the number of shrubs, bedding plants, or bulbs that are needed. Such information can be used to calculate the square footage of lawn, flower beds, and patios. Horizontal measurements are also used in calculating slopes. Measurements may also be needed to determine property boundaries. That is best left up to a professional surveyor who can mark the boundaries based on legal information.

9-5. Examples of tools and equipment used in landscape construction.

Most all landscape measurements in the United States are made using the traditional or English system of measurement. Other countries may use the metric system. If needed, useful conversion tables and formulas are available.

Horizontal distances can be measured or estimated. The best calculations involve accurate measurements. A tape measure, chain, or measuring wheel can be used. Estimates are determined by stepping, pacing, or estimating in other ways.

Measuring a Slope

A landscape contractor shows a slope as a percent relating the vertical rise of the land to the flat horizontal distance.

Use a 48-inch level and a yard stick to measure slope. Put one end of the level on the hillside (slope) and raise the other end until the bubble is in the center of the leveling vial. The level will now be level with the earth's surface. Use the yard stick to measure the distance from the ground to the bottom edge of the level. Measure both distances in inches, not feet. Determine the percent slope of the hill with this formula:

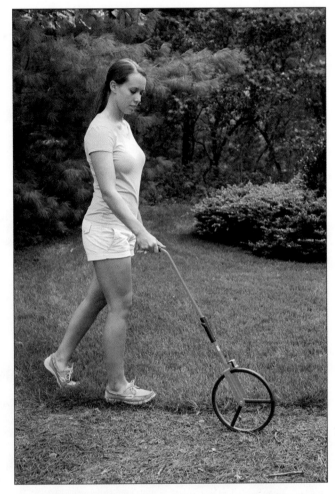

9-6. A measuring wheel is a handy and accurate device for measuring horizontal distances. (Courtesy, Education Images, Inc.)

$$\frac{\text{Vertical Distance}}{\text{Horizontal Distance}} \times 100 = \text{Percent Slope}$$

Example: A vertical distance of 15 inches was measured using the 48-inch level.

$$\frac{15}{48} \times 100 = 31 \text{ percent slope}$$

A transit and target rod, including laser instruments, is another method used to measure a slope. They are covered in the surveying section which follows.

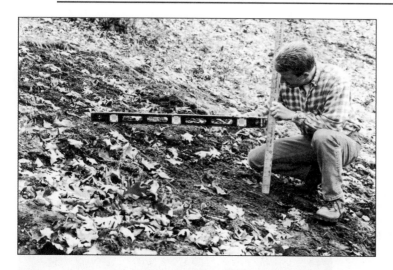

9-7. One slope measuring technique.

9-8. Landscape planting bed and lawn on a slope.

Landscape Activities and Slope

The ideal and the maximum slope percentage for several common components in the landscape are shown in Table 9-1. These are not exact percentages, but serve as a guide to determine how different slopes can be used in the landscape. The percentages are also a guide for changing the slope with grading to allow for different activities.

Table 9-1. Recommended Slope Percent for Different Landscape Components

Landscape Component	Ideal Slope Percent	Maximum Slope Percent
Decks and patios	½ to 1	3
Lawns	2 to 10	30
Walks	1 to 4	8
Driveways	1 to 10	11
Slopes with landscape plants	20 to 30	50
Wheelchair ramps	3 to 5	8
Steps	33 to 50	66

SURVEYING

In the past, landscape surveying dealt with marking property boundaries and dividing farm land into small city lots for home construction. Today, surveying skills help establish the elevation of patios, the leveling of retaining wall foundations, and the layout of drainage systems according to the landscape plan. These skills can also help the landscape contractor establish the correct slopes for a variety of outdoor activities. The transit and target rod surveying instruments are used to determine the present elevation and establish new ones.

Proper drainage of surface water is essential to a well-designed landscape.

9-9. A laser transit and target rod is used to establish elevation.

Most plants do not grow well in poorly drained soil. An underground drain tile system can be installed to remove the extra water from the soil. Surveying skills can help the landscaper correctly grade drainage tile trenches to provide good water flow in the tile.

Standing water from excessive surface runoff can result in temporary ponds that limit the use of the landscape site. Use surveying instruments to construct slopes that will direct water away from buildings and into natural drainage areas. Generally speaking, establish a 2 to 3 percent slope to help surface water drain from the house, patio, walk, and driveway.

LOCATING UNDERGROUND UTILITIES

Before starting a landscape job, the landscape contractor or crew supervisor should call the utility locating service and indicate the type and extent of work to be performed. Most utilities require 48 hours advance notice for locates before starting a landscape job. They will find and mark all underground utilities at the construction site. They do not charge for locating services. Most state laws require contractors to call a utility locating service before digging.

The site should also be reviewed for private utilities that may not have been marked. These could include septic tanks, wells, yard lights, power to outbuildings, etc. Once utilities are located, care should still be exercised when digging.

9-10. Underground telephone lines in this landscape bed have been marked with flags.

TIP: Always call a utility locating service before digging.

9-11. A skid-steer loader being used to level the soil to rough grade at a construction site.

Marking paint and flag colors indicate:

- Red—electric
- Yellow—gas, oil, steam
- Orange—telephone, communication, cable TV
- Blue—water
- Green—sewer

GRADING

Grading involves the moving of soil and the reshaping of the land. Adding soil to the landscape site is called a **fill**, or filling. Removing soil from the site is known as a **cut**. Grade the site to improve drainage patterns, to create an interesting land appearance, and to ensure healthy plant growth. Grading can also make sites with steep slopes more useful for a variety of outdoor activities. Landscapers follow the planting plan and cut and/or fill to establish the desired grade recommended on the plan.

All grading should be done when soil conditions are dry. Soil structure can be destroyed if heavy equipment is used on wet soil. Major changes in the site terrain can alter natural drainage patterns and severely damage or kill the root systems of existing trees. Care should be taken to keep the site terrain in harmony with surrounding property.

Remove and stockpile the topsoil at the construction site before starting any major grading projects. The subsoil can then be reshaped using a skid-steer loader or a backhoe with a front-end loader to create the rough grade. The **rough grade** is the approximate grade or slope of the terrain. The rough grade, or finish, should closely parallel the proposed final grade but is usually 3 to 6 inches below the final grade.

Establishing adequate new drainage patterns should be the number one priority when rough grading a landscape site. Surface water should drain away from buildings but cannot be diverted onto neighboring property. Grade the soil around homes so that there is a 2 to 3 percent slope away from the house to reduce the chance of flooding or seepage into the structure. Construct concave depressions or channels called swales to carry surface water away from buildings. Some sites may need catch basins and drain tiles installed to improve drainage.

After completing the rough grade, spread a 3- to 6-inch layer of topsoil from the stockpile on the rough graded subsoil and establish the final grade. The **final grade** is the elevation of the soil surface after completing all grading operations. Use a rototiller to break up soil clumps into marble-sized particles and remove all rocks and debris before smoothing the surface. Small areas can be hand raked, while larger areas require a tractor with a box-scraper or landscape-rake to smooth the surface and establish the final grade. A transit and target rod should be used to check the exact final grade elevation. The elevation in feet will be found on the landscape planting plan.

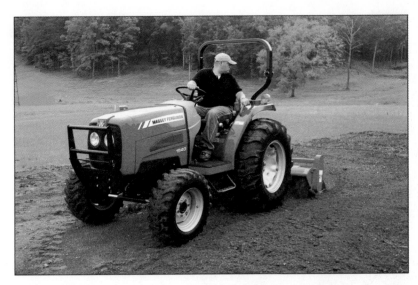

9-12. Good soil preparation is essential in establishing landscapes. A rotary tiller prepares a fine planting bed. (Courtesy, AGCO)

TIP: Landscapers use the term "wet feet" to describe plants growing in very wet or waterlogged soil.

Special Landscape Effects

Proper grading to the designer's plan can create many special landscape effects. The plan may call for a mound of soil called a **berm**. Berms give a flat landscape site an added dimension of height and change the ordinary into the unusual. A berm of any significant size requires large quantities of soil. If the berm is to be mowed, usually the slope will not exceed 30 percent. Berms provide interesting land forms immediately useful and visible in the landscape. Ponds are another example of special landscape effects created from grading. People often enjoy the sight and sound of water in the landscape.

9-13. Berms add interest to the landscape.

STAKING THE SITE

Landscape plans usually do not have measurements. The construction supervisor must use a scale to measure the exact location of each plant. Most landscape plans are drawn using a $\frac{1}{8}$" = 1'- 0" architect scale. The supervisor, using the $\frac{1}{8}$" scale, takes measurements to determine the exact location of each plant on the plan. Transferring the measurements from the planting plan to the outside ground to show the location of each plant is the next step.

9-14. A landscape crew beginning to install plant materials after the site has been staked.

The landscape supervisor will usually stake the site the day before the crew is scheduled on the job. To **stake the site**, the plant name is written on small wooden or plastic stakes, and the stakes are driven into the ground to show the exact center of each planting hole. This shows the crew members where to dig and what to plant. Besides staking plant material location, the supervisor will also locate the patio, walls, fences, and other hard materials with stakes.

SOIL

Soil means different things to different people. Some people think of soil as dirt, the material to wash from clothes or sweep up from the floor. To an agronomist or soil scientist, **soil** is the outer part of the earth's crust in which plant root systems grow. Soil supplies mineral elements, water, and a means of support for plants throughout the world. Mineral particles and organic matter make up the solid part of soil, while the holes in the soil are called **pore spaces**.

SOIL FUNCTIONS

Compare soil to a sponge used to wash a car. The sponge has solid parts, but it also has many holes that can fill with water. An ideal soil will have 50 percent solid material and 50 percent pore space. When the sponge is dry, its holes are filled with air, but when dipped in a bucket of water the air is replaced with the water. The pore spaces in soil can hold water, air, or some of both. Plant roots not only need water but also air for good growth. Therefore, the best soil for plant growth will have its pore space half full of water and half full of air. The total pore space is not as important as the size of the pore space (hole). Small pore spaces hold water, while the larger ones hold air. Mineral particles that make up the soil will determine the size of the pore spaces.

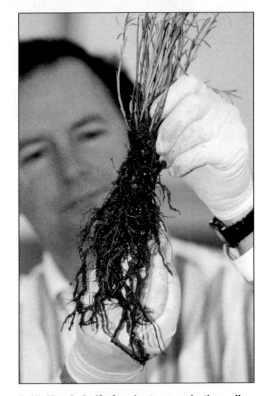

9-15. Nearly half of a plant grows in the soil. (Courtesy, Agricultural Research Service, USDA)

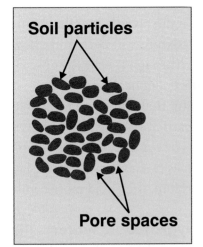

9-16. Pore spaces are the openings between solid soil particles.

Drainage

When there is rainfall, water either enters the soil or flows off the soil as surface drainage. A soil with good texture and structure will absorb a great deal of rainfall. The process of the water soaking into the soil is known as **infiltration**. Once in the soil, the water moves downward. The downward movement of water through the soil

9-17. Water either enters the soil or flows off as surface drainage when there is rainfall. (Courtesy, U.S. Soil Conservation Service)

is known as **percolation**. In heavy rainfall, the pore spaces of soil fill up more quickly than water can drain through the soil. When this occurs, and all pore spaces are filled with water, the soil is considered saturated. Additional rainwater forms puddles or flows downhill on the surface of the soil. A quality soil that allows water movement by infiltration and percolation is said to be **permeable**.

Water found in soils is placed into one of three categories—gravitational water, capillary water, or hygroscopic water.

After a rain, much of the water drains down through the soil through the pore spaces. This is called **gravitational water** because gravity pulls the water down. The water ends up in the ground water below the soil surface. Gravitational water flows quickly through sandy soils that have large pore spaces and more slowly through clay soils with tiny pore spaces.

As gravitational water moves through the soil, it carries with it dissolved minerals, chemicals, and salts. This process is known as **leaching**. The soil texture will determine how quickly minerals, chemicals, and salts are leached, or washed, through a soil. Because of leaching, plants grown on sandy soils need more frequent fertilizer applications.

Capillary water is a second category of water. It is also the water that plants are most able to use. **Capillary water** is the water held between the soil particles against the force of gravity. This water can move through a soil upwards or sideways by capillary action. As surface soil dries out, some water moves up into the open pore spaces by capillary action. Clay soils have a greater number of pore spaces than sandy soils; therefore, they hold more capillary water.

A third category of soil water is called hygroscopic water. **Hygroscopic water** is the water that forms a thin film around individual soil particles. Even the driest soils have hygroscopic water. Plants are unable to absorb and use this type of water.

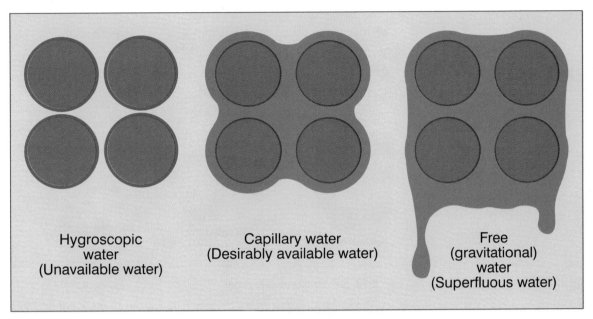

Hygroscopic
water
(Unavailable water)

Capillary water
(Desirably available water)

Free
(gravitational)
water
(Superfluous water)

9-18. Three categories of water are found in soils.

Air

Air is also found in the pore spaces. Roughly 25 percent of the total soil volume should be air. After a rain, many of the pore spaces are filled with water. As that water drains away, air fills the pore spaces. In dry soils, air may take up the majority of the pore spaces. Sandy soils with large pore spaces tend to be well-aerated. Clay soils with their tiny pore spaces often are not well-drained and have a smaller percentage of air.

Most plants perform best when there is a balance between water and air in a soil. Sandy soils are loose and well-aerated but do not hold water very well. Clay soils hold water but are not well-aerated. Soils that have a mix of sand, silt, and clay tend to be both well-drained and well-aerated, which is good for plant growth.

SOIL STRUCTURE

Sand, silt, clay, and organic matter particles in a soil combine with one another to form larger particles of various shapes and sizes. These larger particles are often referred to as soil aggregates. The way in which soil aggregates are arranged is referred to as *soil structure*. There are eight categories of soil structure—blocky, columnar, crumb, granular, platy, prismatic, single grain, and massive.

Soil structure affects water and air movement in a soil, nutrient availability for plants, root growth, and microorganism activity. The pore spaces created by the larger soil particles

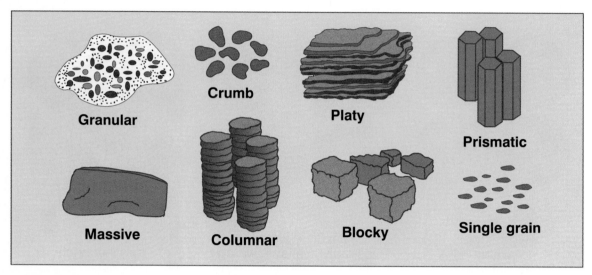

9-19. Soil structure categories.

are larger than those in-between individual particles of sand, silt, or clay. This allows for greater air and water movement, better root growth, and open passageways for small animals. The aggregates are also better able to hold water and nutrients.

Soil structure can be destroyed. A major cause of damage is driving heavy equipment over wet soil. Damage is also caused by working soil when it is either too wet or too dry. These conditions lead to the clay particles clogging up the pore spaces. The soil becomes compacted, and very dense, and when it dries, it becomes very hard. It is very difficult for most plants to survive in a soil whose structure has been destroyed. Soil structure can be improved by adding organic matter.

SOIL TEXTURE

The mineral particles of soil are arranged according to size from very fine to very coarse. **Soil texture** refers to the proportion of sand, silt, and clay particles. Clay describes the smallest soil particles usually less than .002 mm in diameter. Sand particles are large compared to clay with a diameter from .05 to .5 mm. Silt particles are smaller than sand but larger than clay particles, and have a diameter from .002 to .05 mm. Soil texture affects the retention of water and the rate that water moves into the soil after a rain. Loam soils have approximately equal parts of sand and silt with a low percentage of clay. Most landscape plants grow best in a loam-type soil.

SOIL PROPERTY	TEXTURAL CLASS		
	Sand	Silt Loam	Clay
Aeration	excellent	good	poor
Cation Exchange	low	medium	high
Drainage	excellent	good	poor
Erodibility (by water)	easy	moderate	difficult
Permeability (by water)	fast	moderate	slow
Temperature (spring)	warms fast	warms moderately	warms slowly
Tillage	easy	moderate	difficult
Water-Holding Capacity	low	moderate	high
Resistance to Compaction	excellent	good	poor

9-20. Soil properties influenced by soil texture.

TOPSOIL AND SUBSOIL

Before or during construction, grading will usually disturb the original soil. Therefore, very little natural topsoil will be found at the surface. Although the spreading of topsoil following grading may have been accomplished, this layer is usually quite thin. The root system of landscape plants may penetrate 12 to 24 inches in favorable soils.

The excavated material from grading differs from topsoil. It has not been subjected to the mellowing effect of plant roots. It does not have the abundance of soil microbes feeding on dead roots and underground stems. Sandy soils have a low water-holding capacity and are subject to wind erosion. These soils are generally low in nutrients because rainfall has leached the important nutrients from the sand.

Alkaline soils occur throughout drier regions, wherever internal soil drainage is poor. Applying an acid formulation of fertilizer can improve nutrient availability on alkaline soils. Saline soils usually occur on coastal plains where the saltwater penetrates. Selecting landscape plants that like saline soils may be the best solution to this problem.

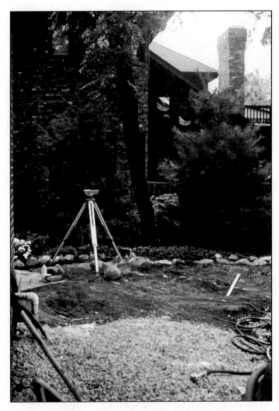

9-21. Topsoil partially spread after grading at this site.

BED PREPARATION

The ***planting bed*** describes the area in the landscape where shrubs and flowers are planted. Remove all sod and grass from the new landscape planting beds before planting shrubs. Never place sod and soil dug from the planting hole on the existing lawn. Put the soil in a wheelbarrow or on a piece of plywood to make the cleanup after tree and shrub planting quick and easy. It is best to back fill the planting hole with the same soil that came from the hole, with no soil amendments added. ***Soil amendments*** are materials added to the soil to improve drainage, moisture-holding ability, and aeration. Sulfur and lime may be added to adjust the soil pH.

Very poor clay soil at the landscape site may require the addition of sand or peat moss to improve soil aeration and drainage. First, cover the existing soil with a 2-inch layer of peat moss followed with a 2-inch layer of sand. Rototill the planting bed to mix the sand and peat into the top 6 inches of soil.

9-22. A 2-inch layer of peat moss has been applied to this planting bed before rototilling.

Many cities recycle grass clippings, landscape waste, and newspapers and sell this compost. This decomposed waste can be used to improve poor soil instead of using peat moss. For best results, always plant shrubs and flowers in a well-prepared planting bed.

TIP: Try to plant annual bedding plants on a cloudy day or in the evening. Hot sunlight can wilt young tender plants.

NUTRIENTS REQUIRED FOR PLANT GROWTH

Nutrients are chemical substances that support the life processes. Plants require 17 elements for good growth. Some elements come from the air, others from water, and the rest from the soil. Plants use large quantities of nitrogen, phosphorus, and potassium (the three primary or macronutrients), but need smaller amounts of the three secondary nutrients. Plants require very small amounts of the minor or micronutrients for good growth.

Table 9-2. Essential Elements Required by Plants

OBTAINED FROM AIR AND WATER		
Carbon		
Hydrogen		
Oxygen		

OBTAINED FROM THE SOIL			
	Element	**Chemical Symbol**	**Available Form**
Primary or macronutrients	Nitrogen	N	NO_{3-}, NH_{4+}
	Phosphorus	P	H_2PO_{4-}, HPO_{4--}
	Potassium	K	K^+
Secondary nutrients	Calcium	Ca	Ca^{++}
	Magnesium	Mg	Mg
	Sulfur	S	SO_{4--}
Minor or micronutrients	Iron	Fe	Fe^{++}, Fe^{+++}
	Manganese	Mn	Mn^{++}
	Copper	Cu	Cu^{++}
	Boron	B	H_2BO_{3-} and others
	Zinc	Zn	Zn^{++}
	Chlorine	Cl	Cl^-
	Molybdenum	Mo	MoO_{4--}
	Nickel	Ni	Ni^{++}

Landscape plants, like other plants, require 17 elements for healthy growth and development. Air and water supply plants with three of the necessary elements—hydrogen, oxygen, and carbon. The remaining 14 elements come from the soil.

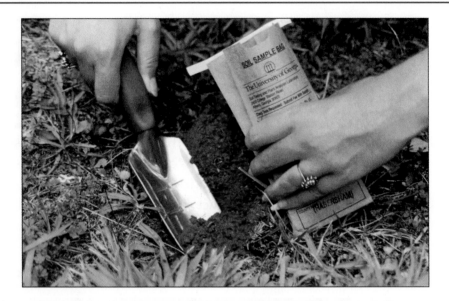

9-23. Collecting a soil sample.

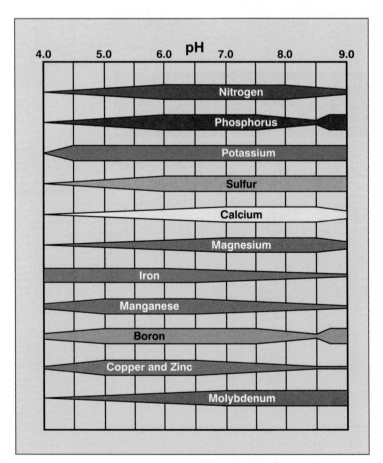

9-24. Nutrient availability as influenced by soil pH.

Large quantities of potassium, commonly called potash, may be present in the soil, but often this potash is not available for plant use. Light, frequent applications of potash will supply plants with this valuable element. Growing plants require more nitrogen than any of the other nutrients. Most fertilizer mixtures contain nitrogen, phosphorus, and potassium. Plants, especially evergreens, growing in alkaline soils may lack iron and have yellow-green foliage. Apply a soluble form of iron to evergreens with yellow needles/leaves and change their color to bright green.

Soil testing shows the ability of the soil to supply the essential nutrients necessary for good plant growth. After testing the soil, apply a fertilizer containing the nutrients recommended by the soil test. Over-application of nutrients can occur when no soil testing is done. Read and follow all the directions on the fertilizer label.

SOIL pH

Soil scientists use a 14-point **pH scale** to explain the acidity or alkalinity of soil. On this pH scale, the middle number, 7.0, is neither acid nor alkaline; it is neutral. Soil with a pH below 7.0 is **acidic**, while soil with a pH over 7.0 is **alkaline**. A soil sample with a pH of 5.0 is more acidic than a sample with a pH of 6.5. Soil scientists called agronomists test soil samples in a laboratory to find the exact pH. Once the pH is identified, amendments can be used to raise or lower it.

The "p" of pH is always a small letter while the "H" is always a capital letter. Agronomists use the pH scale to simplify the reporting of acidity and alkalinity. In a laboratory, agronomists measure the hydrogen ion concentration of a soil sample to be $H+ 10^{-5}$, but will report the soil pH as 5.0. Lemon and tomato juice have an approximate pH of 3.0, while the pH of soap is about 9.0. Most landscape plants grow best when the soil pH is between 5.5 and 7.0. Nutrients are most available when the pH is in that range. Needle evergreens, such as junipers and pines, require an acid soil between 5.0 and 6.0. The same holds true for most broadleaf evergreens.

Soils in the eastern part of the United States are generally acidic (below 5.5), while soils in the southwest are usually alkaline (above 8.0). Midwest soils tend to be in the 6.0 to 7.5 ideal range. Materials can be added to modify the soil pH. When soil tests indicate a low soil pH (below 5.5), add ground limestone to raise the pH into the normal range. Soils with a pH above 8.0 need sulfur compounds, such as ammonium sulfate, added to reduce the pH into the normal range.

9-25. Soil pH is the degree of acidity or alkalinity of a soil.

REVIEWING

MAIN IDEAS

The landscape crew supervisor must identify the locations of all plants required at the landscape site. This individual must transfer all measurements from the planting plan to the landscape site.

Contour lines on the planting plan show the rise and fall of the land. Different terrains suggest varied kinds of use for the site. Use a level and a yard stick or transit and target rod to determine the percent slope at a landscape site. Planting plans use solid contour lines to indicate changes from the original land elevations. A cut will remove soil from the landscape site, while a fill will add soil to the site.

Proper landscape bed preparation is essential for good plant establishment and growth. Improve poor soil by adding peat moss or other organic material. Use soil tests to determine the need for fertilizer applications in the planting bed. There are 17 elements necessary for good plant growth. Three come from air and water, and the remaining 14 come from the soil.

QUESTIONS

Answer the following questions using correct spelling and complete sentences.

1. What is a planting plan and how is it used?

2. What does the term "terrain" mean?

3. Describe two ways to determine the percent slope of a hill.

4. How does a landscape contractor know where underground utilities are located?

5. What is the difference between rough grade and final grade?

6. What is a landscape berm?

7. What is percolation?

8. What does the term "soil texture" refer to?

9. What are soil amendments used for when preparing a planting bed?

10. What are the three primary or macronutrients and their chemical symbols?

CHAPTER SELF-CHECK

Match the term with the correct definition. Place the letter in the blank provided.

a. berm
b. contour line
c. planting plan

d. stake the site
e. grading
f. terrain

g. rough grade
h. nurseries
i. landscape construction

_____1. Developed by the landscape designer

_____2. The crew supervisor does this the day before the landscape crew starts the job

_____3. The rise and fall of land

_____4. The smoothing of the soil surface and the reshaping of the land

_____5. The approximate grade or slope of the terrain

_____6. Mounds of soil that create special effects in the landscape

_____7. These lines on the planting plan show how the terrain changes elevation

_____8. The sources for plant materials used by landscape contractors

_____9. The execution of the planting plan and installation of hardscape features

EXPLORING

1. After drawing a simple landscape plan, practice staking it out at school or home.

2. Determine the percent slope of hillsides near your school or home. Assess how the slopes should be treated in a landscape plan. What kinds of plant materials should be used? What erosion control practices should be implemented? Prepare a report on your measurements and strategy for landscaping the slopes.

3. Borrow landscape plans from a contractor and study the contour lines and determine if cuts or fills will be required.

4. Describe major outdoor activities and determine the best slope for each activity.

5. Prepare a landscape bed at school or home before planting shrubs and flowers.

6. Collect a soil sample and send it to a laboratory for testing.

7. Plan a storage facility for the common hand and power tools used in landscaping. Be sure to consider the protection provided, organization of the storage area, and convenience of locating tools when they are needed. Give an oral report in class on your plans.

Installing Plant Materials

TERMS

annual	flower border	staking
anti-transpirant	geotextile	stomata
balled and burlapped (B&B)	ground cover	sunscald
bare root (BR)	guying	tender plant
bedding plant	hardy plant	transpiration
bed edging	herbaceous plant	vine
container grown	landscape fabric	water requirement
container nursery	mulch	water zone
drought tolerance	perennial	winter burn
field nursery	root circling	xeriscape
flower bed	soil ball	

10-1. Landscape materials must be properly installed and maintained for greatest appeal.

PEOPLE like to see attractive outside areas. They like to see healthy green plants and beautiful flowers. Everyone admires a well-kept lawn. A beautiful landscape does not just happen. It must be planned and properly installed.

Who selects the trees and shrubs planted around new homes? What are B&B, BR, and container grown plants, and how do they differ? What steps should the landscape contractor follow when planting trees and shrubs in the landscape? Why use mulches in landscape planting beds? Where in the landscape should flowers be planted? What is a geotextile and why should it be used? These and many more questions will be answered in this chapter on installing plant materials.

HARVESTING METHODS USED FOR LANDSCAPE PLANTS

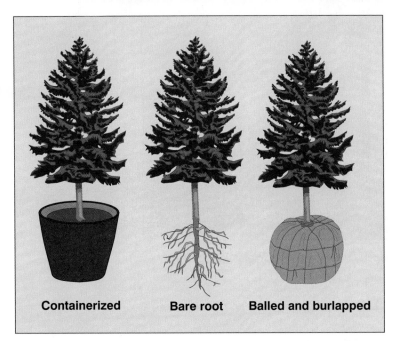

Containerized   **Bare root**   **Balled and burlapped**

10-2. Landscape plants can be sold in containers, bare root, or balled and burlapped.

Planting plans show the plant by name and its location on the plan. Designers recommend planting balled and burlapped (B&B), bare root (BR), or container grown plants depending on the time of year and the budget for each landscape job. A **container nursery** grows nursery crops to marketable size in containers. A **field nursery** grows nursery crops to marketable size in fields. Field nurseries make B&B and BR plant material available. Evergreen shrubs best survive transplanting in the landscape if grown as B&B or container plants. Plant nurseries sell small and medium-sized trees and shrubs as B&B, BR, or container plants. However, large trees transplant best by the balled and burlapped method.

BALLED AND BURLAPPED PLANTS

Plants grown in a field nursery are dug keeping a ball of soil around the root system. The soil ball is covered with burlap. The burlap helps hold the soil and roots together and helps prevent the soil from drying too quickly. Sometimes balled and burlapped plants are also placed in a wire basket. **Balled and burlapped (B&B)** describes this plant harvesting method. Large, power tree spades are used to dig and transplant trees with a trunk diameter of 4 to 12 inches. Using hydraulics, these machines dig trees by pushing three or four large spades into the soil. Balled and burlapped trees should be planted in the spring or fall (early spring in the South).

TIP: Never lift or move a balled and burlapped tree by holding onto the trunk. This can loosen the roots within the soil ball and tree death is almost certain. When moving trees, use special plastic or cardboard trunk protectors to prevent physical damage to the tree trunk.

Steps in Balling and Burlapping Trees

- Loosely wrap the plant branches with twine to keep them out of the way

- Determine the size of the root ball

- Remove weeds and other debris from the digging area

- Mark the diameter of the soil ball with a spade

- Dig a one foot deep circular trench around the root ball with a spade

- Use the spade to taper the soil ball

- Undercut the soil at the bottom of the soil ball

- Slide a piece of burlap under the root ball

- Secure the burlap to the root ball with pinning nails and twine

- Carefully lift the soil ball from the hole by holding onto the twine

10-3. Balled and burlapped trees being planted. (Courtesy, Church Landscape)

The root ball size for balled and burlapped (B&B) trees is based on the trunk diameter. The American Association of Nurserymen has determined the sizes necessary for tree recovery after transplanting.

10-4. Trees must be properly transported and installed. (Courtesy, Church Landscape)

Appropriate Root Ball Sizes for Balled and Burlapped Trees

Trunk Diameter (inches)	Minimum Root Ball Diameter (inches)
½	12
¾	14
1	16
1¼	18
1½	20
1¾	22
2	24
2½	28
3	32
3½	38

BARE ROOT PLANTS

Another popular harvesting technique called **bare root (BR)** describes digging the trees without taking soil from the field. Small and medium-sized trees and shrubs transplanted as bare root have a high survival rate. Most rose bushes and fruit trees sold today use the bare root method. However, most narrowleaf and broadleaf evergreens do not survive when transplanted using the bare root method. Careful attention should be taken not to allow the sun to burn the roots of landscape plants. This root dessication can be prevented by always covering the roots with a piece of burlap during the installation process. Dormant shrubs are usually sold bare root and should be planted in the spring.

10-5. Machine used to dig bare root plants in a nursery.

CONTAINER GROWN PLANTS

Today, many plants are grown in plastic, peat, or recycled newspaper containers. The containers may be filled with a soil-based medium which contains topsoil or a soilless medium that contains organic and inorganic materials. ***Container grown*** describes this cultural method. Container grown plants are easy to handle and move and provide protection for the plant's root system. Container plants grow in confined planting areas, not open farm fields. They can be planted any time during the year when the ground is not frozen.

> **TIP:** In the winter, container grown plants may be moved into small structures that are covered with white plastic.

Bedding Plants

Flowers to be installed in the landscape beds are usually established already growing and ready to begin blooming. A plant in this form is called a ***bedding plant***. The containers these plants are grown in can be plastic or manufactured from organic compounds such as peat moss. The majority of bedding plants are grown in plastic cell packs which are designed to fit into large plastic flat trays.

Herbaceous plants are non-woody plants, such as annuals, bulbs, perennials, turfgrass, and certain vines that die back to the ground each year. Bulbs are classified depending upon their time of planting, time of blooming, and temperature tolerances. Vines and vegetatively propagated turfgrasses are usually available in containers.

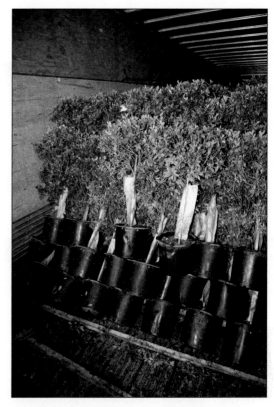

10-6. Container grown nursery stock has been placed in a semi-trailer for transporting from the nursery. (Courtesy, Education Images, Inc.)

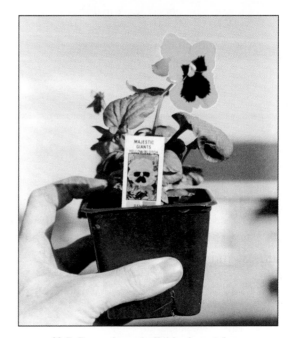

10-7. Pansy in an individual container.

Table 10-1 Advantages and Disadvantages of Various Harvesting Methods

BALLED AND BURLAPPED	
Advantages	**Disadvantages**
• Plants can be held for a long time after digging • Good technique for difficult to transplant species • Large trees can be moved • Popular technique for broadleaf evergreens • Commonly used to move large needle evergreens	• Specialized equipment may be needed • Soil conditions can limit work • Soil balls are heavy and hard to move • Shipping costs are expensive • More skilled labor is required

BARE ROOT	
Advantages	**Disadvantages**
• Harvested plants are lightweight • Plants can be dug in dormant season • Low harvesting costs • Economical shipping costs	• Possible decay of plant roots during storage • Usually dug in the fall or winter and sold the following spring • Special storage facilities are needed • Method is only used on deciduous plants

CONTAINER GROWN	
Advantages	**Disadvantages**
• Rapid production cycle • Plants are more uniform in size and shape • Greater number of plants in a smaller growing area • Less handling damage	• Plants can become pot bound • Plants are susceptible to winter damage from cold • More irrigation is needed • Plants are susceptible to blowing over

PLANT INSTALLATION CONSIDERATIONS

Factors to consider when installing plants include water requirements, growth rate, hardiness, and nutrient and pH needs.

WATER REQUIREMENTS

Water requirement refers to the amount of water plants need to live and grow. Some plants need more water than others. Increasingly, plants that need less water are being selected in landscaping.

Drought tolerance is the ability of a plant to live and grow with low amounts of moisture. The climate in the area being landscaped is important in plant selection. Plants that need an abundance of water should be used in places with high natural moisture.

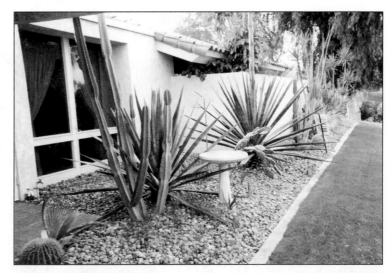

10-8. Landscapes in arid areas often use native, water efficient plants, such as cactus.

GROWTH RATE AND MATURITY

Plants grow at different rates and to different sizes. Plant selection for a landscape must consider the growth of plants. A plant that is very small when planted may grow into a large plant at maturity.

Trees and shrubs are classified by height and spread. Height is how tall a plant grows. It is the vertical space needs of a plant. Some dwarf shrubs grow only a few inches in height. Trees may reach a hundred feet or more. Plants should be selected and placed in a landscape on the basis of mature height.

Spread is the size and fullness of the canopy. It is the horizontal space needs of a plant. Trees may have huge canopies. Small shrubs may have only a few inches of spread. The space available to achieve the purposes of the landscape must be considered. Masses of annuals with little spread may require placing the plants close together.

HARDINESS, HEAT-ZONE, AND OTHER ADAPTATIONS

Hardiness refers to how well a plant is suited to the climate. Some plants withstand cold and are hardy while others are not. Hardiness zones have been established based on plant temperature tolerance. The 11 zones are based on the average minimum temperatures for that part of the country. Zone 1 is the coldest with the average minimum winter temperature below –50°F. Zone 11 has the warmest average minimum winter temperature above 40°F. When a tree or shrub is assigned a hardiness zone rating, it should survive the winter in

10-9. Some plants grow quite well in warm climates, such as the coconut tree in Key West, Florida. (Courtesy, Education Images, Inc.)

that zone or any zone having a higher numbered rating. (Please refer to Figure 7-20 for the Hardiness Zone Map.)

Another useful map is the American Horticultural Society Plant Heat-Zone Map which identifies 12 different zones in the United States based on the average number of days above 86°F. This map is important because many plants that can tolerate cold temperatures do poorly in areas with extended summers and high temperatures. (Please refer to Figure 7-22 for the Heat Zone Map.)

Light requirements differ from plant to plant. Some plants require full sun while others grow well in partial sun or shade conditions. Many small trees need to be planted under the shade of large trees. Some plant leaves will burn and die when planted in full, direct sun.

Only a few plants can grow in soils that are high in salts. Coastal areas, near saltwater, and along highways where salt is used to control snow and ice are both difficult areas in which to grow plants. Plants that tolerate the high salt conditions should be selected for these areas.

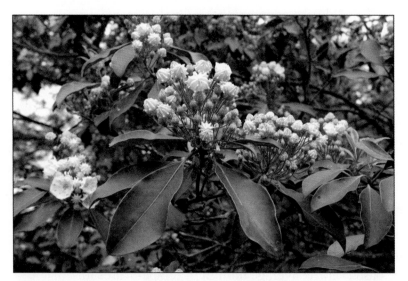

10-10. Some plants are established in areas where the natural landscape includes many appealing plants, such as the mountain laurel shown here. (Courtesy, Education Images, Inc.)

NUTRIENT AND pH NEEDS

Plants vary in nutrient and pH requirements. Soil analysis determines the nutrients available in the soil. Part of preparing the site for planting includes soil tests. Matching the plants to the natural available nutrients and pH reduces cost.

Soil fertility influences species selection as well as growth and overall plant health. Boxwoods prefer fertile, well-drained soils. Hostas prefer fertile and moist but well-drained soil. Junipers will tolerate a range of soil fertility conditions, including dry, chalky, and sandy soils. Yews prefer well-drained, fertile soil. pH is not that important to yews as they will grow in either acidic or alkaline soils. Azaleas (and all other rhodendrons) prefer moist but well-drained soil that is high in humus and has a pH of 4.5 to 5.5. Azaleas often receive fertilizers that are acid-forming.

A good example of the role of pH in plant growth is with the hydrangea. Some 80 species and many cultivars of hydrangeas are grown as pot plants and in landscapes and interiorscapes. The color of the flower of most hydrangeas is influenced by pH. Those grown in acidic soils with a pH below 5.5 have blue flowers; those in soils with a pH greater than 5.5 produce pink flowers. Hydrangea that produce white flowers are not affected by pH.

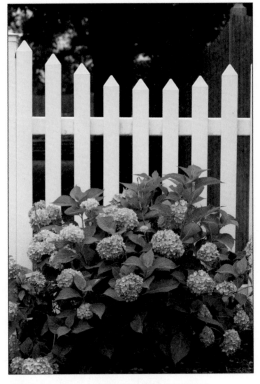

10-11. The color of hydrangea flowers is influenced by soil pH. Blue flowers are produced in highly acidic soils.

PESTS AND HAZARDS

Some areas where landscapes are installed may have problems with pests and hazards. Pests include rabbits, voles, moles, deer, and insects. Rid the area of these pests or choose plants that will not be damaged by the pests, such as deer will

10-12. A pesky rabbit seeks shelter in a holly landscape. (Courtesy, Education Images, Inc.)

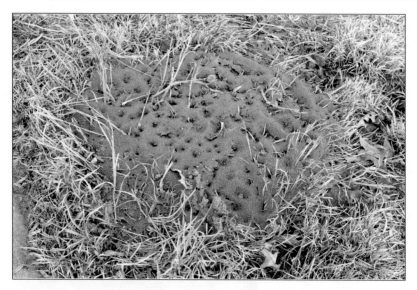

10-13. A fire ant mound in dormant sod. (Courtesy, Education Images, Inc.)

not eat some species of holly. Unfortunately, rabbits will damage holly and most other plants.

Insect pests include a wide range of species. Some pests must be managed before they become problems. Other pests should be eradicated because they damage landscapes and pose hazards to people installing and maintaining the landscape as well as the property owner. An example is the fire ant. Commercial fire ant pesticides are available and should be used according to label several days before landscape work is to be done.

Plants that pose hazards to humans may be growing in the area to be landscaped or present in plant materials. Examples include thorns, spines on leaves and needles, and those that cause allergies. Poison ivy and poison oak are often present in areas to be landscaped or where maintenance is performed. Humans who are allergic to these plants should avoid contact. Carefully spraying with an approved herbicide will eradicate these pests. But, be very careful as the herbicide will also kill desired plants, including those that are being planted.

10-14. Poison ivy is a vine that often climbs trees or shrubs. It is fairly easy to identify because it has a cluster of three leaves. (Courtesy, Education Images, Inc.)

SOURCES OF INFORMATION IN SELECTING AND INSTALLING PLANTS

Good information is needed to help in selecting and installing plants. Landscape designers and landscape contractors need to know plant materials. The important information about plants includes:

- common and scientific names
- whether the plant is deciduous or evergreen
- height and spread of the plant
- growth, training, and trimming requirements
- characteristics of flowers and fruit, if any
- hardiness zone
- heat-zone
- pest resistance and problems
- sun requirements (full sun, partial sun, or shade)
- water requirements
- life span (perennial, biennial, or annual)
- others, such as poisonous foliage, thorns, and potential problems from roots, leaves, and flowers or fruit.

Information about plants is presented in charts that summarize the major features of the species. **Appendix B, Plant Materials List, includes information on common plants used in the landscape by classification.** Reputable local nurseries often have useful information. Agriculture offices at land-grant universities and cooperative extension services usually have information and specialists who can help with plant selection and installation guidelines.

USING XERISCAPING

Xeriscape is water conservation through creative, appropriate landscaping, and water management. The water qualities of an area are determined, and plant materials are selected accordingly. Turf areas are limited and can be replaced with materials

10-15. Lowering the planting bed to catch moisture is one technique to help make efficient use of available water.

such as ground covers, mulches, or hardscape features. An efficient irrigation system may be installed to provide supplemental water. Soil improvements allowing for better moisture penetration and water holding capacity are used. A soil test will be needed. Regular maintenance is needed to preserve the plantings and conserve water.

Water Zones

A **water zone** is an area in a landscape based on the amount of water needed by the plants. Irrigation may be needed if natural moisture supplies are inadequate. Three zones are typically used:

- **Very low water zone**—The very low water zone usually requires no water beyond what is naturally available, except to establish the plants. Plants that are being established may need irrigation. Plants in the very low water zone need to be selected for low water need. Annual flowering plants are not appropriate because of their high water need. Native shrubs, cacti, and other species are often best.

- **Low water zone**—Plants in the low water zone usually need more water than what is available naturally. Some irrigation is needed. Shrubs, ground cover materials, and limited annuals may be appropriate.

- **Moderate water zone**—The plants in the moderate water zone typically need supplemental water. Focal points in the landscape and areas of high use near entrances are in this zone. Annuals and other succulent materials may be used.

TIP: Drip irrigation systems are best for xeriscaping. Water drips out of porous, below surface irrigation emitters. The water is not wasted by evaporation from the soil surface.

10-16. A d-tape irrigation system slowly emits water that soaks into the soil of this bed that is being prepared for planting. (Courtesy, Education Images, Inc.)

Careful Planning

Xeriscaping requires careful planning and installation. A soil analysis is needed to determine nutrient needs. An efficient irrigation system should be selected and properly installed. The amount of turfgrass is limited. (Most turfgrass requires large amounts of moisture.) The use of annual flowering plants is limited. Drought-tolerant perennial flowers and ornamental grasses should be selected. Mulch should be used to cool the surface, prevent erosion, and conserve soil moisture.

PREPLANTING INFORMATION

Successful tree and shrub planting starts with proper care during shipment and ends with correct planting techniques. To prevent drying out and burning of leaves, cover trees with tarpaulins or plastic sheeting when transporting in open trucks or trailers. Failure to properly protect trees and shrubs during transport is a major reason for plant death after planting.

Spring planting has been the standard practice in the landscape business for years, especially when most trees were sold as bare root plants. The short spring season may not allow the landscape contractor time to install all the scheduled landscape projects. Many contractors plant in the fall using B&B and/or container grown plants to increase landscape sales.

TIP: Garden center sales areas should be covered with shade cloth to reduce plant stress from the hot sun.

Some trees and shrubs do not transplant well in the fall in zones 1-6. Therefore, spring planting is recommended. Avoid fall planting of broadleaf evergreens, birches, Bradford Callery pear, hollies, oaks (except pin oak), silver linden, sweetgum, sour gum, and tulip trees. In zones 7-11, most trees and shrubs are planted year around.

Avoid summer planting, especially, during hot, dry periods. However, many landscape contractors find it necessary to install plants in the summer to complete all their projects. Successful summer planting requires adequate irrigation by the homeowner.

GUIDELINES FOR SELECTING TREES

The general appearance of a tree will reveal much about its quality and potential for success when transplanted. Is the trunk straight and is the crown symmetrical? Does the tree show signs of current season growth? Signs of viability include expanding buds, new leaves,

10-17. Balled and burlapped (B&B) plants ready for shipment.

TIP: The soil ball should be 1 foot in diameter for each 1 inch of trunk diameter when selecting balled & burlapped trees.

and elongated shoots. Are there any signs of disease or insect damage? Shade trees should have a strong, well-defined central leader with equally spaced branches forming a symmetrical crown. Trees having multiple leaders, crossing, rubbing, or overly-crowded branches have not been pruned properly and are less valuable.

Discolored, sunken, or swollen areas in the trunk are additional signs to look for when selecting a tree. Bark cuts and scrapes are also undesirable. Trunks with visible wood borer damage and those showing signs of sunscald or cracking should be avoided.

Trees purchased as container-grown should be well-rooted and firmly established in their containers. The root mass should retain its shape and hold together when removed from the container. However, if the roots circle and form a dense web, the tree may be pot-bound. Pot-bound plants are often under stress.

The soil ball for balled and burlapped trees should not be excessively wet or dry and should be securely held together by burlap, twine, or possibly a wire basket. The trunk should be centered in the root ball and should not move independent of it.

Bare root (BR) trees should be stored in a cool, shady area with their roots protected from drying by packing or burlap. Their root system should be damp and flexible. When bare root trees are ready to be planted in the landscape, their root systems should continue to be protected until they are actually placed in the ground. Exposure of the roots to the sun should be limited as much as possible.

PLANTING TECHNIQUES FOR TREES AND SHRUBS

Different landscape contractors may use different planting methods. The following techniques describe common methods of transplanting trees and shrubs.

BALLED AND BURLAPPED PLANTING TECHNIQUES

The **soil ball** is the soil surrounding the root system, which has been balled and burlapped. Always dig the planting hole a minimum of 12 inches larger than the soil ball of the tree or shrub. This will allow a minimum of 6 inches of space between the soil ball and the edge of the planting hole in which new roots can expand. Research has shown that the larger the hole, the better. The top of the soil ball should be level with the surface of the new planting hole and the bottom of the hole should be flat. This allows the tree or shrub to be planted at the same depth as it was originally growing in the nursery. To prevent plant death from root rot, never plant a tree in a hole that is deeper than the height of the soil ball.

When planting B&B stock, carefully place the plant in the hole without removing any burlap or twine and check the hole for proper size. Grasp the plant by the soil ball when han-

Balled & Burlapped plant

Planting hole a minimum of 12 inches wider than soil ball. Cut twine and push burlap back. Form a saucer at the base of the tree and fill with 3" of mulch.

Tree supported by guying

10-18. Planting a balled and burlapped tree.

dling it. Always untie and remove all twine from around the plant trunk or stems. Twine left around the tree trunk can strangle the young tree and cause it to die several years later. With the B&B shrub in the hole, pull the burlap back from the top of the soil ball and push it down between the soil ball and the walls of the planting hole. This will prevent the burlap from acting as a wick, removing moisture from the root ball. Note that synthetic, "burlap look-alike" plastic material should be removed completely before planting.

CONTAINER GROWN PLANTING TECHNIQUES

Before placing a container grown plant in the hole, remove the container. Invert the container plant and tap the container edge on a solid object. The soil ball will slide out of the container. Take care not to disturb the root system. One problem with plants grown in containers is root circling. **Root circling**, also called pot bound, is when a plant grows too long in a container. If the plant is pot bound, cut the roots at the edge with a knife and spread them before planting. Place the soil ball in the hole and check for proper hole diameter and depth. Position the plant in the hole with the best looking side toward the main viewing point.

10-19. If the container plant's roots are circled at the edge, cut them with a knife and spread them at the bottom.

BARE ROOT PLANTING TECHNIQUES

Follow the same general installation guidelines when planting bare root rose bushes, fruit trees, or other bare root plants. Remove the thin plastic covering around the roots and discard any sawdust or other moisture-holding material found inside the plastic bag. Dig a hole

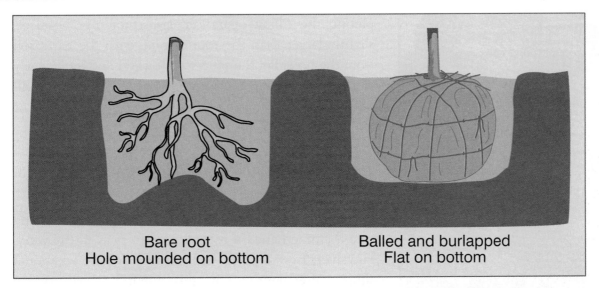

10-20. The harvesting method used for the landscape plant determines the shape of the planting hole.

Bare root
Hole mounded on bottom

Balled and burlapped
Flat on bottom

as deep as the longest root and at least 12 inches wider than the root system. The bark or stem of a bare root plant will usually have a stain marking the level of the original field height. The tree or shrub should be planted at the same depth as it was growing in the nursery. After removing the soil from the planting hole, make a cone-shaped pile of soil in the bottom center of the hole. Rest the plant crown, the junction of roots and stem, on top of this soil cone. Carefully spread the secondary roots to their natural shape. Back fill the hole tamping the soil to remove any unseen pockets of air. Construct a saucer by creating a small berm around the edge of the planting hole to hold irrigation water and clean up the planting area.

BACK FILLING THE HOLE

Break up all large soil clumps with a shovel before using them to back fill the hole. Partially back fill the hole with existing soil and carefully tamp the soil around the root system, but do not pound the soil. Continue back filling the hole tamping the soil to help prevent air pockets from forming around the root system. After com-

2'
2' minimum

10-21 . Establish a water saucer at the plant base.

10-22. Correctly planted flowering tree. Note the saucer around the tree for holding water.

pleting the filling operation, construct a soil saucer, slightly larger than the root system, with the extra soil from the hole. Fill the saucer with water and let it slowly wet the root system and surrounding soil. The saucer will help retain rain or irrigation water for use by the tree or shrub.

SUPPORT BY STAKING OR GUYING

Some new research shows that the trunk of a young tree is strengthened if it is allowed to sway in the wind. However, trees 6 to 12 feet tall may require additional support after planting. Give this support by driving two or three long wooden stakes next to the soil ball and attach a wire between the stakes and the tree trunk. Protect the soft trunk tissue by covering the wire with a short piece of rubber hose. This method of support is called **staking**. Note that shrubs rarely require additional support.

10-23. A crepe myrtle has been braced with support stakes. (Courtesy, Education Images, Inc.)

10-24. Bracing a tree by guying.

Newly planted trees more than 15 feet tall need cables or wires attached to the tree trunk and to three equally-spaced stakes driven around the tree base for support. The wires between the stakes and the tree trunk are split in the middle with a turnbuckle, which is used to adjust the wire or cable tension. The tree trunk should be protected by covering each wire with a short piece of rubber hose. This support method is called **guying**. Guying cables need to be visibly flagged for safety.

WATERING PRACTICES

Newly transplanted trees and shrubs require deep and thorough watering for the entire first year after planting. Homeowners may forget to water trees and shrubs regularly after planting. The following watering technique will thoroughly wet the soil 12 inches deep and is an easy way to provide adequate soil moisture for most plants. Slowly empty a 5-gallon bucket of water in the soil saucer of shrubs. Use two 5-gallon buckets of water on large shrubs and trees. Instruct homeowners to continue this weekly watering practice for the first growing season on all landscape plants when no rainfall has occurred during the week. Most landscape contractors only water plants once after installing them. The homeowner should then assume the watering responsibility and should continue weekly watering for the first growing season.

> **TIP:** Always water plants immediately after planting. Do not wait until the end of the day or several days. Water at once.

FERTILIZER AND ANTI-TRANSPIRANT

Most landscape contractors do not fertilize trees and shrubs at the time of planting. Over-fertilization can cause more stress to newly transplanted trees than no fertilization.

Leaf burn from excessive water loss can occur when transplanting trees and shrubs in full leaf. **Transpiration** is the loss of water from the plant through the leaves in the form of water vapor. The **stomata** are small openings in the epidermal layer of plant tissue where transpiration occurs. Root loss and stress from transplanting can cause an increase in transpiration resulting in leaf scorch. Spray the foliage with an anti-transpirant to reduce water loss when transplanting trees and shrubs. An **anti-transpirant** seals the stomata and reduces transpiration which can help prevent leaf scorch or leaf burn. Apply anti-transpirant in the late fall to reduce winter burn on evergreens caused by dry winter winds.

> **TIP:** Two to three days before transplanting evergreens, spray the foliage with an anti-transpirant to reduce wilting after planting.

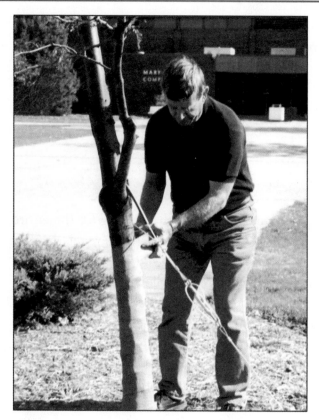

10-25. Newly transplanted tree with trunk protected with tree wrap.

TRUNK WRAPPING

Many landscape contractors wrap tree trunks with a heavy paper, tree wrap material to reduce the possibility of sunscald and to protect them from rodents or other pests. **Sunscald**, or **winter burn**, describes a condition in which bark blisters from the intense winter sunlight.

Start wrapping the paper spirally around the trunk from the ground level and continue up to the first branch. Securely attach the tree wrap paper to the trunk with twine or tape. Never damage the trunk if it can be avoided.

PLANTING TECHNIQUES FOR GROUND COVERS AND VINES

Ground cover refers to a woody or herbaceous plant that forms a mat less than 1 foot high covering the ground. It is generally regarded as a special purpose plant. A **vine** is a woody or herbaceous plant that climbs naturally with some type of support or creeps along the ground.

GROUND COVER INSTALLATION

Most ground cover plants have a maximum height of 12 inches. In the past, ground covers were used mainly on steep banks to hold soil and reduce erosion. For years, landscapers also recommended ground covers under trees or in other shady areas where grass would not grow. Today, ground covers are an important part of a well-designed home landscape planting. They create living mulch that will cover the soil and reduce weed growth in landscape planting beds.

Because ground cover plants do not have much individual form, their design form is determined by the shape of the landscape bed. Most ground covers are perennial plants that grow year after year without replanting. Most are also evergreen plants, keeping their leaves all year; however, a few are deciduous and drop their leaves in the winter. Some ground covers have showy flowers; while others have interesting and unusual leaf colors or patterns.

Ground covers are often used instead of grass to cover the soil. Ground covers improve the appearance of the ground, hold the soil, and prevent erosion on steep slopes. They may be difficult to establish and completely cover an area. Frequent watering, during this establishment stage, will speed the spread of the ground cover plants. Weeds can be difficult to control in the ground cover bed during the establishment stage. Pulling weeds by hand from between the plants may be the only effective method of control. Herbicides that control most weeds will also kill the desirable ground cover plants.

10-26. Ground cover is often used to control erosion and provide an attractive landscape bed covering.

Table 10-2. Calculating Amounts of Ground Cover

NUMBER OF PLANTS NEEDED	
Specified Distance Apart	**Multiply area to be covered (sq. ft.) by:**
4" o.c.	9.0
6" o.c.	4.0
9" o.c.	1.78
12" o.c.	1.0
15" o.c.	0.64
18" o.c.	0.44
24" o.c.	0.25

Spacing of the plants will help determine how quickly or slowly the soil will be completely covered. Most ground covers are planted 8 to 12 inches o.c. The term "o.c." stands for "on center" or the distance between the center of one plant and the center of the next plant. Appendix B, Plant Materials List, provides specific spacing requirements for ground covers.

Many ground covers will grow faster than low-growing evergreens. Do not plant fast-growing ground covers (English ivy, *Hedera helix*; crown vetch, *Coronilla varia*; or honeysuckle, *Lonicera sempervirens*) in the same planting bed with low-growing evergreens.

VINE INSTALLATION

A landscape plant whose stem requires support for upright growth is called a vine. They may be deciduous or evergreen. In many parts of the country, vines are not as popular today as in the past. Vines, especially in the north, require more care than most other landscape plants. Use vines for overhead protection, over a patio or other areas, as an alternative to shade trees. Plant vines next to walls and fences to soften their harsh construction lines. Many vines are planted for their beautiful flowers or colorful fruit.

A decorative support called an arbor or trellis can be used to support the weak stems of climbing plants. Climbing plants have three different methods of support: tendrils, twining, or holdfasts. Small special stems called tendrils, wrap around the support structure and help many climbing plants stay on the trellis. Some vine plants hold onto the support structure by twining or simply wrapping their entire stem around the support. Other vines have developed special root-like structures, called holdfasts, on their stems that penetrate wood, brick, or mortar to secure the plant to the wall or fence.

Holdfast   Twining   Tendril

10-27. Examples of vine attachment—holdfast, twining, and tendril.

Vines growing on brick or wood homes can cause structural damage. The holdfast structures of the vine can weaken the brick wall by damaging the mortar between the bricks. Thick-growing vines may hold extra moisture around wood window frames and cause the wood to rot. In the south, the Virginia creeper (*Parthenocissus quinquifolia*) is a fast-growing vine that can smother shrubs and large trees in the landscape.

Clematis is one of the most popular vines in the country. Large, fragrant, white, blue, red, or purple flowers can add interest to any landscape. The stems containing the red-orange berries of the American bittersweet vine add color to dried, fall floral arrangements.

PLANTING TECHNIQUES FOR FLOWERS IN THE LANDSCAPE

Vivid flower colors contrasted with green shrubs attract attention to the landscape. Homes built before 1950 contained large flower beds in the front yard. Bright-colored flowers attract the public's eye and can detract from the total home appearance. Today, designers normally place the flower beds in the backyard where they can be enjoyed close up by family and friends. Planting flowers in the private area also adds many colorful features to the landscape.

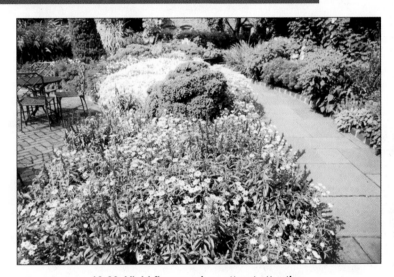

10-28. Vivid flower colors attract attention.

FLOWER BORDERS, BEDS, AND GROUPS

Flowers in front of shrubs in a planting bed create a **flower border** with the shrubs providing the back drop. A **flower bed** is a planting bed that only contains flowers. Tall-growing flower varieties should be planted at the back of the flower bed and short varieties at the front edge. Flower bed design should be kept simple. Try to plant groups of the same flowers together.

Annual flowers are plants that germinate from seed, grow to maturity, flower, and produce seed in one growing season. Annual flowers give the landscape quick color at a reasonable price. They can also be used in perennial flower beds to help maintain color throughout the year. Annuals planted in the spring will die each fall and need to be

TIP: Annual flowers usually are vivid, bright colors while perennials are more subdued; not as showy.

10-29. Annual flowers in shady area.

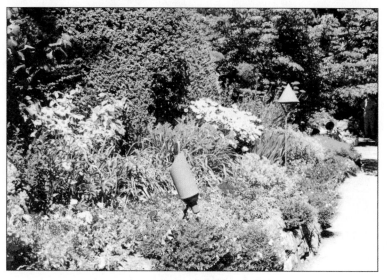

10-30. Perennial flower bed.

replanted each spring. **Perennial** flowers are plants that live for more than two growing seasons. Perennials may be placed in subgroups of herbaceous or woody types.

Plants can be further classified by temperature tolerance. Tender plants are more sensitive to temperature extremes than hardy plants. Hardy bulbs planted in the fall will flower each spring for many years. Plant tender bulbs and tubers in the spring for summer flowering but dig up in the fall before frost and store inside through the winter. Planting time, plant cost, and general maintenance requirements should be considered by the designer when selecting the best flowers for each landscape job. Appendix B provides cultural information for annual and perennial flowers used in the landscape.

Perennial Gardens

One of the fastest growing segments of landscaping is the perennial garden. Perennials offer a vast array of colors and textures. The proper choice of perennial plant material can mean beautiful blooms from spring, through summer, and into the fall.

There are several considerations when selecting a site for a perennial garden. The amount of sun or shade the site is exposed to plays an important part in plant selection. The amount of sun the site receives during the day must be known. Another key is proper drainage. The site selected should have good drainage so the plants do not sit in standing water. A good way to determine if the site has good drainage is to dig a hole at the site and fill it with water. Let the water drain and fill the hole again. If the water drains out at less than 1 inch per hour, the drainage will need to be improved, or plant material that will thrive in wet conditions must be selected.

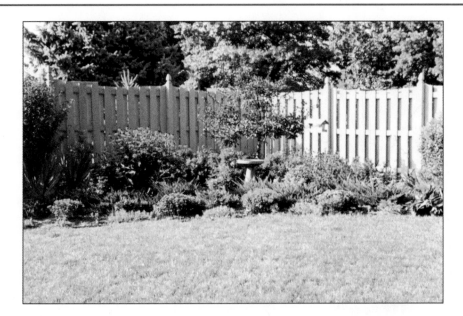

10-31. Perennial gardens are often used to add color and beauty to the private area.

After the site has been selected and the needs have been determined, the perennial bed pattern shape can now be laid out. An easy way to accomplish this is to lay a garden hose or rope on the ground in the desired shape of the garden. The shape of the bed should be in harmony with the rest of the landscape. If other landscape beds are curved, the perennial bed should be curved. If they are straight or 45 degree angles, the perennial garden should be also. For ease of maintenance, design planting beds to be no deeper than 5 feet.

The selection of plant material is the most important decision for the perennial garden. Perennials are available in a variety of colors, sizes, and flowering times. In addition, sun requirements and drainage needs have to be considered. Colors and sizes that create a balanced garden should be selected. A number of groupings of plants generally look better than single plants spread throughout the garden. Taller plants should be placed towards the rear with shorter ones toward the front. There should be a plan used when selecting plant material.

Generally, perennials are planted in the spring or in the fall. Site preparation should begin some time before the actual planting. The bed should be tilled about 6 inches down and the soil mixed thoroughly. Organic material such as peat moss or leaf compost should be added. The soil should be kept loose until planting. Soil should be tested in order to determine fertilizer requirements and pH.

Flowering Bulbs/Tubers/Corms

Plant hardy flowering bulbs, such as tulips (*Tulipa sp.*), daffodils (*Narcissus* sp.), and hyacinths (*Hyacinthus sp.*), in the fall. They will give the landscape added color the following spring. In cold climates, plant tender plants, such as canna (*Canna sp.*) in the spring and enjoy their glorious blooms through the summer. Come fall, dig up the bulbs and tubers and

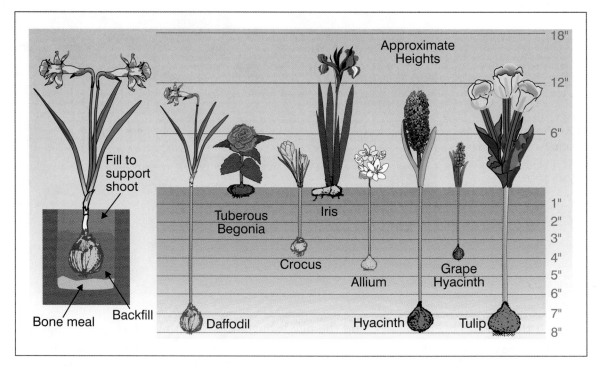

Fill to support shoot

Bone meal

Backfill

Approximate Heights

18"
12"
6"

Tuberous Begonia

Iris

1"
2"
3"

Crocus

4"

Allium

Grape Hyacinth

5"
6"

Daffodil

Hyacinth

Tulip

7"
8"

10-32. Planting technique for bulbs and tubers. Spring flowering bulbs can be planted from September through early November in a sunny, well-drained location.

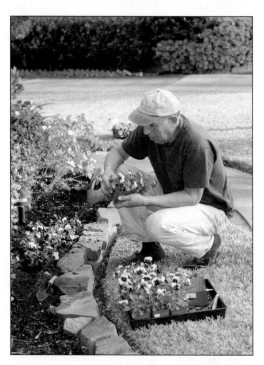

10-33. Pansies should be planted in beds that have been well-prepared.

store them through the winter for planting next spring. Appendix B provides cultural information for bulbs and tubers used in the landscape.

FLOWER PLANTING

Flowers grow best in well-prepared beds. The planting bed should be free of all turf. Organic matter, such as peat moss, leaf compost, or manure, should be added and tilled into the top 6 inches of the soil to improve soil texture and increase water holding capacity.

Some flowers require full sun, while others need a shady planting location. Always know the different kinds of flowers and their individual growth requirements. Plant them in the right place. Some flowers can survive a variety of planting conditions while others cannot.

AFTER-PLANTING CARE

Flower beds need hand watering and require regular weeding. Without an intense maintenance program, flower beds look terrible. Immediately after planting, apply a preemergent herbicide to prevent weed seeds from germinating in the flower bed. As with all pesticides, always read and follow the label directions. Weed seed germination can also be reduced or prevented by using mulch around the individual plants.

Fertilize flower beds once or twice a year by applying a liquid flower fertilizer when watering. Follow the manufacturer's recommendations for proper mixing. Over fertilization has killed more flowers than under fertilization. Follow the label instructions for additional applications throughout the season. When in doubt about whether to fertilize or not to fertilize flowers, do not fertilize.

FINAL PLANTING STEPS

Edging the planting bed and applying a landscape fabric can enhance any landscape project and eliminate weed growth. Many different types of landscape mulch are available. Installing mulch along with the final cleanup of the job site will complete the landscape installation process.

BED EDGING

Bed edging is the area where the landscape bed joins the lawn area. The landscape area may be naturally edged or may have a permanent, finished edge. Use a sharp spade to make a clean, crisp line between the grass lawn area and the landscape bed. Naturally edged beds look great right after the edging but need frequent touch up to keep them looking good. A variety of materials are available to put a permanent, finished edge on the landscape bed. This type of edging minimizes hand trimming and helps contain mulches, such as stone and bark, within the bed area. It will also help to keep more water in the planting beds by slowing surface runoff.

TIP: When installing metal stakes in plastic bed edging, drive the stake at a 45 degree angle from the planting bed side under the grass next to the bed.

Plastic, steel, aluminum, pavers, timbers, and treated wood are used as bed edging materials. During the last 10 to 15 years, the most widely used edging materials have been heavy duty polyethylene/vinyl types. These edging materials have a variety of shapes, such as the common round bead tops and a series of horizontal groves, v-lips, or fins on the bottom help prevent frost heaving. Vinyl edging sizes vary, but 4 inches wide by 20 feet long is the normal size. A variety of thicknesses are available.

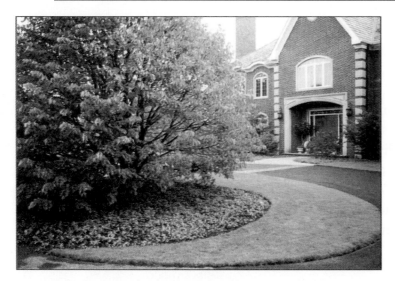

10-34. Natural-edged bed without plastic or metal edging.

Steel edging provides a more permanent edge, but at an increase in cost. Commercial landscape sites usually specify steel edging on the landscape planting plans. Steel landscape edging material is sold in 4 inch widths with thicknesses of 1/8, 3/16, or 1/4 inch and lengths of 10, 16, or 20 feet.

Aluminum edging is available in similar sizes to the steel edging. It comes in several colors—natural, black, green, bronze and black. Special stakes hold all edging materials in the soil and prevent the edging from heaving out of the ground during freezing and thawing conditions.

Treated landscape timbers 4" ´ 6" ´ 8' provide a different bed edging effect. The inability to construct curved bed edges is a main difference between wood and other edging materials. Large landscape projects can use railroad ties for bed edging. However, railroad

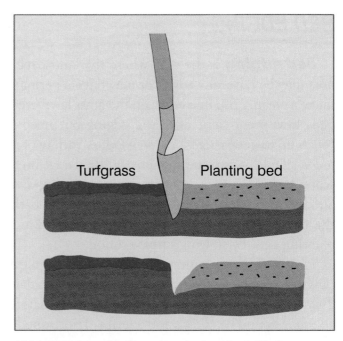

10-35. Edging installed around a landscape planting bed.

10-36. The sharp drop in a natural-edged bed will slow rhizome turfgrasses and stop bunch grasses from spreading.

ties may appear too large in the average home landscape.

Installation

Dig a trench deep enough to bury the edging with ½ to ¾ inch exposed above the mulch. Follow the manufacturer's directions to install the stakes provided with the edging. Drill 9/16-inch diameter holes through railroad ties. Drive 18-inch long, ½-inch diameter reinforcing rods into the soil to secure the ties. However, when using landscape timbers or in heavy clay soil, only 3/8-inch diameter, 18-inch long reinforcing rods are needed.

10-37. Installing reinforcing rods in landscape timbers.

LANDSCAPE FABRIC

Landscape fabric is a plastic sheet placed in the landscape bed to reduce weed competition with the landscape plants. Solid, black plastic sheets were used in the 1970s. The solid sheets prevented air and water movement into the soil. Modern landscape fabrics, called geotextiles, have replaced the solid plastic sheets. **Geotextiles** are woven strips of plastic landscape fabric that allow the movement of air, water, and fertilizer into the soil. Some landscape fabrics also contain herbicides to control weeds. Landscape fabric is covered with mulch after installation.

Clear the area to bare soil and unroll the fabric over the planting bed. If placed over an existing bed, cut an "X" over each plant, slip plants through the opening and push fabric under the plant base. If placed over a

TIP: Cover the landscape planting bed with a landscape fabric after planting shrubs, but before spreading mulch. Do not use a weed barrier in annual flower beds. It is very time consuming to cut individual holes into the fabric to plant the annual flowers.

10-38. Landscape fabric is used to prevent weed growth in the landscape bed.

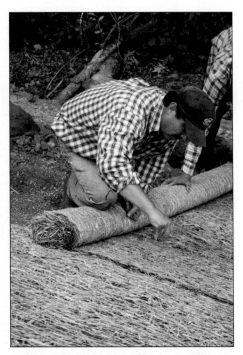

10-39. A roll of straw matting is being placed on a slope. Note that a tie is being used to help hold the mat in place. (Courtesy, Education Images, Inc.)

new bed, roll fabric over the soil and cut an "X" for each hole where the plant and its roots will be placed. Fold excess fabric under and cover it with a minimum of 4 inches of mulch. Do not leave any fabric exposed since it will deteriorate after prolonged exposure to direct sunlight.

Some locations may require the use of materials to prevent soil erosion to water. Various practices can be used to protect the soil including diverting any runoff, covering with sod, using mulch, using stone or rock, and covering with mats. In some locations, straw mats are placed over soil. Grass seed can be planted over the mat. As the grass or vegetation grows, the mat rots away and disappears.

LANDSCAPE MULCH

Landscape mulch covers the soil or landscape fabric in planting beds. **Mulch** is the material used around plants to reduce water loss, prevent weed growth, keep soil temperatures uniform, or prevent erosion. Mulching improves the general appearance

10-40. Bark mulch also can prevent weed growth in planting beds.

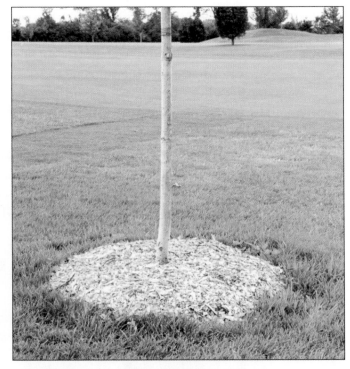

10-41. Wood mulch spread at the base of a tree to control weeds and keep soil moist.

of planting beds. Organic and inorganic mulch give the landscape designer or contractor two major kinds of mulch from which to choose. Spread the mulch uniformly 1 to 4 inches deep in the planting bed area.

Organic Mulch Materials

Organic mulches are often from products or materials that might be wasted or discarded if not used as mulch. They are from materials that were once living—ground tree bark, pine needles, rice hulls, wood chips, pistachio hulls, corn cobs, and cocoa bean hulls. Each region of the country produces several different kinds of organic mulch materials. Therefore, many of these mulch materials will not be available in all parts of the country. While organic mulches have a very pleasing earthy appearance, they decay quickly in the landscape. Normally, beds require a yearly top dressing with new mulch to keep them looking good. Large-particle mulches last longer. Organic mulch should be replenished periodically, but the landscape fabric should last for years.

Inorganic Mulch Materials

Inorganic mulches, called aggregates, come from materials that were never living. Inorganic mulch materials are more permanent and seldom require top dressing with new mulch. Gravel, crushed stone, sand, and brick chips furnish the landscape contractor a variety of materials to choose from.

10-42. Pine needle mulch is popular in the southeastern United States.

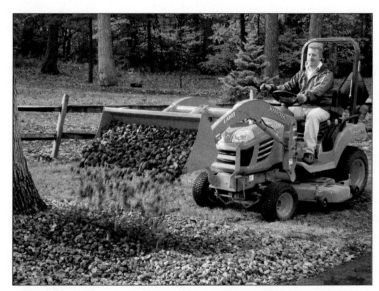

10-43. Gravel is an inorganic mulch that is sometimes used in landscape beds.

To complete the planting operation, clean up the planting site by removing debris from the planting holes and discarding plant containers. Landscape construction jobs may require a crew to work for several hours or many days at one job site. Each day brings a crew new challenges and opportunities to provide customers a beautiful and functional landscape.

REVIEWING

MAIN IDEAS

Landscapers install bare root, balled and burlapped, or container grown plants in the home landscape. Follow these simple rules when transplanting trees and shrubs. Always use a clean sharp spade. Dig the hole a minimum of 12 inches larger than the soil ball size. Plant the tree so the top of the soil ball is level with the soil at the site. Remove any plastic containers from the soil ball before planting. Remove twine from around the trunk of the tree. Spray evergreens with an anti-transpirant to reduce water loss.

Plant flowers in flower beds or flower borders. Hardy bulbs should be planted in the fall to give the landscape color in the early spring. Always prepare flower bed soil before planting the flowers. Use a herbicide to control weeds in flower and landscape beds. Mulch flower beds to reduce hand watering.

Edge planting beds to create a crisp line between the lawn area and the bed. Plastic, steel, aluminum, pavers, timbers, and treated wood make excellent bed edging. Install a landscape fabric to prevent weed growth in the planting bed. Mulches add the finishing touch to a well-designed and installed landscape bed. Organic mulches, such as bark or wood chips, give the bed a natural look. Gravel mulch will last many years without any additional maintenance.

QUESTIONS

Answer the following questions using correct spelling and complete sentences.

1. What is the difference between bare root, balled and burlapped, and container grown plants?

2. What is xeriscape?

3. How deep should the hole be when planting a tree or shrub?

4. Why should an anti-transpirant be used after planting evergreen shrubs?

5. What is sunscald?

6. How many ground cover plants are needed for 10 sq. ft. if they are spaced 6" o.c.?

7. What is the difference between a flower bed and a flower border?

8. Why install bed edging around landscape planting beds?

9. What is the purpose of landscape fabric?

10. What are the two major kinds of landscape mulch? What are the advantages of each?

CHAPTER SELF-CHECK

Match the term with the correct definition. Write the letter by the term in the blank provided.

a. guying
b. sunscald
c. geotextile
d. container grown

e. flower bed
f. stomata
g. pine needles
h. hardy bulbs

i. gravel
j. flower border

_____1. Holes that let air and water into the leaf

_____2. Trees and evergreens grown in plastic containers filled with a special soil mix

_____3. Attach cables between the tree trunk and a stake to support the newly transplanted tree

_____4. Many landscape contractors wrap tree trunks with a paper wrap to prevent damage from the sun

_____5. A landscape planting containing flowers, not shrubs

_____6. This material should be installed under mulch to prevent weed growth in landscape planting beds

_____7. A landscape planting containing both flowers and shrubs

_____8. An organic type mulch

_____9. An inorganic type mulch

_____10. Planted in the fall and flower the next spring

EXPLORING

1. Go to a garden center and identify bare root, balled and burlapped, and container-grown plants. Note the species and prices of the plants. Determine where such plants might be used in a landscape. Prepare a report on your findings. Present an oral report in class.

2. Apply an anti-transpirant material to flower and vegetable transplants in your home garden.

3. Install plastic edging and landscape fabric in landscape beds at school or home. Make digital images of before and after. Prepare a presentation that uses your images.

CHAPTER 11

Turfgrass Establishment

OBJECTIVES

1 Distinguish between warm and cool season turfgrasses.

2 Describe how to establish turf.

3 Name the factors necessary for good seed germination.

4 Explain vegetative propagation of turf.

TERMS

cool humid region
cool season turfgrass
knits down
mono-stand
plains region
plug

sod
sprigs
topdressing
transition zone
turfgrass
turfgrass blend

turfgrass mixtures
warm arid and semi-arid region
warm humid region
warm season turfgrass

11-1. Well-kept turf is important to the overall beauty of the landscape.

BEAUTIFUL, green turfgrass is appealing and useful in many ways. People enjoy lawns, playing fields, parks, and other places with turf. Turf is an integral part of the landscape.

Having good turf is more than throwing out a few grass seeds. Turf requires the same care as other plants. The soil must be tested and fertilized, the seedbed properly prepared, good grass seed selected, the soil watered, and pests managed.

Southern and northern turfgrasses need many of the same general practices. The manner in which plants grow is the same. The differences are in the grass species and the cultural practices used in growing each. People also have different objectives and goals for turfgrass in varying locations.

TURFGRASS USE IN THE UNITED STATES

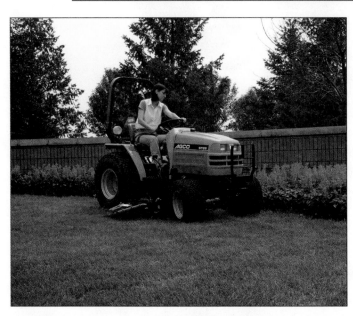

11-2. Mowing at the proper height with good equipment is essential in turf maintenance. (Courtesy, AGCO)

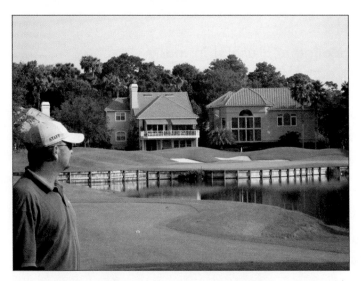

11-3. Attractive turf has a major role in the aesthetics of a gated golf course community. (Courtesy, Eddie Seagle, Abraham Baldwin Agricultural College)

People like the beauty of lawns, athletic fields, parks, golf courses, and other places where turf is grown. Turf is an integral part of the landscape in the United States. Good turf requires more than throwing out a few grass seeds and hoping for the establishment of a green lawn. Often, good turf management practices are put into effect at the wrong time of the year. This chapter provides a good foundation in proper turfgrass installation and establishment techniques.

TURF FUNCTIONS

Turfgrass is a collection of grass plants that form a ground cover. Quality turfgrass requires regular maintenance practices. Grass has three different uses in the landscape—ornamental or beauty, utility, and sports. Turf quality is related to the common visual factors of density, texture, uniformity, and color. All grass lawns and athletic fields must look good.

People enjoy seeing a large green lawn around a home, business, or park. A well-maintained yard can increase the property value of a house. Turfgrass planted along roads can stabilize the soil and reduce erosion. Turfgrass plants also have a cooling effect in hot weather and can clean air by removing toxic emissions. Athletes like the good surface that natural turf provides. It can reduce player injuries in many sports.

CLIMATE AND TURFGRASS LIFE CYCLE

Turfgrasses are often placed in two groups—southern and northern. These groups are based on the ability of a species to grow and serve a useful purpose in a specific climate. The **cool season turfgrasses** grow best in a temperature range of 50 to 75°F. They can withstand very cold winter temperatures but may die during very hot spells. The **warm season turfgrasses** grow best in the range of 70 to 95°F, but become dormant in weather below 40°F. Most warm season turfgrass plants can survive very hot temperatures, but cannot survive cold winter temperatures. The life cycles of grasses are related to the season in which the grasses grow.

Table 11-1. Examples of Common Turfgrasses

Common Name	Scientific Name	Description/Notations
Grasses for warmer climates:		

Bermudagrasses
  Common
  Bradley
  Megennis
  Others
	Cynodon dactylon
	C. bradleyi
	C. magennisii
		specialized varieties and hybrids make it popular; fine-textured; established by seed or sod, depending on the kind; often used on athletic fields and home lawns; prefers full sun; mow at a height of 0.5 to 1.5 inches, except for varieties on golf greens that can be mowed shorter

Centipedegrass	*Eremochloa ophiuroides*	medium-textured grass; adapted to a wide range of soil conditions; minimal maintenance needed; mow 1 to 2 inches high
Saint Augustine	*Stenotaphrum secundatum*	coarse-textured and aggressive growing; prefers well-drained sandy soil; not cold tolerant; will tolerate shade; subject to fungus diseases; easy to propagate with sprigs or runners; mow at a height of 2.5 to 3.5 inches
Zoysiagrass	*Zoysia japonica*	medium-textured grass; grows slowly; will tolerate some cold; mow with a reel mower at heights of 0.5 to 1 inch
Grasses for cooler climates:		
Kentucky Bluegrass	*Poa pratensis*	medium-textured grass; often established on lawns with sod; prefers moist, temperate climates; mow at a height of 2.5 to 3.5 inches
Bent grass	*Agrostis palustris*	common on closely cut areas, such as putting greens; grows by creeping along the ground; not a good home lawn grass

Fescue
  Fine
  Tall
	Festuca rubra
	F. arundinacea
		popular grasses; fine textured; tolerant of some shade; mowing height depends on variety, with fine fescue mowed 1.5 to 2.5 inches high, and tall fescue never mowed below 3 inches high

Perennial Ryegrass	*Lolium perenne*	widely used in home lawns; difficult to have good appearance after mowing; mow at a height of 1.5 to 2.5 inches

TIP: Warm season grasses grow best when the weather is warm in late spring through summer and into fall. Cool season grasses grow best during the cool temperatures of spring and fall.

Seeded annual turfgrasses complete a life cycle in one growing season. This includes the vegetative, reproductive, and senescence (death) stages. The life cycle of perennial grasses includes vegetative, reproductive, and dormancy stages. Most turfgrasses planted in the United States belong to the perennial group. Mowing helps keep turfgrasses in the vegetative stage, rather than following a natural schedule of flowering and seed production.

If cool season turfgrasses go into summer dormancy from extended periods of heat and drought, they may not survive. Irrigation and syringing (misting for surface cooling) can help minimize summer dormancy problems. Warm season turfgrasses go into winter dormancy and may die if the temperatures go too low. Warm season grasses growing in tropical climates will remain green all year.

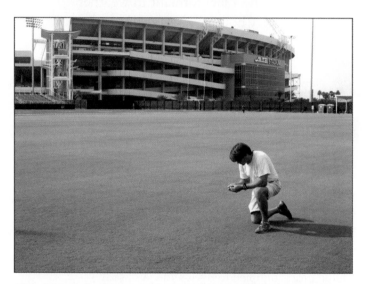

11-4. Athletic facility grounds superintendents place a premium on quality turf. (Courtesy, Eddie Seagle, Abraham Baldwin Agricultural College)

TURFGRASS REGIONS

Climate, soil conditions, and length of growing seasons differ greatly throughout the country. These ecological differences help divide the country into four major turfgrass regions. The kinds of grasses grown and the management practices differ in each of these regions.

Cool Humid Region is suited to cool season grasses, such as bluegrass, ryegrass, fescue, or bentgrass. The soils are generally acidic and some irrigation may be needed to supplement natural rainfall. Planting seed is the common way of starting new lawns in the cool humid region.

Warm Humid Region is suited to warm season grasses, such as Bermudagrass, Zoysiagrass, Bahiagrass, Centipedegrass, Carpetgrass, and St. Augustinegrass. These soils are generally strongly acidic and may be relatively infertile. Most warm season turf is established by vegetative techniques, not by seed. Sodding, plugging, and sprigging are common methods used to install new lawns in the warm humid region of the United States.

Plains Region is a dry part of the United States where buffalograss and blue grama grass grow naturally. Cool season turfgrasses will only grow in this region with adequate irrigation. Buffalograss and blue grama grasses are both established by seed.

Warm Arid and Semi-Arid Regions will only support the warm season turf if irrigation is used to supplement the very low natural rainfall. Soils in this region are usually alkaline and low in fertility. Lawns are established by sodding, plugging, and sprigging in the warm arid and semiarid regions.

TRANSITION ZONE

A **transition zone** is an area between two major climate zones. The transition zone separates temperate and subtropical zones in the eastern United States. This zone goes east and west at approximately 37° north latitude and varies from 100 to 200 miles wide. Bluegrass, bentgrass, and fescue meet the limits of their southern exposure in this transition zone, while Bermudagrass meets the limit of northern exposure due to cold winter temperatures in the transition zone.

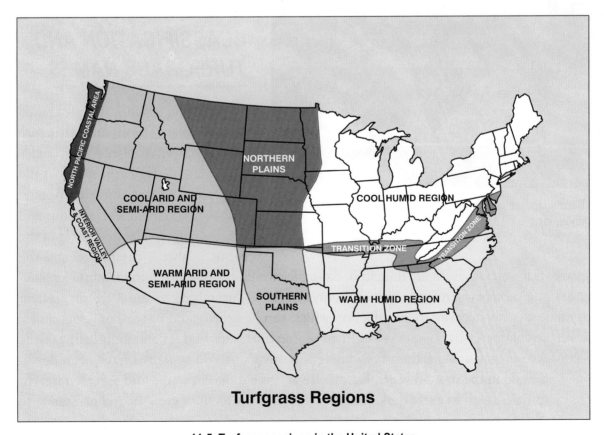

11-5. Turfgrass regions in the United States.

Several warm season and cool season turfgrasses can be grown in this transition zone, but the climate is not really optimum for any turfgrasses. Zoysiagrass is the most cold tolerant of the warm season turfgrasses and is commonly grown here. However, Bermudagrass can be grown in this transition zone with some winter-kill occurring. Tall fescue is the best cool season turfgrass to grow in the transition zone.

ESTABLISHING TURF

There are several commonly used methods of establishing turfgrasses—seeding, sodding, plugging, and sprigging. Establishment by seeding is the most common method in the cool humid region because it is usually the least expensive method. In the South, lawns are usually established by sodding, plugging, or sprigging of warm season turf species.

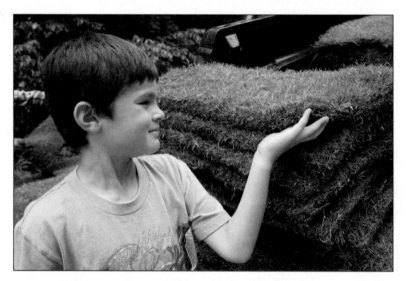

11-6. Quality Bermudagrass sod is ready for placing. (Courtesy, Education Images, Inc.)

SCIENTIFIC CLASSIFICATION AND TURFGRASS NAMES

Scientific classification is based on the plant form and structure (morphology) of plants. The scientific name is the Latin name of the grass plant written using the Roman alphabet and includes the genus and species names. The first letter of the genus is always capitalized and the species is lowercase. Both are italicized. Examples would be: *Poa pratensis* (Kentucky bluegrass) or *Cynodon dactylon* (common Bermudagrass). Turf managers use the term cultivar to name a cultivated variety or selection which can be propagated by seed or sprigs and is available commercially. Glades is a cultivar of *Poa pratensis*, and is commonly called Glade Kentucky bluegrass. More than 500 different cultivars of *Poa pratensis* have been developed and sold in the past 50 years. Each cultivar has a different name and several different characteristics, such as extra dark green leaf color, short habit of growth, and resistance to certain diseases.

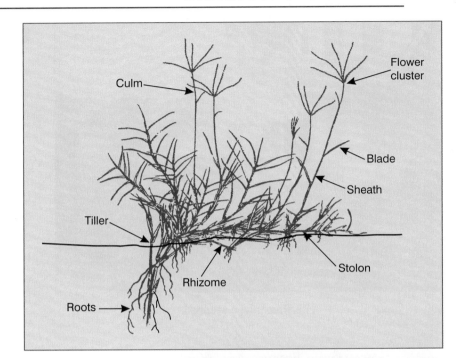

11-7. Major parts of a Bermudagrass plant.

Culm

Flower cluster

Blade

Sheath

Tiller

Stolon

Rhizome

Roots

TURFGRASS ESTABLISHMENT BY SEED

The advantages of establishing a lawn with seed are a greater selection of cultivars, development in the environment in which they must ultimately survive, and lower establishment costs. When establishing a lawn from seed, the following factors are necessary for good seed germination and growth: (1) high quality live seed, (2) adequate soil moisture, (3) sufficient soil warmth, and (4) adequate soil aeration. Early spring (March and April) or late summer (August and September) provides the ideal weather conditions for good grass seed germination in the cool humid region. Warm season grasses should be established in early summer or just prior to their peak period of growth. It is important that irrigation be available during the summer when lack of adequate rainfall can kill new immature turfgrass plants.

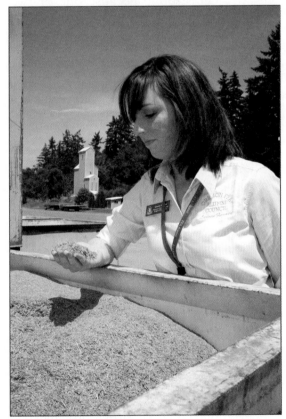

11-8. Newly harvested fescue seed on the Triangle Farm in Oregon. (Courtesy, Education Images, Inc.)

11-9. Preparing a seedbed.

Blends and Mixtures

When selecting turfgrass seed, choose cultivars that have been recommended by your local Extension Office. Turf managers may select a single cultivar, a blend of several different cultivars, or a mixture of several different grass species. Planting only one cultivar may create future maintenance problems. The cultivar may be very susceptible to a disease and the entire lawn could die. Combining several different turfgrass cultivars can help prevent this kind of major catastrophe because one or two of the other cultivars may be resistant to a particular turfgrass disease.

A **turfgrass blend** is a combination of several different cultivars of the same species. Blends should have cultivars that are similar in appearance and competitive ability. At least one cultivar should be well adapted to the planting site. Blends usually have at least three cultivars. Combine three different cultivars: Adelphi, Glade, and Touchdown to create a blend of Poa pratensis (Kentucky bluegrass).

Turfgrass mixtures are combinations of two or more different turfgrass species. Combine *Poa pratensis* (Kentucky bluegrass), *Festuca rubra* (red fescue) and *Lolium perenne* (perennial ryegrass) to create a good cool season turfgrass mixture. Today, landscapers commonly sow a mixture of three different Kentucky bluegrass cultivars and two different Perennial ryegrass cultivars. At least one of the cultivars should adapt and grow in each different area of the lawn. The individual cultivars will be different for each turf installation depending on what part of the cool humid region the turfgrass will be grown.

SEED SELECTION

In the cool humid region, most landscapers plant a mixture of 50 percent Kentucky bluegrass and 50 percent perennial ryegrass in sunny lawn areas. Shady lawn areas will require a mixture of 20 percent red fescue with 40 percent Kentucky bluegrass and 40 percent perennial ryegrass. Most landscapers plant tall fescue seed by itself. Check with the local Cooperative Extension office for specific cultivar recommendations for your area. Landscapers usually sow 3 to 5 pounds of grass seed mixture per 1,000 sq. ft. to establish a good home lawn.

Table 11-2 Where to Use Major Turfgrass Species.

Species	Sun/Shade	Region Common in	Major Use	Propagated by
Kentucky Bluegrass	Sun	Cool humid	Home lawns & athletic turf	Seed
Perennial Ryegrass	Sun	Cool humid	Home lawns & athletic turf	Seed
Red fescue	Shade	Cool humid	Home lawns	Seed
Tall fescue	Sun/Shade	Cool humid & transition	Home lawns & athletic turf	Seed
Bentgrass	Sun	Cool humid	Golf course greens, tees, & fairways	Seed
Buffalograss	Sun	Arid & semiarid	Low maintenance turf areas	Seed
Blue gramagrass	Sun	Arid & semiarid	Low maintenance turf areas	Seed
Bermudagrass	Sun	Warm humid	Home lawns & golf courses	Sprigs
Zoysiagrass	Sun	Warm humid & transition zone	Home lawns & athletic turf	Plugs
St. Augustinegrass	Shade	Warm humid	Home lawns	Plugs
Carpetgrass	Shade	Warm humid	Low maintenance turf areas	Sprigs

Site Preparation

Proper preparation of the planting site can reduce future problems. These include drainage, poor soil aeration, extreme soil pH levels, and other soil fertility problems that may not become evident until after the lawn is established. It is harder to correct these problems after the turf is established than during establishment. Proper site preparation steps include: (1) controlling existing weeds at the planting site, (2) rough grading the site and removing debris, (3) adding top soil if needed, (4) conducting a soil test and applying soil amendments as necessary, (5) thoroughly mixing the amendments into the top 4 to 6 inches of soil, (6) compacting soil with a water-filled roller, and (7) establishing the finish grade for the site.

11-10. The desert regions in the Southwest present additional problems in seedbed preparation and turfgrass selection. This shows established turf next to California desert sand.

Eliminating weeds, especially perennial grassy weeds, will reduce competition with the new developing turfgrass plants. Some herbicides (weed killers) such as Roundup® can be used to eliminate weeds prior to lawn establishment. After the weeds have been eliminated, rough grade the site to improve surface drainage. Generally, a 1 to 2 percent slope away from buildings is adequate. This is a drop of 1 to 2 feet for every 100 feet of run. Remove all debris, such as roots, stones, and other materials brought to the surface by rough grading.

11-11. Laser-guided leveling equipment is being used to prepare this soccer field for sod. (Courtesy, U.S. Department of Agriculture)

Add topsoil if needed at the planting site. Turfgrass plants grow best in 4 to 6 inches of good top soil. When good top soil is not available, add sand and peat moss to amend and improve existing soil. A soil test can determine soil pH and nutrient deficiencies.

If the soil pH is below 6.0, add limestone to adjust the pH between 6.5 and 7.0. Your Cooperative Extension office can recommend the quantity and specific materials to apply for your area. Landscapers normally apply 50 pounds of lime per 1,000 sq. ft. to raise the soil pH one-half point. In the warm arid region, many soils have a high pH which is alkaline. Soil with a pH above 7.5 may need the addition of sulfur containing compounds to lower the pH. It will take 10 to 20 pounds of sulfur per 1,000 sq. ft. to lower the soil pH one-half point (from 7.5 to 7.0).

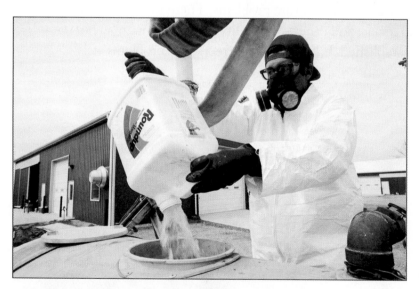

11-12. Wear appropriate protective clothing and equipment when mixing and applying pesticides. (Courtesy, U.S. Department of Agriculture)

Soil testing can also indicate deficiencies of certain required nutrients. The phosphorus (P) test results should be in the 30 to130 pounds per acre for good turfgrass growth. For potassium (K), the test results need to be in the 200 to 400 pound range per acre. If your soil test readings are low, add extra phosphorus or potassium as recommended by the testing service.

This is also the time to apply a starter fertilizer to the lawn. Select a fertilizer that is high in phosphorus because young grass seedlings need it to develop into dense lush turfgrass plants. A common starter fertilizer analysis is (12-24-13) where the 24 represents 24 percent phosphorus. Follow label directions which usually recommend applying approximately 5 pounds of the starter fertilizer per 1,000 sq. ft. Use a rototiller to uniformly incorporate all the above nutrients into the top 4 to 6 inches of soil.

After rototilling, use a heavy, water-filled roller to smooth the soil and remove any air pockets which could cause an uneven surface after seeding. Establish the final or finish grade by using 36" wide aluminum landscape rakes.

TIP: Smooth soled shoes, without heels, will prevent landscapers from leaving footprints in the seedbed.

TIP: The finish grade for a seeded lawn should be ½" below all sidewalks and driveways.

Planting the Grass Seed

The seed label provides valuable information about the grass seed contained in the bag. When selecting seed, look for a high purity and germination percentage, date of seed test within the last year, and seed with low weed seed content. Different turfgrasses have different seeding rates. They vary according to the size and weight of the various seeds.

11-13. An example of a grass seed label.

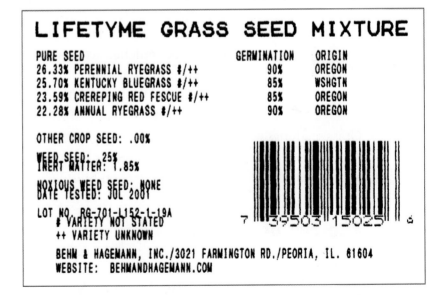

```
LIFETYME GRASS SEED MIXTURE

PURE SEED                        GERMINATION    ORIGIN
26.33% PERENNIAL RYEGRASS #/++      90%         OREGON
25.70% KENTUCKY BLUEGRASS #/++      85%         WSHGTN
23.59% CREREPING RED FESCUE #/++    85%         OREGON
22.28% ANNUAL RYEGRASS #/++         90%         OREGON

OTHER CROP SEED: .00%

WEED SEED: .25%
INERT MATTER: 1.85%

NOXIOUS WEED SEED: NONE
DATE TESTED: JUL 2001

LOT NO. RG-701-L152-1-19A
  # VARIETY NOT STATED
  ++ VARIETY UNKNOWN

BEHM & HAGEMANN, INC./3021 FARMINGTON RD./PEORIA, IL. 61604
WEBSITE:  BEHMANDHAGEMANN.COM
```

After choosing the turfgrass seed mixture, determine the correct seeding rate which can be found in Table 11-3. Use a rotary-type (broadcast) or drop-type spreader to apply the grass seed uniformly over the prepared seedbed. Most landscapers sow the seed in two directions, at 90-degree angles, to ensure uniform seed distribution. Avoid high seeding rates that can produce crowded or weak plants and increase disease problems.

Table 11-3. Size and Seeding Rates

Species	Seeds per Pound	lbs./1,000 sq. ft.
Kentucky bluegrass	1,000,000 to 2,200,000	2–3
Red fescue	350,000 to 600,000	3–5
Perennial ryegrass	250,000	5–7
Tall fescue	170,000 to 220,000	7–9
Creeping bentgrass	5,000,000 to 7,000,000	1–2

TIP: Cut a one-inch square hole in a standard sheet of notebook paper and randomly drop the sheet on the seeded area. Count the seeds in the square. There should be 20 to 30 seeds in the one-inch square.

After the seed is in place, the next two steps are crucial to successful turfgrass establishment. First, make sure there is good seed-to-soil contact and then protect new seedlings from drying out. Use a leaf rake to lightly rake the seedbed and mix the seed into the upper ¼" of soil. After raking, lightly roll the seedbed with a roller half full of water. Rolling not only increases seed-to-soil contact, but also firms the seedbed and slows the drying of the soil.

The seedbed area should be mulched to slow soil drying. A thin layer of clean straw is commonly used. Do not apply too much mulch. The soil beneath the straw should be visible. Usually one bale (35 to 50 lbs.) will cover 1,000 sq. ft. of seedbed. The straw should not be removed after the seed germinates. Raking off the straw can injure the young grass plants. Grass seedlings will grow up through the light straw layer and gradually cover it as the straw decomposes. Several new mulch materials have been developed including paper materials and special meshes for erosion control on hillsides.

Aftercare of Seedbed

Proper site preparation and seeding techniques must be followed by good watering practices to ensure successful seed germination. After planting the seed, heavily water the entire seedbed. On the following day, start light daily watering to keep the top ½" of soil wet. Continue irrigation during the germination period, which can take several weeks. Water less frequently but more thoroughly (deeply) as the turfgrass seeds germinate. Remember, grass seeds need both water and air for good germination. Over-watering can fill all the soil pore spaces with water, eliminate air from these pore spaces, and prevent good seed germination. Too much foot traffic on a newly seeded lawn can also reduce seed germination. The amount of traffic on a newly seeded lawn should be limited until the new lawn is mowed several times.

First Mowing

The new lawn will be ready to mow when the turfgrass plants are approximately one inch higher than the height at which they will normally be maintained. For example, if the lawn will be cut regularly at 2" inches, set the mower at 2" and mow for the first time when the seedlings are 3 inches tall. The general rule is to never remove more than 1/3 of the turfgrass leaf blade at a single mowing. Avoid mowing when the grass is wet. A sharp mower blade is very important. Dull mower blades can rip, shred, and pull out small turfgrass seedlings instead of cutting them. This can also make the turfgrass plants more susceptible to diseases and other problems.

VEGETATIVE PROPAGATION

Instead of sowing grass seed, various grass parts can be planted to develop a new lawn. The technique of planting grass parts is called vegetative propagation, which is establishing turf without seed. Sodding, plugging, and sprigging are three different, but popular, techniques of vegetative propagation. **Sod** is the surface layer of mature turf. It includes the grass plants and a thin layer of soil. Sodding is a common technique for lawn establishment in the cool humid and the warm humid turfgrass zones. It can provide the homeowner with an "instant" lawn.

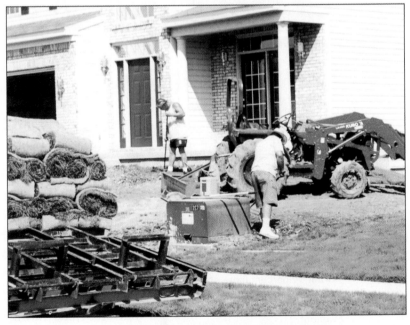

11-14. Preparing the soil surface prior to sodding.

Warm season turfgrasses are usually started with plugs or sprigs as opposed to sod. Most landscapers recommend a **mono-stand** when using warm season turfgrass plants. A mono-stand of turfgrass contains only one cultivar of grass, never a mixture of several cultivars. Southern landscapers do not mix different turfgrass cultivars or species in a single home lawn as is common in the cool humid region. Install sod that contains suitable grass varieties for the area to be covered, that is, shade-tolerant grasses for shaded locations, drought-tolerant grasses for steep slopes, etc. In the cool humid region, use a sod containing a mixture of grass varieties that are well adapted to your area. Too often, sod is selected and installed with little regard for the kinds of grass plants present in the sod or the environmental conditions of the site.

11-15. A trailerload of sod being delivered to the landscape site.

11-16. Pallets of dormant Bermudagrass.

TIP: Order 10 percent more sod than determined by site measurement to make sure you will not run out.

While speed of establishment is usually the reason for sodding, erosion control is also a valid reason to install sod. Sod is harvested in rolls, squares, or strips. The sod is cut at the turf farm with a mechanical sod cutter. It removes a thin layer of soil with the grass plants. In the northeast and midwest U.S., the pieces of sod are usually 18 inches wide, 6 feet long, and 5/8 of an inch thick. Other sod sizes are available in different parts of the country. After the sod is cut, it is rolled and stacked on a wooden pallet for delivery. Each roll usually contains one square yard of sod. High quality sod is dense, uniform, and free of weeds and disease. It should be transported and installed as soon as possible (within 24 hours).

The best time of year for laying sod in the cool humid region is in the early fall. The normal cycle of new root formation begins during this time. However, sod can be laid in almost any season provided the soil is not frozen. Plant sod

11-17. Sod pieces are staggered when laid so the ends do not line up.

during the spring or summer in the warmer regions of the United States. Adequate irrigation should be available for the grass plants to become established in their new location.

The steps in site preparation for sodding are the same as in seeding a new lawn area. After tilling, level and roll the soil to provide a good base. Just before laying the sod, dampen the prepared planting area. Position the first piece of sod along a straight edge, such as a walk or building foundation. Be very careful handling sod pieces to prevent tearing and stretching. Unroll the first piece of sod. Butt the end of the next roll tightly against the first piece, and unroll the second piece. Lay sod pieces in a staggered or checkerboard manner. Some landscapers call this pattern a running brick bond. Lay rolls in a parallel manner, staggering the ends. Use a roller half full of water to ensure good sod-soil

> **TIP:** Water the site the day before laying sod.

> **TIP:** The finish grade for a sodded lawn should be ½" below all sidewalks and driveways.

11-18. Newly laid dormant Bermudagrass sod.

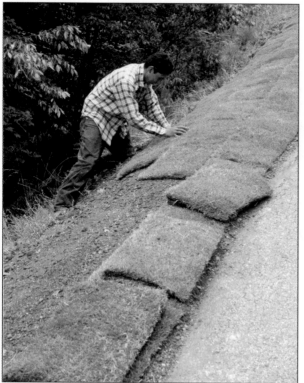

11-19. Bermudagrass sod is also excellent in controlling erosion on slopes adjacent to lawns. (Courtesy,

11-20. Hand sprigging a lawn with Bermudagrass.

contact. After rolling, water the sod enough to wet the sod and the soil below the sod strips. Homeowners sometimes only water the sod, and do not wet the soil below. The sod never **knits** down, or establishes its roots into the soil at a new site.

Plugs of turf are mainly used to establish subtropical turfgrasses. A **plug** is a small 2-inch square or round piece of sod that is 2 inches thick. Grass plugs look like biscuits. Plugs are sold by the tray or box. They are used to establish turf without making a solid cover over the entire area. Follow the same site preparation steps used before seeding or laying sod. Use a steel plugger to make holes 6 to 8 inches apart on a prepared seedbed. After planting, firm the soil around each plug and keep the area moist for two to three weeks. The plugs will grow and cover the entire area in one season. Zoysia grass is usually established using plugs in the late spring or early summer.

> **TIP:** Carefully spot-spray any weeds growing between the plugs.

Sprigs can also be used to establish a lawn. **Sprigs** are special grass stems, called runners or stolons, with roots attached. They consist of at least three or four nodes (joints). Sprigging is accomplished by making shallow furrows 2 to 3 inches deep and 10 to 18 inches apart in the planting area. The sprigs are planted in the furrows and the soil is firmed around the stems. Bermudagrass is normally established with sprigs planted either by hand or with a machine.

After sprigging, topdress the sprigs by lightly covering them with good top soil.

Covering turfgrass with 1/4" to 3/8" of soil is called ***topdressing***. Topdressing will cover any parts of the sprigs that did not get planted and help level the site after sprigging. Lightly firm the soil and topdressing by rolling or tamping. Water the lawn area after sprigging and continue to keep the soil wet until the sprigs grow and cover the site. Mow the newly sprigged lawn when grass plants are one inch taller than the lawn's normal mower height.

TIP: Plant 2 bushels of sprigs per 1,000 sq. ft. when starting a home lawn.

11-21. A mechanical sprig planter sprigging Bermudagrass on an athletic field area. (Courtesy, Eddie Seagle, Abraham Baldwin Agricultural College)

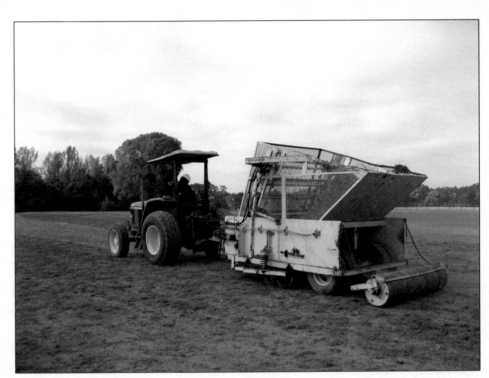

OVER-SEEDING

Some home lawns may have a thin stand of turfgrass from past poor cultural practices. A homeowner may wish to start over and establish a new lawn. However, an alternative to replacing the entire lawn is called over-seeding. Over-seeding is planting one grass in another established grass without destroying the existing grass. A slit seeder is used to plant the new seed. As the grass seed germinates and grows, the turf will become thicker and denser.

Slit seeding can be done in the spring or fall at the normal times new lawns are established. Raking, rolling, or mulching is not required when a slit seeder is used. After seeding, a starter fertilizer should be applied at the rate of 5 pounds per 1,000 sq. ft.

REVIEWING

MAIN IDEAS

In the North, new home lawns are usually established by seed. Kentucky bluegrass and ryegrass are the most popular lawn grasses in the northern part of the United States. Red fescue, perennial ryegrass, and tall fescue cultivars are also planted for special conditions, such as shade or low maintenance practices. Most landscapers plant a mixture of several different grasses in home lawns.

Kentucky bluegrass should be mowed with a sharp mower blade set at 2 to 3 inches in height. This will allow the grass to compete with lawn weeds. Never remove more than 1/3 of the grass leaf blade at a single mowing.

Sod, plugs, and sprigs are commonly used in the warm humid region to start new lawns. Landscapers in the South usually plant a mono-stand, only one cultivar of grass. Some lawn areas are seeded. Bermudagrass, St. Augustinegrass, and Carpetgrass are the popular lawn grasses in the southern part of the country.

Zoysiagrass and tall fescue are popular in the transition zone. Buffalograss and blue grama grass do well in the cool arid region of the country and are established with seed.

QUESTIONS

Answer the following questions using correct spelling and complete sentences.

1. What are the best times of the year to establish a lawn by seed in the cool humid region?

2. Identify the popular grasses grown in the warm humid region.

3. Identify the popular grasses grown in the cool humid region.

4. What is a transition zone?

5. What is sprigging?

6. Describe the size and shape of a grass plug

7. Describe where the turf transition zone is in the United States.

8. List the four factors for good seed germination and growth.

9. Explain the use of the genus and species names in scientific classification.

10. Describe substances that can be used to amend soil when good topsoil is not available.

CHAPTER SELF-CHECK

Match the term with the correct definition. Place the correct letter in the blank provided.

a. turfgrass mixture   d. plug   g. Phosphorus
b. Buffalograss   e. Zoysiagrass   h. Bermudagrass
c. sprig   f. sod   i. turfgrass blend

_____1. A small 2-inch square or round piece of sod, biscuit shaped

_____2. Grass plants that have a thin layer of soil attached

_____3. Special grass stems used in starting new lawns in the warm humid region

_____4. New grass seedlings need a lot of this nutrient

_____5. A popular grass in the transition zone

_____6. A warm season turfgrass that is not very cold tolerant

_____7. A native grass growing in the arid western part of the United States

_____8. A combination of several different cultivars of the same species

_____9. A combination of several different turfgrass species

EXPLORING

1. Select a golf course in your community and scout the course observing all features and playing areas. Try to identify the different kinds of turfgrass growing in each area. You may wish to interview the grounds superintendent about turfgrass. Find out the species/variety; how it is maintained; pest management; irrigation; fertilization; and other features. Prepare a report on your findings.

2. Prepare a seedbed following the procedures discussed in this chapter.

3. Calculate the number of square yards of sod needed for a home lawn or area on the school grounds. Measure the horizontal dimensions and calculate the yards of sod required to cover the turfgrass area. Remember, 9 square feet of area require 1 square yard of sod. Develop a cost estimate for sodding the area. Prepare a report on your findings and give an oral report in class.

4. Establish a lawn by using plugs. Keep a record of the planting date and see how long it takes to completely cover the lawn.

CHAPTER 12

Installing Patios, Decks, and Walks

OBJECTIVES

1 List advantages and disadvantages of surfacing material.

2 Determine patio size for a family of four.

3 Describe the different materials used to construct patios.

4 Demonstrate the techniques used when installing concrete walks and patios.

5 Know the installation steps for paver blocks.

6 Describe wood-treating techniques to prevent rot.

7 Identify deck components and correctly size each.

8 Calculate dimensions for outdoor steps.

TERMS

accelerator	deck boards	plate compactor
baluster	eased	retarder
beam	exposed aggregate	riser
broom finish	float	screeding
cement	form	soft paving
cleat	joist	tread
cubic yard	patio	trowel
cure	paver blocks	
deck	paving	

12-1. A deck connects the interior rooms with the outdoor landscape. (Courtesy, R.S. Hursthouse & Associates, Inc.)

PATIOS, decks, and gazebos connect the interior rooms with the outdoor landscape. Patios and decks are attached or adjacent to the house. A gazebo is a freestanding structure or pavilion within the landscape. These serve as outdoor dining rooms, game areas, or places to relax. They must be designed large enough to handle the normal amount of traffic with overload capability built into the surrounding landscape.

Walks are the pathway entrance to and from the residence. They are built to eliminate cutting across lawns or corners. The primary walkways should be wide enough so two people can walk side-by-side. Secondary walkways only need to accommodate one person.

What materials can be used to construct a patio? How large should the patio be? What kinds of brick are available for patio construction? How do you install a concrete patio? What materials should be used when building a deck? These and many other questions will be answered in this chapter. Regardless of what you have, always begin with a plan.

LANDSCAPE PAVING

12-2. A paver block walk is being installed at this residence.

12-3. Installing a slate patio. (Courtesy, R.S. Hursthouse & Associates, Inc.)

Covering the soil with a hard surface material to prevent soil erosion and compaction from traffic is called **paving**. Aggregates are often used for paving. Gravel or concrete driveways can prevent soil compaction problems. Sidewalks and patios provide a strong surface for people traffic in the home landscape. Grass or other plant materials cannot provide a permanent surface for either car or people traffic. Paving materials can be divided into two groups—hard paving and soft paving materials. As the name implies, hard paving includes such materials as poured concrete, brick, stone, tile, and wood.

Soft paving materials lack the solid form that hard paving materials provide. Many landscapers use the term loose aggregates to describe soft paving. Soft materials may be very durable but may require more maintenance to keep them looking good in the landscape. To prevent injuries, use soft paving materials in children's play areas. Install soft surfacing materials for walks and drives that get little traffic. These materials can also be used as a temporary surface before installing a permanent, hard surface material.

The following loose aggregate materials provide soft paving surfaces: wood or bark chips, sand, gravel, and ground-up tires. Ground-up tires will not make a good driveway paving surface. However, they can provide an

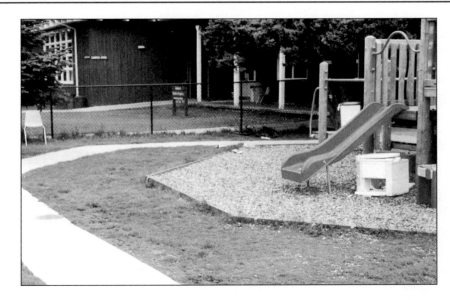

12-4. A playground covered with wood chips.

excellent paving material under children's playground equipment. Use loose aggregate material for little-used garden walks and drives. Rake occasionally to keep the loose aggregate materials looking good.

Hard surfaces provide the home landscape with a strong, durable, low-maintenance surface suitable for many different activities. However, the sun can heat hard surface materials limiting daytime use. Some hard surface materials are very slippery when wet and may present additional hazards. The cost of material and installation for hard surfacing is high.

The landscape designer or contractor will guide the homeowner in selecting the patio surfacing material and will also suggest guidelines for overall patio size. It is easy to build one that is too small. Landscapers recommend the following guidelines for patio design. All sides of a well-designed patio should be at least 8 feet long. A good patio for a family of four will contain at least 300 square feet of surface area. Consider both guidelines as minimum recommendations and increase them as money and space allow.

Entrance walks and other heavy traffic walks should be 4 feet wide while secondary paths can be 2 feet wide. Again, consider the above sizes as minimums and increase as the situation demands.

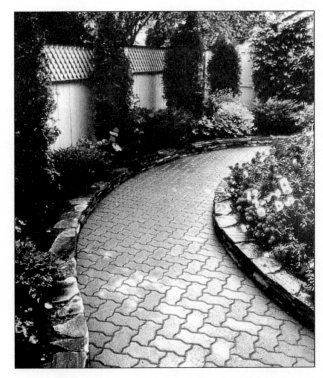

12-5. A walk in the outdoor living area constructed with pavers. (Courtesy, Pavestone Company, Dallas, TX)

PATIOS

Before 1960 in the United States, few families spent time outside in the backyard. As Americans started moving outdoors into the backyard during the late 1950s and the early 1960s, the patio was born. The patio provided the hard surface needed to keep family members' feet out of the grass and mud and prevented chair and table legs from sinking into the ground. Shortly after creating the patio, the Americans began grilling hot dogs, hamburgers, and steaks on the grill. The house contractor built many of these new patios from concrete before the landscape contractor was hired.

A ***patio*** provides a hard surface outdoors for a variety of family activities, such as eating, dancing, playing games, or just relaxing and talking. The patio can be constructed from a variety of building materials and several different construction techniques can be used for each material.

The cost of construction for patios will vary with the different building materials. Gravel will cost the least. Flagstone will cost the most. The homeowner and the landscape designer will select the material to use and decide how to construct the patio.

12-6. Flagstone patio on concrete base.

12-7. Concrete blocks filled with soil and planted with grass seed provide a living driveway.

TIP: Paved patios will drain water better if they have a slight slope to one side. Ideally, a ¼-inch drop for every 4 feet of run should be used. Example: if the patio is 12 feet wide, one side should be (3 ′ ¼") ¾ inch higher than the other.

CHOOSING THE RIGHT PATIO MATERIAL

The shape of a patio may dictate the choice of building material. It is difficult to construct curved edges out of brick or flagstone, but concrete will easily conform to many odd-shaped layouts. If the site is hilly, a wooden deck may be more appropriate than leveling the site and building a concrete patio.

Most people think brick patios are beautiful, while a concrete patio

12-8. Deck on a steep hillside.

is very ordinary. Each material has a different aesthetic quality. A concrete patio will last a long time, but one made from inexpensive patio stones may need replacing in five years.

Yearly maintenance requirements will also affect the selection of patio materials. Wood will need frequent treatment with preservatives to keep the boards looking good and prevent rot. A brick-over-concrete patio will last for 30 or more years with very little yearly maintenance. Cost is usually the major factor in selecting the best patio material for each landscape site.

After the customer selects the patio material, the landscape contractor must correctly install the patio. Some landscape contractors do not install all types of patios, but subcon-

Table 12-1. Patio Construction Materials

Construction Material	Material Cost	Aesthetic Quality	Durability and Life	Maintenance and Upkeep
Gravel	very low	low	medium	high
Concrete	medium	low	high	low
Brick over sand	medium	high	medium	medium
Patio pavers over sand	medium	medium	medium	medium
Flagstone over sand	high	high	medium	low
Brick over concrete	high	high	very high	low
Wood decks	high	high	medium	medium
Clay tile over concrete	very high	very high	low	low
Flagstone over concrete	very high	high	medium	low

tract this work to other companies. The subcontractor works directly for the landscape contractor and only completes a small part of the total landscape work. Many companies specialize in building brick or flagstone patios, while others only construct wood decks.

CONCRETE PAVING

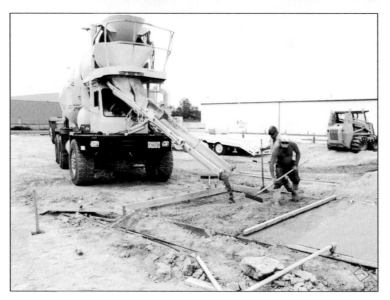

12-9. Pouring ready-mix concrete.

Concrete is the most popular patio surfacing material. It is easy to install and can be poured into almost any desired shape. Low maintenance and durability make concrete a good choice when selecting patio surfacing materials. Properly mixing sand, gravel, cement, and water together creates concrete. **Cement**, the "glue" that holds the sand and gravel together, is a mixture of lime, clay, iron, and silica. Most communities have ready-mix concrete companies that mix and deliver concrete in large trucks to the building site. A chemical reaction changes the soupy liquid mixture into a solid form a few hours after pouring. Temperature and humidity will affect this chemical reaction, but nothing can stop it. When the concrete truck arrives, be ready to pour and finish the concrete.

FORMS CONSTRUCTION

Use 2" × 4" boards to construct wood forms before pouring concrete walks or patios. Set the forms so the top edge of the 2" × 4" is the desired surface height of the finished concrete pad. Steel or wood stakes hold the 2" × 4" in place while pouring concrete. Most walks and patios will be 3½ inches thick, the same as the actual thickness of the form. Concrete driveways are usually 6 inches thick.

Layout the patio and remove any existing turf. Excavate the site to a depth of 6 inches below the finish surface of the patio. Next, add a 2½-inch layer of crushed gravel or hard-

TIP: After driving in stakes to support the form, cut the top of the stake level with the top of the 2" × 4" form. This will make screeding easier.

core as a base material in the excavated site. Use a plate compactor to compact the gravel. A **plate compactor** is a mechanical plate vibrator used to compact base materials and pavers. It has a small gasoline engine that vibrates a heavy steel plate that tamps the base material.

MIXING CONCRETE

Most concrete is prepared at a plant and delivered to the construction site in trucks that continue the mixing process until delivery. Small amounts can be mixed with a portable mixer or by hand in a large tub, wheelbarrow, or wooden box. Generally, ready-mixed concrete is used for all jobs requiring one or more cubic yards of concrete.

12-10. 2" × 4" forms before pouring a concrete walk.

EQUIPMENT FOR CONCRETE WORK

Elaborate equipment is not needed for mixing and placing concrete, although, for efficient work, certain simple tools are essential. They are:

- Water and pail for washing tools.

- Square-pointed shovels for turning and mixing.

- Tamp for compacting concrete or foundation bases.

- Steel wheelbarrow for moving aggregates and concrete mixtures.

Wood float

Edger

Bull float

Jointer

Metal trowel

Power trowel

12-11. Examples of tools used in concrete work.

TIP: Cleanup will be easy if you spray water on all tools (shovels, trowels, and wheel barrow) before working with concrete.

- Mixing box or platform if concrete is mixed by hand for small jobs.

- Screed (straightedge board) for leveling concrete.

- Wood float and trowel for finishing concrete.

ORDERING AND POURING CONCRETE

Ready-mix companies sell concrete by the cubic yard. A **cubic yard** is a volume measurement 3 feet wide, 3 feet long, and 3 feet high. There are several ways to compute the quantity of concrete necessary. Patios and walks are usually poured 3½ inches thick. One easy way is multiply the length times the width of the patio to find the square feet and divide this answer by 81 (square feet per cubic yard). A patio 27 feet long and 12 feet wide will require 4 cubic yards of concrete.

$$27' \times 12' = 324 \text{ sq. ft.} \quad \frac{324 \text{ sq. ft.}}{81 \text{ sq. ft./cu. yd.}} = 4 \text{ cu. yds. concrete}$$

When ordering ready-mixed concrete, give the following information:

1. Use to be made of ready-mix. Will it be used for patio, walk, or driveway?

2. Amounts of exposure the concrete will receive. Will it receive severe exposure, normal exposure, or mild exposure?

3. Amount of ready-mixed concrete needed.

12-12. Drawing of a patio, 27' × 12'.

FORMS

A **form** is a frame or mold that holds liquid concrete to shape until it has set. The forms for concrete must be strong and rigid to prevent sagging, bulging, and spreading.

Forms may be removed easily without the concrete sticking to them if they have been coated on the inside with motor oil before they are used. All pieces of concrete should be removed from forms before they are used again.

12-13. Form with plastic and steel reinforcement ready for placing a concrete slab. (Note bracing to keep form from warping or collapsing under the pressure from the weight of the wet concrete.)

REINFORCING CONCRETE

The tendency of concrete to crack has been an accepted problem in construction. To reduce cracking, landscapers incorporated metal wire mesh when pouring concrete. Wire mesh will not prevent concrete from cracking, but will hold the cracked pieces together. Wire mesh can also rust and discolor the concrete.

Today, many landscapers use plastic fibers instead of metal wire mesh to add strength to the finished concrete. Fibrillated polypropylene fibers, bundles of interconnected strands, reduce the formation of shrinkage cracks and increase the tensile strength of the concrete slab. Fibermesh® is a popular brand of polypropylene fiber. The fibers are engineered exclusively for concrete use. When the bundles of fibers are added to the concrete mix, at the rate of 1½ pounds per cubic yard, the mixing action causes them to open and separate into millions of individual fibers. The fibers are uniformly distributed throughout the concrete in all directions, providing effective secondary reinforcement for shrinkage crack control. The fiber will not rust or stain surfaces, is non-corrosive and alkali-proof, and will not affect the finishing characteristics of concrete.

PLACING CONCRETE

The ready-mix truck will pour the concrete into the constructed forms. Use shovels to move the concrete and fill the forms. Level the concrete surface by working a 2" × 4" straight edge across the narrow sides of the patio form. This leveling technique is called **screeding**.

TIP: Spray wood forms with water just before pouring concrete. It will help prevent the concrete from sticking to the forms.

Screeding will move the excess concrete from high spots and fill in the low spots. When the concrete starts to get hard, use a bull float to make the surface smooth and work the large aggregates down from the surface. Use an edger to put a curve on the edge of the concrete next to the forms.

A concrete mixture should be placed in the forms when it is thoroughly mixed. Concrete will begin to set within 30 to 45 minutes after the water is added. A shovel or thin board may be used to work the mixture against the forms. A powered vibrator is used for larger jobs. It can be rented from an equipment rental business.

Several stages of hardening take place as concrete **cures**, gets hard. The slower the concrete cures, the stronger the patio. Cover newly

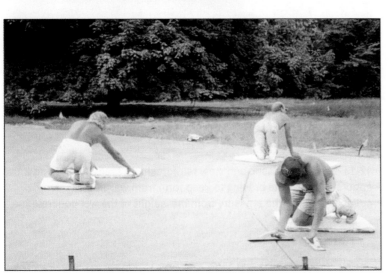

12-14. Finishing a concrete driveway.

poured concrete for at least seven days with a sheet of plastic to slow the curing process. The initial hardening takes only a few hours. Several days later, the concrete goes through a second curing stage and gets harder. After one month, concrete completes a third curing stage. No traffic should be allowed on the concrete during the first and second stages of curing, about three to seven days. After this time, the forms can be removed and light traffic will not damage the concrete. Heavy traffic should not be permitted until concrete has cured for one month.

Concrete poured in the summer may cure too fast. Ready-mix companies can add a chemical **retarder** to slow this hardening process. Cold winter temperatures may slow the curing process too much, causing the water to freeze before the concrete hardens. Chemicals called **accelerators** are added to speed the hardening process.

FINISHING CONCRETE

A **float** is a tool used for initially smoothing the surface after screeding. A metal trowel is a tool used to bring a thin film of cement to the top after the concrete has initially set, making a very smooth surface. This film of cement does not wear as well as a cement and sand mixture, and is slippery when wet.

Concrete can have a variety of surface finishes depending on the wants and needs of the customer. A glassy smooth surface may look great, but it can be very slick when wet and may reflect light into nearby buildings. Drag a broom over the concrete just before it hardens to create a rough, nonskid **broom finish** on the surface.

Many landscapers expose the gravel used to make the concrete by washing away some of the cement just before the concrete hardens. **Exposed aggregate** can create an unusual patio from ordinary concrete. Skill is needed to know when to expose the aggregate. Washing too early can destroy the concrete. If you wait too long, the concrete may be too hard to remove the cement particles. Timing is very important.

REMOVING FORMS

Forms are removed when new concrete has set sufficiently so it will not be damaged in the process.

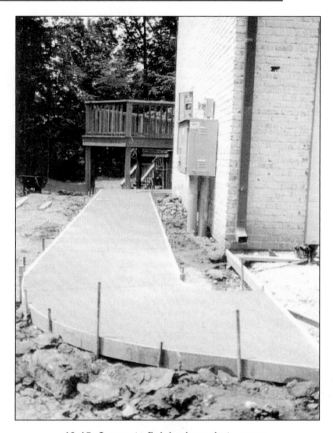

12-15. Concrete finished, ready to cover.

Ordinarily, during warm weather, two or three days should be sufficient for forms to remain in place for walls and small objects. In cold weather, the forms should remain in place about twice as long.

In determining when to remove forms, weather, temperature, and nature of the work must be considered. In no case should the forms be removed until, by careful examination, the concrete has thoroughly set and there is no danger of it breaking apart or becoming damaged. It is often an advantage to leave the forms in place during curing to help retain moisture in the concrete.

CONCRETE WALKS AND DRIVEWAYS

Walks and driveways are carefully planned for attractiveness and use. Walks are built for convenience and to eliminate cutting across lawns or corners. Walks are of great importance to both the utility and beauty of the landscape.

Here is how to construct a walk:

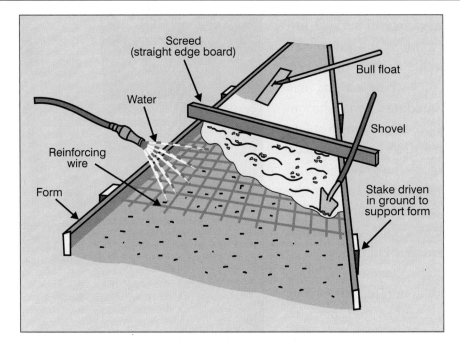

Screed
(straight edge board)

Bull float

Water

Shovel

Reinforcing
wire

Form

Stake driven
in ground to
support form

12-16. Procedures in placing a concrete walk include keeping the soil moist, working with the concrete with a square-point shovel, striking with a two-by-four, and using a bull float to smooth the surface.

1. Estimate the quantities of cement and aggregates or ready-mix that will be required. Most walkways are 36 to 48 inches wide and 4 inches thick.

2. Prepare a level, well-drained, compact base. Build up the base so the top of the walk will extend ½ inch above the ground.

3. Use two-by-fours for side forms. Use stakes to hold the forms in position. Level tops of forms so the concrete will be of the desired thickness; ordinarily a thickness of about 4 inches is sufficient. A slight slope to one side of 1/8 inch per foot will allow water to drain off rapidly.

4. Place partition strips at intervals of 4 to 6 feet.

5. Level with a screed (straight edge board).

6. Finish with a broom for a rough, non-slip surface.

7. Cover with plastic after the concrete has hardened slightly. Cure for at least seven days.

A good driveway is attractive and serviceable. The arrangement and location of a driveway should be planned with care. Driveways for single vehicles are 9 to 10 feet wide. Most are made of concrete 6 inches thick. A compact, well-drained base is more critical for driveways than walks.

The center of the base should be 1 inch higher than the edges, and the base should be rounded uniformly so the concrete will have a uniform thickness of 6 or more inches. Use 2" × 6" lumber for side forms. Level the forms and stake them securely. Place partitions about

12-17. Finishing a walk involves using a trowel to separate wet concrete from the form, using an edger to slightly round the edge, and using a jointer to make a joint.

20 feet apart and allow space for the expansion and the contraction of the concrete. Add reinforcing wire once the forms are in place. Strike off so the center will be 1 inch higher than the outer edges. Finish and cure similarly to walks.

PAVER BLOCKS

Many companies manufacture paver blocks and bricks. *Paver blocks* are specially made units constructed from compressed concrete into many types, styles, colors, and sizes. The concrete mixture is compacted under extreme pressure and high frequency vibrations to give the finished paver a compressive strength of 8,000 psi. The pavers have maximum water absorption of 5 percent and resist freezing and thawing cycles. Paveloc® Industries, Inc. and Unilock® license manufacturers throughout the country to produce concrete pavers. The most common size of pavers available is 2 3/8 inches thick, 8

12-18. A patio constructed using paver blocks. The edging material keeps the pavers in place. (Courtesy, Church Landscape)

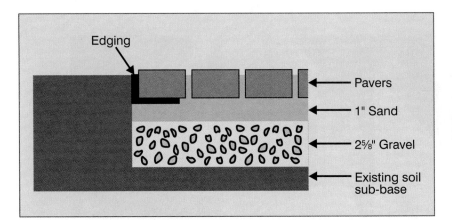

12-19. Cross-section of paver installation technique.

Edging

Pavers

1" Sand

2⅝" Gravel

Existing soil sub-base

TIP: Rent a power masonry saw with a diamond blade to cut paver blocks.

inches long, and 4 inches wide. Pavers can be cut using any masonry saw or by hand using a brick chisel. Wood, aluminum, steel, or plastic edging must be used on all sides of the surface when laying the paver blocks.

12-20. The steps to installing pavers are: (1) mark and excavate the site, (2) prepare the base and compact, (3) install edge restraint, (4) screed the sand base, (5) lay pavers starting in a corner, (6) cut pavers as necessary, (7) fill the joints with coarse sand, (8) use a plate compactor for final compaction of the pavers, and (9) sweep more sand into joints and rinse off with a gentle spray from a hose. (Courtesy, Pavestone Company, Dallas, TX)

Mark off the area and remove any existing turf from the site. Excavate the site to a depth of 6 inches below the finished surface. Prepare the base using a 2 5/8-inch layer of crushed gravel. Use a plate compactor to compact the gravel. Landscape fabric can be placed over the gravel to help keep the entire paver surface uniform by restricting heaving caused by freezing and thawing conditions.

Install edge restraints to keep the pavers in place. BrickEdg® by Oly-Ola Sales, Inc. and Permaloc aluminum edging are specially made for this purpose. Landscape timbers or railroad ties can also be used. Next, add a 1-inch layer of sand. Take special care to level (screed) this sand layer.

Place the pavers in position starting in a corner. Cut pavers as necessary for the edges. Level the pavers and fill the joints with coarse sand. Use a plate compactor for final compaction going over the top of the pavers in several different directions. Sweep more dry, coarse sand into the cracks between the pavers. Rinse off the excess sand with a gentle spray from a water hose to complete the job.

TIP: When using pavers for a walk, always start laying the pavers next to the house or steps. Usually the end of the walk farthest from the house can be shortened or lengthened to accommodate full-length pavers. This will reduce the number of pavers that need to be cut.

TIP: When installing pavers, lay several 1-inch metal electric conduit pipes over the compacted gravel. Fill the area between the conduit pipes with sand and use a 2" × 4" to screed and level the sand. Remove the pipes and fill with sand before installing the pavers.

BRICK PATIOS

Bricks have been used in construction for thousands of years. Clay dug from the ground is heated in a kiln to several thousand degrees for several days. Different clays will create different colors of brick. The standard brick size is 3¾ inches wide by 2¼ inches thick and 8 inches long. Bricks made from clay will last hundreds of years in the landscape. Lay bricks on a sand base using the same technique as used when installing concrete pavers. Never use house bricks for constructing surfaces.

Bricks can also be laid over a bed of concrete. This technique is twice as expensive as placing the bricks on a sand base. Dig out the site to a depth of 7 inches and pour a 3½-inch concrete base. After the concrete base has hardened, cover it with a 1-inch bed of mortar. Gently place each brick in the mortar and use a level to create a flat surface. Leave a ¼-to ½-inch space between the bricks. Fill these cracks the next day by sweeping a dry mixture of mortar and sand into each crack. Use a fine stream of water to wet the dry mortar mix and complete the brick installation.

12-21. Patio paving designs.

DECKS

12-22. An example of an elevated deck.

Deck describes a patio with a wooden surface area raised above the ground level. Decks first became popular during the late 1960s as a way of adding outdoor living space on hillside lots. However, many decks today are built on level ground. Decks can be built just inches high or elevated well above the ground. They may be free-standing or attached to the home or other buildings. Decks can even be built on a second-story above a garage, carport, or other roofed structure. The landscape site may suggest the use of a wooden deck instead of other patio materials.

Usually, the deck is the same height as the house floor so people can walk onto the deck without stepping up or down. A bi-level deck, one with two or more levels, can solve the problem of small changes in elevation from the house floor to the yard. The upper deck will be level with the house floor and the lower deck only one step above the yard. Wooden steps connect the two deck levels.

DECK MATERIALS

Decks are usually constructed of wooden lumber or composite materials made to have the appearance of wood. Wood has been the long-standing material of choice. In recent years, the new manufactured materials have gained widespread use. In choosing material, you want one that is compatible with the climate and will have a long life—one that will not readily decay. You also want material that is strong, durable, attractive, and easy to clean.

Redwood and bald cypress are two naturally decay-resistant woods. High price and limited availability make them poor choices for deck construction. Other woods can be used when pressure-treated with chemicals that discourage decay and insect infestation. These chemicals are forced into the wood by a high-pressure treatment technique. Today, Southern yellow pine is pressure-treated with Amine Copper Quat (ACQ). A few years ago, lumber treated with Wolman® chromated copper arsenate (CCA) was used but it was found to be hazardous to humans and should not be used.

Composite materials are made of wood and plastic fibers that have been blended and formed together. The manufacture of these materials uses recycled wood and plastic, such as used grocery bags, or materials that would otherwise be wasted. In short, these materials are made of materials that are sometimes said to be scrap. The end product is decay-resistant and does not require painting, staining, or preserving. A drawback is that the product is not good at load bearing; therefore, the under structures of a deck are made of wood timbers. These materials have work qualities that are similar to wood. It is measured, marked, and cut like wood. Rather than nails, it is attached with drive screws. Using drive screws speeds the construction process over driving nails. A common trade name for this product is Trex® though other brand names are available, such as TimberTech®.

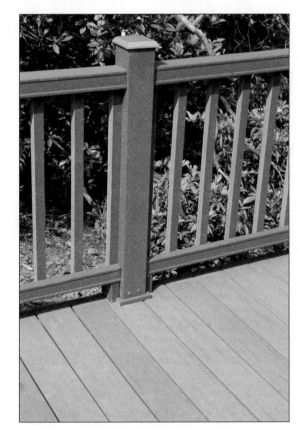

12-23. Composite materials have been used to construct a deck. (Courtesy, Education Images, Inc.)

SAFETY PRECAUTIONS WHEN BUILDING A DECK

A few simple safety precautions to follow when building a deck are:

- Follow safety rules, including wearing goggles for eye safety.

- Use all tools properly and in a safe manner.

- Wash hands after handling CCA treated wood and before eating.

- Wear a dust (particulate) mask when cutting and sawing materials, particularly treated lumber.

- Use CCA lumber only on outside projects.

- Never burn wood scraps; take them to a sanitary landfill.

- Never construct a food preparation area with CCA lumber.

12-24. Treated lumber label.

CONSTRUCTION TIPS

- Always nail a thinner board to a thicker board.

- Drive nails in the deck board at a slight angle, toward each other, for greater holding power.

- When toenailing, stagger opposing nails so they pass each other.

- Nails and other hardware should be hot-dipped, zinc-coated.

- To reduce splitting, drill a pilot hole about three-quarters the diameter of the nail.

- For maximum holding power, use spiral-shank nails or deck screws.

- The nail should penetrate the thicker piece of lumber twice as deep as the thickness of the thin piece of lumber.

- Blunt the nail point with a hammer to reduce the chances of splitting the wood.

Deck boards are held together with special fasteners created just for heavy-duty outdoor use. Nails are identified by a "d" designation, which stands for penny. A 16d nail is called a 16-penny nail. Use spiral-shank, galvanized nails that "screw" into wood when driven with a hammer. These nails are also called deck nails.

Galvanized buglehead screws (deck screws), similar to black drywall screws, can also be used when building decks. These screws have a #2 Phillips head and are installed with an electric drill or screw gun. Install large lag screws for major structural connections on the deck. Use a wrench or socket to install lag screws with a square or hex head. Always use washers and pre-drill the holes to reduce the splitting of wood.

DESIGN

Decks are made up of five major parts—posts, beams, joists, decking, and railings. The three basic considerations when selecting building materials and deck design are function, structural stability, and appearance.

12-25. Parts of a deck.

Dig holes for support posts 48 inches deep, place CCA treated 4" × 4" or 6" × 6" posts upright in the hole. Use a level to keep the posts plumb while filling the holes. Fill the hole with a bag of dry premixed concrete. Wet the dry concrete mix around the post to start the chemical curing of the concrete.

12-26. Layout and site preparation for deck or patio construction.

Use Tables 12-2 and 12-4 to select the correct post size and spacing. **Beams** are 2-inch thick boards, 8- to 12-inches wide, which connect the posts and provide the support for the joists in deck construction. **Cleats** are the short boards attached to the posts for the beams to rest on. **Joists** run at a 90-degree angle to the beams and are usually spaced 16- or 24-inches "on center" (o.c.). Use Table 12-3 for joist size and spacing. **Deck boards** cover the joists and provide the flooring surface of a deck on which people walk and where furniture is placed. Always install the deck boards with the bark side up to reduce cupping action as the boards weather. Several different sized deck boards are available. Deck boards are also available with squared edges or rounded edges called eased-edges. Eased-edged deck boards resist splitting and look better. Deck boards will usually be either a 2" ´ 6" (1½ inches thick by 5½ inches wide) or a five-quarter, 5/4 ´ 6" (1 inch thick by 5½ inches wide). Most deck boards are made from Southern pine or Douglasfir.

Table 12-2. Minimum Beam Sizes

Length of Span (ft.)	Spacing Between Posts (ft.)						
	4	**5**	**6**	**7**	**8**	**9**	**10**
6	(2) 2 × 8s	(2) 2 × 8s	(2) 2 × 8s	(2) 2 × 10s	(2) 2 × 10s	(2) 2 × 10s	(2) 2 × 12s
7	(2) 2 × 10s	(2) 2 × 10s	(2) 2 × 10s	(2) 2 × 10s	(2) 2 × 10s	(2) 2 × 12s	(2) 2 × 12s
8	(2) 2 × 10s	(2) 2 × 10s	(2) 2 × 10s	(2) 2 × 12s	(2) 2 × 12s	(2) 2 × 12s	(3) 2 × 12s
9	(2) 2 × 10s	(2) 2 × 10s	(2) 2 × 12s	(2) 2 × 12s	(2) 2 × 12s	(3) 2 × 12s	*
10	(2) 2 × 10s	(2) 2 × 12s	(2) 2 × 12s	(3) 2 × 12s	(3) 2 × 12s	*	*
11	(2) 2 × 12s	(2) 2 × 12s	(3) 2 × 12s	(3) 2 × 12s	*	*	*
12	(2) 2 × 12s	(2) 2 × 12s	(3) 2 × 12s	(3) 2 × 12s	*	*	*

*Beams larger than 2 × 12 recommended. Consult a designer for appropriate sizes.

Table 12-3. Maximum Allowable Spans for Deck Joists

Joist Size (inches)	Joist Spacing (inches)	
	16	**24**
2 × 6	9'-9"	7'-11"
2 × 8	12'-10"	10'-6"
2 × 10	16'-5"	13'-4"

Table 12-4. Minimum Post Sizes

Height (ft.)	Load Area (sq. ft.) = Beam Spacing × Post Spacing				
	48	**72**	**96**	**120**	**144**
Up to 6	4 × 4	4 × 4	6 × 6	6 × 6	6 × 6
Up to 8	6 × 6	6 × 6	6 × 6	6 × 6	6 × 6

Vertical loads figured as concentric along axis.
No lateral loads considered.

Install deck boards using deck nails or buglehead screws. Use a block of wood or nail as a spacer to set the boards 1/8 to 1/4 inch apart. This will allow water to drain from the deck boards. Trim the edge of the deck boards, after nailing, to create a straight line. Do not allow the deck boards to overhang the deck support member by more than 1½ inches.

12-27. Installing deck boards.

Next, install the posts for the railing. The support posts can also be used for the railing support. Standard railing height is 36 inches above the deck surface. The vertical pieces of wood between the top and bottom rails are called **balusters**. Balusters are commonly placed 6 inches apart. However, local building ordinances may require them to be placed closer together.

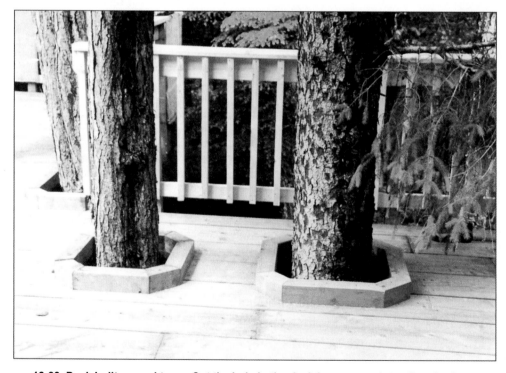

12-28. Deck built around trees. Cut the hole in the deck large enough to allow for future tree growth.

STEPS

Patios, decks, and walks may have several levels or they may be used in combination. Steps are necessary to allow access to or to connect these different levels. The material selected by the designer for the steps usually matches the levels being connected. However, the surface area should take into account that outdoor steps can become slippery when wet.

There are two basic components of steps. The riser is the elevating vertical part of a step and the tread is the level part of the step on which the foot is placed. The slope of the incline of steps should be 33 to 50 percent. In unusual situations, an incline up to 65 percent is acceptable. Steps in a landscape should be constructed to allow the user to maintain a natural stride pattern. The steps should be constructed so that the total length of two risers and one tread is 26 inches. As the tread dimension increases, the riser dimension decreases. The formula for calculating dimensions for outdoor steps is Tread + 2 Risers = 26". Therefore, a riser of 7 inches would have a tread of 12 inches, or a riser of 5 inches would have a tread of 16 inches.

12-29. Parts of steps.

REVIEWING

MAIN IDEAS

Grass or other plant materials cannot provide a permanent surface for vehicular or foot traffic. Hard surface and loose aggregate materials provide a durable surface for high traffic areas in the home landscape. The patio became popular in this country during the early 1960s. A patio must be large enough for the family's outdoor activities. Concrete, manufactured paver blocks, brick, and flagstone are popular construction materials for home patios.

A patio made from wood is called a deck. Decks can be constructed level with the ground or elevated well above the ground. They may be freestanding or attached to the home. Construct the deck using redwood, bald cypress, or treated lumber. Follow all safety precautions when using CCA treated lumber. Always consult engineering charts when selecting posts, beams, and joists for deck construction. Deck boards now are commonly sold as 5/4- × 6-inch boards. Their edges can be square or rounded.

QUESTIONS

Answer the following questions using correct spelling and complete sentences.

1. What size should a patio be for a family of four people?

2. Why may it be necessary to build a deck instead of a patio?

3. What are four different kinds of common paving materials?

4. What is screeding concrete?

5. Why use treated lumber when building a deck?

6. How many cubic yards of concrete should be ordered to pour a patio 27 feet long, 12 feet wide, and 3½ inches thick?

7. How thick should the sand layer be under a patio constructed using pavers?

8. What are the five major parts of a deck?

9. What minimum size beams should be used for a deck when the post spacing is 6 feet and the length of span is 7 feet?

10. What are the two basic components of steps?

CHAPTER SELF-CHECK

Match the term with the correct definition. Place the letter in the blank provided.

a. pressure-treated

b. loose aggregate

c. retarder

d. plate compactor

e. screeding

f. ready-mix

g. bi-level deck

h. beam

_____1. A mechanical vibrator used to compact base materials and pavers

_____2. Concrete delivered by truck to the building site

_____3. A deck with two or more levels

_____4. A chemical sometimes added to concrete poured in the summer

_____5. Leveling the sand before placing the patio bricks

_____6. Large boards attached to the deck posts that will support the joists

_____7. The term used to describe soft paving materials

_____8. Technique used on lumber so it will discourage decay and insect infestation

EXPLORING

1. Examine your or a neighbor's patio and measure the length and width. Describe the building materials. Is this patio the correct size?

2. Talk to a landscape construction company and visit a site where they are building a deck.

3. Try finishing a small concrete pad using a bag of premixed concrete. Make a wooden form using 2 × 4s, 2 feet square. Use correct concrete finishing tools.

4. Calculate the cost of materials to install a 27 feet long by 12 feet wide patio using pavers. Start by visiting a local landscape or building supply company. Determine with them how much crushed gravel 2 5/8-inches thick and how much sand 1-inch thick will be needed, as well as the cost for each. Next, select the pavers to be used and record the unit cost. Calculate the number of pavers needed and their total cost. Determine how much all materials will cost for your patio.

Installing Fences and Walls

TERMS

bay	infill	post
covenant	line post	retaining wall
enclosure	main post	screen
fence	microclimate	wall
frost line	mortarless block wall system	weep hole
gate	ordinance	wrought iron
gate post	pilaster	

13-1. This fence serves several useful roles in the landscape—mark property lines, contain large animals, and deter trespassing. It is also aesthetically attractive.

FENCES and walls serve to enclose a section of the landscape. They may provide protection or privacy. They can change the climate of a small area by reducing wind or the sun's rays. They may serve safety or engineering needs by holding back soil on a slope or enclosing an electrical transformer. They can mark the property boundary. They are the walls in the outdoor room of the landscape design.

Why install a chain link fence in a backyard? From what materials can a retaining wall be made? Why put weep holes in concrete retaining walls? What is a microclimate? How do fences and screens differ? How deep should a fence post hole be dug? What material should be used when backfilling around fence posts? What is a restrictive covenant and how is it important when building fences? What is a mortarless block wall system?

LANDSCAPE FENCES AND WALLS

Landscapers use the term **enclosure** to describe both fences and walls used in the landscape. A **fence** is an enclosure having posts, rails, and infill usually constructed from wood, metal, or plastic. Concrete, brick, stones, and blocks are used to construct more substantial enclosing elements called walls. A **wall** is an upright structure serving to enclose, divide, support, or protect an area.

MAJOR REASONS FOR FENCES AND WALLS

- protect property
- provide security for children and pets
- ensure privacy
- create sound barriers
- maintain microclimates
- screen objectionable views
- mark property lines

13-2. A louvered fence screens the air conditioner units, but allows good air circulation.

TIP: Fences made of wood will require painting or treating with preservatives to keep them looking good and to make them last longer.

13-3. Wrought-iron fence sections around the front yard.

Fences can serve any or all of the above purposes in the home landscape. Fences should solve specific problems in the yard. Do not build fences just to build fences. Keep fences as a background for landscape planting. Do not let them become the main attraction. Some fence materials may require constant painting and maintenance.

The temperature, precipitation, humidity, and wind of a small area, such as a backyard, is called a *microclimate*. Well-designed fences will allow cooling breezes into the yard, but prevent strong, cold winds. A strong, prevailing wind can make an outdoor living area unusable or at best uncomfortable much of the year. A wall constructed near the patio can deflect the wind and allow greater use of the outdoor area. Glass or plastic fence materials are commonly used around swimming pools to control unwanted cool winds.

13-4. A white vinyl fence is decorative in this landscape.

13-5. This split-rail fence defines property lines.

Fences are usually constructed along the property line for both security and visual privacy. Walls can be constructed inside or along the property line for the same reasons. Many landscapers use the term screen to describe a fence or wall used to create only visual privacy in the landscape. Screens do not have to be on the property line, but can be moved closer to the patio for increased privacy. Screens will not provide security or property protection.

13-6. A preassembled plastic, basket weave fence.

13-7. A white picket fence in the tourist residential area has been constructed along the sidewalk to retain palm trees. (Courtesy, Educational Images, Inc.)

TIP: Plants growing in front of a solid-screen fence should be either shorter or taller than the fence.

Plant material can also provide the homeowner with the same visual privacy that fences do. However, living screens are usually 4 to 6 feet wide, while fence materials are 4 to 6 inches wide. Small city properties usually do not have the space necessary for living screens.

Fence materials should be similar to the house construction materials. Ideally, brick homes should have matching brick outdoor walls. Wood fences look best when used around homes constructed of natural wood. Size restrictions of the lot and budget limitations may prevent using identical home and fence construction materials.

LEGAL CONSIDERATIONS WHEN BUILDING FENCES AND WALLS

> **TIP:** Check your local building codes and laws to determine the height and material required for fences around swimming pools.

An **ordinance** is a governmental regulation or statute. City ordinances and building codes cover the location, size, and construction of fences and walls within the city limits. Many cities restrict all fences or walls to a maximum of 6 feet in height in the backyard. Some cities limit fence height in the front yard to 4 feet. City ordinances usually do not regulate the type of fence material used.

A **covenant** is an agreement made between two or more parties to do or keep from doing a specific thing. Many subdivisions have restrictive covenants that regulate fence construction within the subdivision. Some covenants regulate the fence material, while others restrict the height and location of all fences in the subdivision. Some people believe chain-link fences, animal wire fences, and electric fences are not attractive and do not want them in the subdivision. (Most covenants can be changed by a vote of the property owners in the development. This means that restrictions on fences and other structures such as gazebos can be changed.)

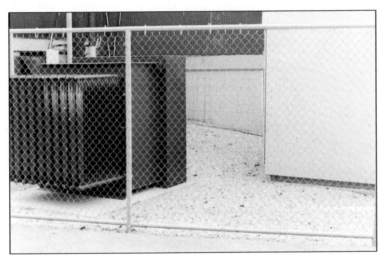

13-8. Chain link fence provides security around this electric transformer.

FENCE MATERIALS AND PARTS

Several kinds of materials are used to construct landscape fences. The most popular kinds are wood, ornamental iron, vinyl, chain link, brick, and stone. Some fences may be combinations of two materials such as brick and ornamental iron. Barbed wire, net wire, and other specialty wire designed for animal management are primarily used on farms and ranches and in animal keeping. They are not widely used in residential landscaping. In addition to fence materials, gate automation and access controls may be used in fence construction. The lifetime and maintenance requirements vary widely. For example, a vinyl fence does not require painting but it often needs to be cleaned of mildew and can snap in very cold weather.

Wood, vinyl, and metal fences can be built on site or preassembled sections can be erected. Preassembled fence sections are built in a factory and are ready to install without additional construction. Today, landscape companies usually install preassembled sections of fence. Most fence sections are either 4 or 6 feet high and usually 8 feet long.

Wooden fences have posts, rails, and infill. A **post** is a strong upright material that supports a fence. Two kinds of posts are typically found: main and line.

A **main post** is at a corner or a gate. The post to which a gate is attached is known as a **gate post**. **Line posts** are between corner and gate posts. Rails are the horizontal supports between posts. Most fences with infill have two rails. Rails are sometimes known as stringers. Some fences are built only of rails attached to posts.

The distance between two posts is known as a **bay**. **Infill** is the material fastened to the rails that ensures security and privacy. Infill may also be known as screening. With fences that have a public view, the rails are put on the inside. Rails are often on the outside of a decorative patio or backyard fences.

A **gate** is a movable barrier in a fence. Most gates are attached with hinges on one side. A latch on the side opposite the hinges keeps the gate securely fastened. Some latches may have locks that help prevent unauthorized entry. Gates are typically designed using material similar to the fence structure.

A common metal fence used in commercial and residential landscapes is the chain link fence. This is usually an all-metal fence. It is strong and can be constructed in various heights. Chain link fences offer full visibility of the protected areas.

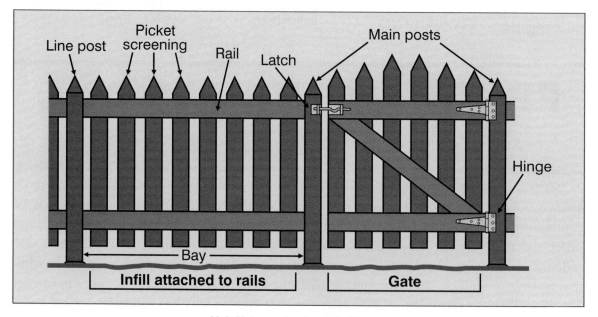

13-9. Major parts of a picket fence.

Chain link fence fabric does not come in preassembled pieces. The wire fabric is galvanized number 9- or 11-gauge wire. It is set 1½-inch pipe posts, 2½ feet deep, in holes that are 10 feet on center. Backfill the holes with concrete. Install a top pipe rail before stretching and attaching the wire chain link fabric to the pipe frame.

The fence material may be galvanized steel, aluminum, or vinyl-coated steel mesh. Only galvanized posts and rails should be used. A top rail may be used with only a tension wire at the bottom. The mesh wire must be stretched taut between the posts. Specially-made bands and post tops are used with chain link fences. Purchase preassembled gates.

13-10. Parts of a chain link fence.

KINDS OF FENCES IN THE LANDSCAPE

A white, picket fence defines property and controls pets and children without creating a closed-in feeling. The original, split-rail fence built in the early 1700s did not use posts. Today, either two or three rails are held up with posts. This fence provides a visual backdrop for landscape planting and defines property lines. The basket-weave fence is a very popular style throughout the country. It is an interesting and beautiful fence that provides total privacy and security for children and pets.

13-11. Natural-wood picket fence built on site.

13-12. Ornamental picket fence with large wooden posts.

Boards, 6 to 8 inches wide, made of wood or plastic are used to construct the modern board fence. The boards can be next to each other to provide a solid screen or spaced to allow air circulation, while still providing good visual privacy. Wood fences require constant painting or staining to keep them looking neat and clean. Plastic fence material looks like painted wood but does not require maintenance.

Table 13-1. Popular Types of Enclosures

Type	Description	Use in the Landscape
WOOD FENCES	made of natural wood or plastic, build on site or buy preassembled sections	
Board on Board	wood or plastic, usually 6" wide board, 6' high, painted or natural stain, construct on site or buy pre-assembled	privacy, security, screen objectionable views, create microclimates, sound barrier
Solid board	wood, usually 6" to 10" wide, 6' high, painted or natural stain, construct on site or buy preassembled	privacy, security, screen objectionable views, create microclimates, sound barrier
Basket weave	wood or plastic, very thin boards, 6' high, painted or natural stain, usually preassembled	privacy, security, screen objectionable views, create microclimates, sound barrier
Picket	3' to 4' high, wood or plastic, usually painted to match color of house	security for children and pets, mark property lines
Rail	wood or plastic, rough split and stained or finished painted boards, 2 or 3 rails	mark property lines
Louvers	6" wide boards angled to restrict view but permit air movement, natural or painted	privacy, security, screen objectionable views

(Continued)

Table 13-1 (Continued)

Type	Description	Use in the Landscape
CHAIN LINK	galvanized fabric, 1½" pipe posts	
Standard Mesh	galvanized or aluminum fabric, not a good background for shrubs	security, mark property lines
Colored Mesh	wire covered with black or green vinyl coating to improve the look	security, mark property lines
Plastic/Metal Inserts	inserts fit all standard fabric	security, mark property lines, privacy, screen objectionable views
WROUGHT IRON	solid, square pieces of wrought iron, heavy and very expensive	
Hollow Tubing	hollow steel or aluminum tubing used instead of solid wrought iron, posts 1" square, upright tube ½" square	security, mark property lines
MASONRY WALL	very large and massive, used on large building sites, not in a small backyard	
Plain Concrete Block	4" thick blocks with 8" blocks used to create columns every 16 feet	privacy, security, sound barrier, create microclimates
Brick	variety of kinds and colors, if possible match brick used in house, can curve to create interest	privacy, security, sound barrier, create microclimates
Poured Concrete	6" thick wall, use forms	privacy, security, sound barrier, create microclimates

Wrought iron is an iron that contains some slag and very little carbon. It is corrosion-resistant, tough, and ductile. Wrought-iron fences have been used around cemeteries for hundreds of years. Use wrought iron as a see-through fence when security and beauty are required. Today, large estates have installed hollow steel or aluminum tubes that look like the old-fashioned wrought iron. This new fence material is less expensive than the old material. However, this type of fence is still very expensive. Large,

13-13. Concrete blocks are used to construct this wall-type fence.

brick posts, 2 or 3 feet square, can be used to create an interesting and unusual fence to designate property lines. Decorative accessories, such as scrolls, finials, and ball caps, are available to match wrought-iron fences. Walk gates and large industrial gates are available that match the style of the wrought-iron fence. This type of fence will enhance the beauty of a swimming pool while providing needed security.

13-14. An example of a wrought iron fence with brick columns.

INSTALLING FENCES

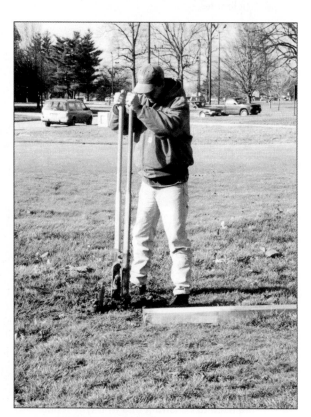

Locate and verify all property boundaries before installing fences on or near the property line. Start fence construction by locating one corner post hole. Stretch a line from this post to the end of the fence. Measure 8 feet and mark the center of each post hole.

Setting posts involves digging holes, positioning the post in the hole, and placing fill around the post. Holes can be dug with a power auger or with hand diggers. Dig the hole with the center below the on-center location of the post on the line. The line will need to be slightly pushed to one side for digging.

A guideline is to make the depth of holes for wood posts in ornamental fences one-third the height of the post above the ground plus 6 inches. If a post is to extend 6 feet above the ground, use an 8-foot (or slightly longer) post and dig the hole 30 inches deep

TIP: A power post hole digger should have a reverse switch to help remove the auger from the soil.

13-15. Hand digging a fence post hole.

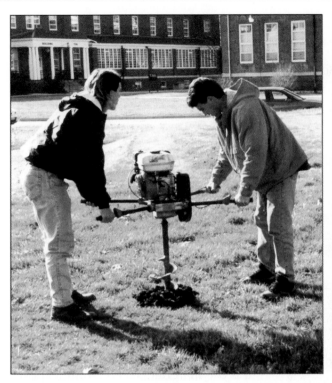

13-16. A 2-person power auger used to dig post holes.

13-17. Use a level to position the post.

(24 inches for post and 6 inches for gravel underneath post). In colder climates, the depth of the hole is determined by the frost line. The *frost line* is the maximum depth at which the ground will freeze. The bottom of the post must extend below the frost line so it does not heave during freezing and thawing conditions. The diameter of holes depends on the size of posts and the fill to be used.

Use a 6-inch hand auger or clam shell post hole digger to dig several post holes. In hard soil conditions or on large jobs, a gasoline-powered auger can be used. Dig a clean hole, try not to make the hole wider than 6 inches. This will help support the post and fence. After setting the post, fill the hole with concrete mix and let the concrete cure for several days before constructing the fence.

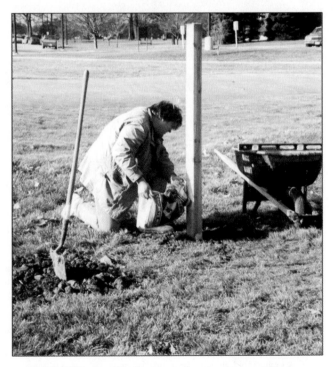

13-18. Fill hole with dry concrete mix after positioning.

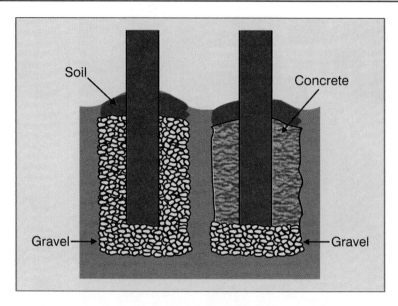

13-19. This shows holes around posts filled with gravel that has been tamped (left) and concrete (right). (Note the layer of gravel in the bottom of the hole below the end of the post.)

13-20. Original style of split-rail fence.

Use a level to position the post vertically in the hole. Hold the level on two sides of the post to be sure it is vertical. Fill is the material placed around a post in the hole. Either concrete or gravel may be used. Many people prefer concrete because of post stability. The bottom of the hole should be filled with 6 inches of gravel or crushed stone. The gravel will allow moisture to escape and make the wooden post last longer. Backfill the hole one-half full with a dry mixture of concrete. Pour a bucket of water into the hole to moisten the concrete mixture. Fill the hole to the top with more dry concrete mixture and wet with more water. Check and make sure the post is still vertical after filling the hole. The concrete can also be mixed with water before placing it in the hole. Use one bag of premixed concrete to set each post.

RETAINING WALLS

A **retaining wall** is an enclosure constructed to retain or hold soil in place. Well-constructed retaining walls can increase the available flat ground on hilly landscape sites. A variety of materials are available to construct a retaining wall. Poured concrete has been used for years in constructing retaining walls. Use railroad ties or treated landscape timbers to create strong but aesthetically pleasing walls. A variety of modern concrete block retaining wall systems are available. These new blocks are mortarless and easy to install. They come in a several different surface textures and colors.

Masonry constructed walls require a 12-inch wide by 12-inch deep poured concrete footing below the frost line. Concrete blocks or decorative bricks can be laid on top of this footing using mortar

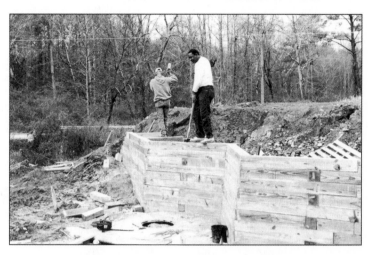

13-21. A 6" × 6" landscape timber retaining wall.

to hold the blocks together. Every 16 feet down the wall, a large square column called a pilaster is constructed. A **pilaster** is a rectangular support or pier projecting partially from a wall. The pilasters provide a visual break in a long wall and structurally support it.

CHOOSING THE TYPE OF RETAINING WALL

The height and strength required, shape, drainage, and cost are all factors when the designer selects a particular type of retaining wall. Solid walls require footings, bracing, and reinforcement. The architecture and other parts of the hardscape features can also affect the type of wall to be used.

Sometimes a retaining wall serves a special purpose in the landscape. For example, the grade may have been raised around an existing tree. If the tree is to be saved, a retaining wall will have to be built around its base holding it to the original grade. This special purpose retaining wall will need vertical tiles set in a radial pattern beneath the dripline of the tree with crushed stone underneath. The crushed stone extends into the base of the retaining wall at the original grade. If the lawn area has been lowered around a tree, it will also need a retaining wall to hold the original grade.

Before beginning construction, analyze the site and develop a general layout and plan. Design the wall so surface water will flow around the ends of the wall, not over the top. Check all local building codes, lot lines, and buried utility lines before starting construction.

CONCRETE WALLS

Concrete walls are strong but are not beautiful. Water pressure can build up behind solid walls and can push them over. When building a solid wall, it is important to provide an exit

13-22. Concrete retaining wall.

for water trapped behind the wall. Every few feet down the wall, holes are made through the wall to release the built-up water pressure. These holes are called **weep holes** as water will weep through them. Few landscape contractors build retaining walls using poured concrete.

RAILROAD TIE WALLS

Build railroad tie walls by stacking the ties on top of each other or placing the ties upright in a trench. Ties are treated with creosote to prevent rotting and measure 6 inches wide by 8 inches high and 8½ feet long. Most landscapers construct railroad tie walls a maximum of 4 feet high. Taller walls can be built, but they require additional bracing, called dead-man, set into the hillside. Note that creosote can irritate the skin. Always wear long-sleeve shirts and gloves when handling railroad ties.

13-23. Railroad tie retaining wall.

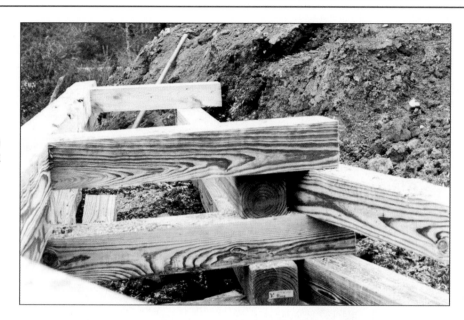

13-24. Use of dead-man timbers extending back into the hillside to support the wall.

Place the first railroad tie on level, compacted soil. Drill three, 11/16-inch diameter holes at a slight angle through each tie (a hole at each end and one in the middle). Drive a 3-foot long, 5/8-inch diameter reinforcing rod into the soil to hold the first row of ties. Set each row of ties back 1-inch from the row below. This will slant the wall into the hillside and provide greater support for the ties. Stagger the ties like brickwork. Continue drilling three, 11/16-inch diameter holes in each railroad tie. Use 12-inch long, 5/8-inch diameter, reinforcing rods to hold the ties together. Pole barn nails (40-penny) can also be used to hold the ties in place. Pre-drill all holes to prevent splitting the ties.

13-25. Installing reinforcing rods.

13-26. Landscape timber or railroad tie wall construction using dead-man bracing.

Labels in figure: 1', Spike, 4', Finished grade, Dead-man brace (railroad tie), 5/8" reinforcing rod, 6 x 8 Pressure-treated lumber, Finish grade, Compacted subgrade, 2', Drain tile

13-27. Retaining wall constructed by placing the railroad ties or posts vertically in the ground. Note that the tops can be even or uneven (as shown).

POST WALLS

Post or ballard walls offer variety in the landscape design. They are usually constructed with landscape timbers or railroad ties. They are installed by digging a trench. The posts are cut and placed side-by-side in the trench. The top of the posts can be even or uneven depending on the appearance wanted by the landscape designer. After the posts are in proper position, the trench is backfilled. This can be done with soil and gravel layers or with equal amounts of concrete on both sides.

When installing post walls, generally there is as much post under ground as there is above ground. Higher post walls will require larger diameter posts. Weep holes may be needed to allow excess water to drain from behind the wall.

MORTARLESS CONCRETE BLOCK WALL SYSTEM

Mortarless block wall construction systems became popular in the 1980s. A ***mortarless block wall system*** uses precast concrete blocks, with various surface textures and colors, stacked on top of one another without mortar to hold them together. One popular block system is called Allan Block®. These blocks are $7\frac{5}{8}$ inches high, 12 inches deep, and $17\frac{5}{8}$ inches long. A junior size that is $7\frac{1}{2}$ inches long is also available. They are stacked on top of each other without using mortar to hold them in place. The built-in interlock is provided by a raised front lip and notched bottom. It provides a built-in set back and a tight wall with clean lines. The Keystone® mortarless block system uses special reinforced fiberglass pins to hold each block in place. Both block systems automatically establish the necessary setback angle, lock each course of blocks together, and provide some built-in drainage through the wall.

Measure the wall length and multiply by the average height to compute the surface square feet of wall. Multiply the total square footage by 1.4 to find the total number of

TIP: Use a plate compactor to compact the base of the footing before installing the first row of a mortarless block wall system.

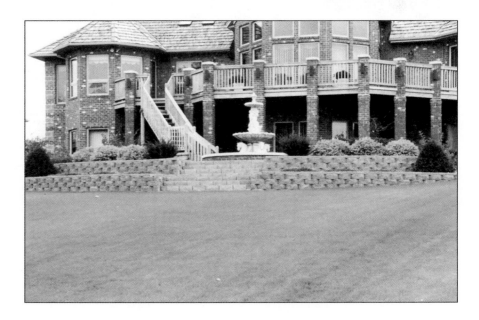

13-28. A mortarless retaining wall system is attractive in this landscape.

13-29. Curved landscape flower bed created using mortarless blocks.

13-30. Diagram of installation technique for a Keystone® mortarless block wall system.

blocks needed. Retaining walls less than 4 feet high do not require a concrete footing. Concrete footings will be needed on walls higher than 4 feet.

Dig and level the bottom of the footing. Compact the base of the footing before adding a 3-inch layer of pea gravel. In heavy soil conditions, install a plastic drain tile behind the base course of blocks to remove water. Place blocks side by side on the prepared foundation. Level each block from side to side and from front to back. Check level often and use a string line to keep the wall straight. Carefully backfill with pea gravel around the base blocks and pack the gravel to lock the blocks in place.

Backfill behind the base course and each successive course with sand or pea gravel. Clay or topsoil are not recommended as backfill. Fill the voids in and between the blocks with the pea gravel. Position the second and additional layers of blocks over the base course by staggering the edges to be in the middle of the block beneath it. The setback angle is automatically established by placing the block tightly against the front lip of the block beneath it. Backfill as each course is completed.

13-31. Mortarless block wall systems are often used to create raised planting beds or to provide transition in topography of the land.

Curved and serpentine walls are easy to construct using the mortarless blocks. Inside curves are built by placing the front faces edge to edge and fanning the blocks to meet the curve. Taller walls require special design techniques; consult the block distributor for pre-engineered plans. The block company may recommend installing a plastic landscape fabric behind the wall to provide additional stability for large-scale projects.

REVIEWING

MAIN IDEAS

There are several reasons for building fences in the home landscape. Privacy and security for children and pets are the most important reasons. However, well-designed fences also create sound barriers, screen objectionable views, create microclimates in the yard, and mark property lines. No single fence material can do all of the above. The landscape designer and homeowner must decide which style fence to install.

Fences can be constructed on the property line or built away from the property line. The term screen usually describes fences or walls built inside the property line to create visual privacy. Check city ordinances and building codes for restrictions on location and size of fences. Some subdivisions also have restrictive covenants that not only regulate the size and location of fences, but may also restrict certain fence materials.

In the past, the board fence was not only the most popular fence but the only style of fence. Today, landscapers have a variety of fence materials to select from. The fence may be made from plastic boards, not natural wood as in the past. When choosing fence materials and design, consider the amount of maintenance needed to keep the fence looking good.

Select fence material that is similar to the house construction material. Natural wood fences look best next to wood-sided houses, not brick homes. Build fences that complement the general architectural style of the home. Use split-rail fences in the country. Wrought-iron fences are elegant and need large lots to effectively show them off. In some parts of the country, masonry walls are used as fences.

Retaining walls hold soil and provide additional flat areas in the landscape. Poured concrete walls are strong, but they are not attractive. Stack railroad ties on top of each other to create an interesting retaining wall. Landscape timbers can also be used instead of railroad ties for wall construction. These walls are usually 4 feet or less in height. Install reinforcing rods to hold the ties or timbers in place.

During the 1980s, a new style retaining wall was developed called the mortarless block wall system. Plants throughout the United States manufacture concrete blocks with interesting surface textures and colors. These blocks are designed to stack on top of each other without using mortar to hold them together.

QUESTIONS

Answer the following questions using correct spelling and complete sentences.

1. What are five reasons for installing fences in the home landscape?

2. Define microclimate.

3. What is a screen used for in the landscape?

4. What is a restrictive covenant? Why is it important when designing and installing fences?

5. Name four different kinds of wood fences.

6. What are the two major types of metal fences?

7. How is water pressure from behind a retaining wall released?

8. How is a mortarless block retaining wall constructed?

CHAPTER SELF-CHECK

Match the term with the correct definition. Place the letter in the blank provided.

a. covenant	d. wrought iron	g. weep hole
b. pilaster	e. Allan block	h. pea gravel
c. retaining wall	f. chain link	i. enclosure

_____1. Walls constructed to hold soil and create flat surfaces in the landscape

_____2. Mortarless retaining wall block system

_____3. Columns built every 16 feet on brick walls

_____4. Holes in solid retaining wall to relieve water pressure

_____5. A fence that will provide security but is not beautiful

_____6. A beautiful fence that can provide security

_____7. Backfill around mortarless block wall systems with this material

_____8. Special rules that some subdivisions have restricting fence construction techniques

_____9. A term that describes both fences and walls used in the landscape

EXPLORING

1. Visit landscape sites where fences are being constructed. Use a digital camera and record the materials and methods used. Prepare an electronic presentation for your class.

2. Try installing several fence sections at home or school. Follow the steps discussed when installing the posts.

3. Visit a landscape site where retaining wall construction is taking place.

Using Light and Water to Enhance the Landscape

TERMS

accent lighting
backflow prevention device
cross lighting
down-lighting
drip irrigation device
ecosystem
filtration system
ground fault circuit
   interrupter (GFCI)

high-voltage
irrigation controller
low-voltage
mirror lighting
night-landscaping
path lighting
photocell
point-of-connection
pop-up rotating sprinkler

preformed pool
security lighting
shadow lighting
silhouette lighting
solenoid valve
spotlighting
spray head sprinkler
station
up-lighting

14-1. Water appeals to the sense of sight and sound in the landscape. (Courtesy, R.S. Hursthouse & Associates, Inc.)

LIGHTING in the landscape provides safety for people, security for the grounds, and an enrichment to the night landscape. Dramatic focal points can be created in the landscape at night. Lighting also provides the homeowner with the necessary illumination to use the outdoor room at night.

Water features provide great visual impact in the landscape. Moving water is an ideal source of relaxation. A quiet reflecting pool mirrors the elements around it. Water features are focal points that enhance the landscape.

Landscape plants require adequate water to survive. The water that plants receive affects their growth and development. Determining when to water landscape plants is important in the maintenance of a healthy landscape.

LIGHTING THE LANDSCAPE

Safety, security, and enhancement of property are reasons for lighting the landscape around residential and commercial sites. Landscape lighting increases the usefulness of the landscape. Instead of having to move indoors when it gets dark, people can stay outside and enjoy their surroundings. However, safety and security are the most important considerations when lighting business landscapes. While corporate and residential lighting needs may differ in degree, the desire for safety and attractiveness is the same.

Law enforcement agencies recommend lighted areas to deter criminal activities. **Photocells** are light sensitive switches that automatically turn lighting on at dusk and off at sunrise. Security systems now include low-voltage lighting connected to motion detectors for increased safety around the home. For additional protection, timers can also vary the times that lights are activated.

For years, landscape lighting consisted of one or two spotlights attached to the back of the house. Today, modern, low-voltage lamps not only provide security, but also add beauty to the landscape. **Night-landscaping** describes the use of ornamental lighting to enhance the landscape after dark. Landscape designers can choose from hundreds of different style lamps to solve a variety of night-landscaping problems.

Up-lighting is a general term used for light sources which shine upward. This is a popular technique for business and commercial installations. Up-lighting is becoming more popular with homeowners as it uses ambient light techniques which can be softer on the eye than other methods of illumination. **Down-lighting** is the lighting of an object, area, or surface from above. The light source can be a floodlight, a specialized lamp, a unique fixture, or even Christmas lights.

LIGHTING TECHNIQUES

There are ten major night-lighting techniques—path or safety, mirror, spotlighting,

Accent Lighting

Spotlighting

Shadow Lighting

Mirror Lighting

14-2. Examples of up-lighting techniques.

shadow, silhouette, accent, moonlighting, area, cross, and security lighting. ***Path lighting*** or safety lighting offers improved safety for pedestrians while providing an interesting lighting effect in the landscape. It is a technique which focuses on illuminating paths and steps at night. Some safety lights are built into the actual steps or railings to provide a dim glow which illuminates the steps. Path lighting can use indirect lighting from other lighting techniques or it can use direct methods involving actual fixtures installed along the walkway or path.

Mirror lighting technique uses reflected light on water to add interest in the landscape. Mirror lighting puts small but powerful up-lights at the base of specimen plants or art-

14-3. Path lighting (safety lighting) next to garden steps.

work to create a mirror effect in a body of dark water nearby. It is especially effective when used on mature trees next to a still body of water. ***Spotlighting*** gives focal glow to an object within the landscape by directing an intense beam of light toward it. It focuses the eye on objects which are considered to be the most important elements of the design plan. Spotlights are frequently used on specimen trees, statues, or dramatic entryways. Shadow lighting is a particularly attractive variation on silhouette lighting.

Instead of playing up a plant's silhouette, ***shadow lighting*** lights the plant to create a distinct pattern of light and shadow on a plain wall or backdrop. It can create very beautiful

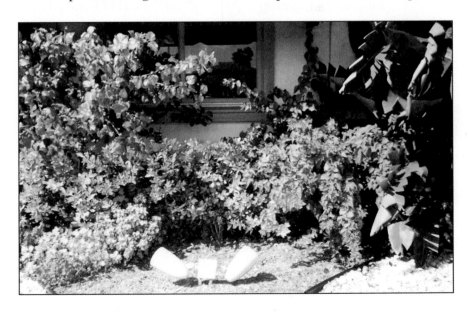

14-4. Lighting has been used to highlight the shrubs in this landscape.

14-5. Up-lighting at the base of a tree.

Security Lighting

Silhouette Lighting

Cross Lighting

Moonlighting

Area Lighting

14-6. Examples of down-lighting techniques.

and subtle lighting effects. By placing the lamp close to the plant, the shadow will be larger. Move the lamp away from the plant and the shadow will be smaller.

Silhouette lighting is when a light is directed at a wall or other plain backdrop in the background to show off the silhouette of a plant or statue in the foreground. It is a subtle and attractive way of showcasing a specimen tree or shrub. Not all silhouette lights are down-lights.

Accent lighting is when small lights are used to highlight a particular plant, small garden element, or work of art. Accent lighting typically uses a low voltage fixture. Often the accent light itself can be an unusual shape. Not all accent lights are up-lights; some can be down-lights or diffuse lights.

Cross lighting is when two or more spotlights are shown down onto the same general area but from different angles. It creates an attractive play of light and shadow on the ground below. A particularly effective form of this, known as moonlighting, is when dim light fixtures are placed high in mature trees to shine down through the leaves and branches.

Area lighting is designed to illuminate an outdoor room. It can be achieved through a variety of means, but down-lighting is the most common choice, and the easiest. Area lighting needs to be bright and uniform without being glaring. Well-designed area lighting should not be intrusive to neighbors, yet should be bright enough to create a functional space.

Security lighting is when light is used to protect property from vandalism or theft. Floodlights installed on house eaves and directed into the viewer's eyes are a bad example of security lighting. When installed well, there is no need to sacrifice beauty for function. Proper security lighting should illuminate the area without being harsh or glaring. Some systems are activated by motion detectors or photocells.

VOLTAGE SYSTEMS FOR OUTDOOR LIGHTING

Two main lighting systems are now available. *High-voltage* lighting systems use conventional 120-volt electricity while low-voltage systems convert the 120 volts to 24 volts. The high-voltage system allows for large lamps that produce more light in the landscape. Outdoor electric cable installation must conform to all local electric codes. These cables will usually be buried 18 inches underground by a licensed electrician.

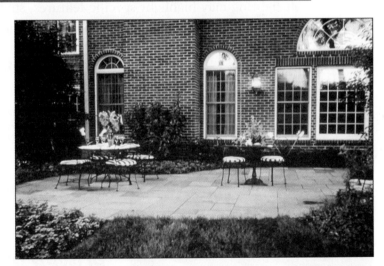

14-7. High-voltage outdoor lighting illuminates this patio. (Courtesy, R.S. Hursthouse & Associates, Inc.)

Avoid using high-voltage sodium lights around landscape beds. Sodium lights give off a yellow cast making green plants appear unnatural in color. High-voltage mercury vapor lights give off a clear glow and work well for lighting large exterior walls that also have landscape plants.

Low-Voltage Lighting

Low-voltage lighting systems run on 24 volts of electricity. By using 24 volts, it is safer, less costly, and adaptable to a variety of conditions.

Low-voltage systems have several advantages over 120-volt systems. Low-voltage systems may not have to be installed by an electrician. Low-voltage cable is buried 6 to 8 inches underground without using electrical conduit. Reduced voltage prevents electrical shocks even when touching the bare wires or accidentally cutting a buried cable with a garden tool.

Low-voltage lighting systems consist of three components. The heart of any low-voltage lighting system is the power pack. Operating off a standard 120-volt electrical outlet, the power pack converts the electrical current to a safe 24 volts for use by the lighting fixtures. Electric cables transmit the 24-volt electric current from the power pack to the individual lighting fixtures. Electric cable comes in a variety of wire sizes, with 10- and 12-gauge being the most common. Follow the manufacturer's recommendations on cable selection. Different lighting fixtures provide a unique lighting effect to a landscape.

LANDSCAPE LIGHT FIXTURES

Always use as few lights as possible to accent focal points that make the landscape and building unique. Today, the trend is toward a softer, more natural look in the landscape. Soft lighting may highlight specific features, such as plantings, walls, decks, or entrances. Avoid the runway look of light along walks. Place lamps close to walks and throw pools of light onto these surfaces.

14-8. Lights placed along a sidewalk to improve safety.

Try to locate landscape light fixtures either above or below eye level. Lighting fixtures can be incorporated into a retaining wall or under steps or house eaves to accent design points. Good lighting can wash a landscape wall and highlight the uneven textures of the wall. Trees with white bark provide striking points of interest in the night landscape. Flower beds can be beautiful at night when properly lighted.

POWER PACKS

Power packs are available with various wattage ranges. Find the correct size of the power pack by adding the wattage of each bulb in the circuit. The power pack's rating should always be greater than the total lighting fixture wattage with all fixtures turned on. Controller options include manual, dusk-to-dawn, and timer-operated models. They also may have a remote control or built-in motion/heat sensors.

Timer-operated power packs automatically turn the lights on and off at a predetermined time. A photocell can turn the lights on at sunset and off at sunrise. Motion/heat sensor

14-9. Components of a low-voltage lighting system.

power packs use a timer that turns the lights on and off at predetermined times each day. However, if someone enters the protected area when the lights are off, the passive infrared motion sensor automatically turns the lights on for a set period.

INSTALLING LOW-VOLTAGE LIGHTING

City ordinances may require that a licensed electrician install all outdoor lighting. Always check the local laws before working with electricity. Install a ground fault circuit interrupter (GFCI) device on all outdoor lighting equipment. A ***ground fault circuit interrupter (GFCI)*** is a safety device designed to protect people using electricity in areas that may be wet or have water. The GFCI will disconnect the electrical circuit when it detects a short or moisture.

Begin at the power pack and stretch the cable to each light fixture. Install the cable by following the landscape's natural contour and barriers leaving 1 to 2 feet of extra cable at each fixture site to allow for future adjustments. Low-voltage cable is self sealing and weather resistant. It can be buried in the ground, covered with mulch, or hidden under shrubs or foliage. Assemble the fixture, as required, and connect it to the cable using the supplied connector. Push the fixture into place in the ground. Adjust the position of the fixtures, so they create the desired lighting effect.

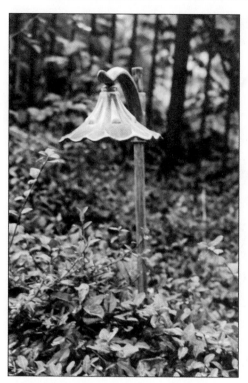

14-10. Many different styles of lighting fixtures are available.

SEVEN STEPS FOR HOME LANDSCAPE LIGHTING

- Evaluate the customer's landscape. Locate the focal points that need emphasis and plan the lighting around those points. Consider walks and driveways for safety and security lighting.

- Keep it simple. Try not to hang lamps from the top of large trees. Not only will installation be difficult, but replacing bulbs will also be difficult. Ground lights that shine into the trees can convey the same effect.

- Choose the fixtures. Some customers want the fixtures to blend into the landscape and be natural or not seen. Other customers want the lighting fixtures to make a statement and be very ornamental. Do not forget the weather. A beautiful fixture near the ground may be difficult to locate and avoid during snow removal.

- Select the bulbs. Large trees, large walls, and large parking lots will require larger-wattage bulbs. A clarity of brightness directs the eyes to the dominant point. From there, your eyes will drift to the rest of the landscape.

- Choose the correct wire size. Outdoor 12-gauge cable with a ground wire for high voltage is the standard in the landscape industry. Low-voltage cables are usually 10- or 12-gauge.

- Choose a transformer or power pack. The transformer will convert the power from 120 volts to 24 volts. Add the wattage of all the bulbs in the circuit to determine the correct transformer size.

- Install the system. Use basic electricians' tools to install the lamp fixtures. Remember, electricity is always a potential danger. Bury low-voltage wire 6 to 8 inches underground. Make a drawing of where the wires lay, in case you want to do some digging in the future and as reference for the homeowner.

CARE AND MAINTENANCE

Low-voltage lighting systems require little care once installed. Occasionally, clean dirt, leaves, and other debris away from the fixtures. Periodically, check the fixtures for proper adjustment. Once a year, remove the bulbs and spray the lamp sockets with a silicone-base spray. Inspect the cable yearly for damage or fraying near the connection points. If a bulb burns out, replace it immediately. Voltage no longer used by damaged bulbs continues to flow to the operating bulbs. This extra voltage can reduce the life of the remaining bulbs.

LIGHTING WATER FEATURES

Water features are especially interesting when lit. Fountains look best when accented from under-lighting. The water conducts the light and begins to glow. Colored or clear bulbs can be used to light water features. However, water and electricity, even with low-voltage systems, are hazardous. Follow all manufacturers' recommendations for proper installation of lamps in and around water features.

THINK SAFETY

Working at night, the landscape crew locates the lamp positions. During the next day, the crew

14-11. Night-lighting increases the beauty of water features. (Courtesy, R.S. Hursthouse & Associates, Inc.)

permanently places the lighting devices in the landscape. Landscape crews should always have safety foremost on their minds while installing landscape lighting devices.

WATER IN THE LANDSCAPE

Water features are important because they appeal to the senses of sight and sound and add magic to a landscape. A gently flowing stream, a cascading waterfall, or a peaceful lily pond can change a simple landscape into a breathtaking experience. The feature can be as formal as a circular fountain set into a patio area or as casual as a brook flowing through the backyard. In most home landscapes, the backyard provides the best location for water features. They should be in proportion to the landscape area.

Safety issues arise when water features are established in a landscape. Water gardens are especially hazardous to small children. Most pools are not very deep thus minimizing hazards associated with deep water. But, it doesn't take much water for a small child to drown. Additional safety issues occur when electricity is used to operate pumps and light the area. Electricity and water do not mix. Always use GFCI protected circuits and ensure proper grounding.

WATER GARDEN PLANNING AND INSTALLATION

The most important consideration in water gardening is site selection. Most water plants need 6 to 8 hours of sun per day to thrive. The area should be level and not low where surface drainage would run into the pond. It should also be away from trees that would drop leaves into the pond in the autumn. The water garden should be placed where it can be enjoyed and viewed from areas frequented in the house or landscape.

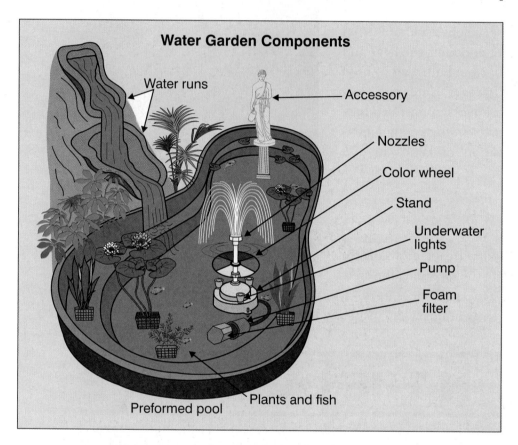

Water Garden Components

Water runs

Accessory

Nozzles

Color wheel

Stand

Underwater lights

Pump

Foam filter

Plants and fish

Preformed pool

14-12. Components of a water garden.

A water garden is a closed **ecosystem**, a confined community. Included in this environment is water, air (oxygen and carbon dioxide), plants, and fish and snails. It is important that the environment be kept balanced. There needs to be good water circulation, oxygenating plants, proper plant coverage of the water surface, proper number of fish and snails, and proper maintenance. The smaller the pond, the more important these needs are. A common water gardening mistake is creating a pond that is too small.

Guidelines for proper balance in a water garden are:

• Circulate the water volume every one to two hours.

• Floating plants should cover 65 to 75 percent of the pond surface.

- Oxygenating and marginal/bog plants should number one plant per 2 square feet of pond surface, taking into account that the total number of plants in the pond should cover 2/3 to 3/4 of the water surface.

- There should never be more than 1 inch of fish per 5 gallons of water (for example, six 5-inch long fish would require a pond with at least 150 gallons of water; $6 \times 5 = 30 \times 5 = 150$ gallons).

- There should not be more than 1 inch of snails per square foot of bottom surface area.

14-13. Some water garden installation steps include (1) excavating and installing the pond liner; (2) grading the site for proper drainage; (3) installing power, lighting, and landscape plants; (4) planting water plants in containers or baskets; (5) acclimating fish to the pond's water temperature; (6) enjoying the plants and fish in the water garden.

Water used to fill a pond may have elements that are harmful to plants and fish. City water may have chlorine, chloramine, or heavy metals. Chlorine will dissipate in 3 to 5 days. Chloramine needs to be treated and heavy metals neutralized. Country or well water may have nitrates or pesticides present. The best practice is to have the water tested. The water pH level is also important. A pH of 7.0 is best for fish and plants. The water pH should be tested and adjusted if necessary. It is best to treat or make adjustments to the water and wait 7 to 10 days before adding fish and plants.

Proper water circulation is important. The proper sized pump should circulate the entire water volume every 1 to 2 hours. A larger pump will be needed if the water garden has a waterfall, fountain, or other features which involves lifting water. Pumps are rated by gph (gallons per hour). The pump should be placed a minimum of 12 inches below the water surface. The return line from the pump should be placed away from the intake for proper circulation. Some ponds may need a mechanical **filtration system**, a pump with a filter to remove impurities and keep the water clean and clear. A layer of gravel on the bottom can also provide a habitat for bacteria which will act as a biological filtration system.

Water plants are an essential part of a water garden. When plants are fully developed, they should cover between 2/3 and 3/4 of the water surface area. Most water plants such as water lilies prefer full sun for 6 to 8 hours per day to thrive. Plants that require containers should be placed at the proper depth. They should be fertilized once a month with pond tabs from spring to fall, and twice a month during hot weather. Brown or yellow growth should be clipped off down to the crown of the plant. It is also important to note that water lilies do not like too much turbulence. They need to be placed away from waterfalls and fountains.

TYPES AND MAINTENANCE OF PONDS

Several types of ponds may be used in the landscape. Each has specific maintenance features that must be considered.

Pond Types

Pond types include preformed liner ponds, concrete shells, brick forms, and membrane (EPDM) ponds. Some are more involved to install and tend to be more permanent than others.

Flexible pond liners can be used to create ponds of any shape and size. They come in various grades and quality, and in a range of prices. PVC (polyvinyl chloride) is the least expensive and the thicker grades are often guaranteed for 10 years. EPDM (ethylene propylene diene rubber membrane) is more expensive, but is generally considered much better material. The most important consideration is that the liner material be specifically intended for use in ponds. Some materials may contain chemicals that are harmful to plants and fish.

Preformed pools are ready-made pond shells of fiberglass or molded plastic (polyethylene). They come in a variety of colors and shapes. Good support is crucial because the pressure of the water can warp the shell if it is not properly supported. Other materials such as concrete, nonabsorbent tile, or brick can also be used to build ponds.

14-14. **Examples of types of ponds.**

When computing the number of gallons a pond will hold, all measurements must be in feet. Don't mix feet and inches when measuring. To determine the approximate number of

14-15. **Pool installation steps using a liner include (1) excavate the site and remove any sharp objects; (2) spread sand over the bottom or cover the bottom with plastic or old newspapers; (3) drape the liner loosely in the pool with the edges anchored, and fill with water; (4) trim away excess liner, leaving an adequate flap around the edge at ground level; (5) line the perimeter with rocks or pavers to hide the liner edge for a finished look.**

gallons (water volume) a pond holds, use the following formulas based on the shape of the pond:

- Rectangular Pond: Length × Width × Depth × 7.5 = gallons
- Oval Pond: Length × Width × Depth × 6.7 = gallons
- Circular Pond: 3.14 × ½ Diameter × ½ Diameter × Depth × 7.5 = gallons

Pond Maintenance

If the pond water turns green, it is called an algae bloom. This is a natural occurrence. Treatment is usually unnecessary. An average algae bloom lasts for 10 to 14 days. It will disappear virtually overnight if the pond is properly balanced. Avoid fertilizing water lilies as long as the algae problem persists. Healthy water will often be slightly green. However, the water should be clear enough to see at least 6 to 8 inches below the surface.

Growing more aquatic plants can also help to inhibit algae. Algae needs sun to grow and reproduce. Water lilies and other desirable plants covering 2/3 to 3/4 of the pond surface will leave very little open water to catch the sun's rays. This is easily accomplished in mid-summer. However, early in the season before water lilies start to spread, algae will receive more of the sun's rays. As a spring control, floating plants like water lettuce (*Pistia stratiotes*) or water hyacinth (*Eichhornia crassipes*) can be added to help cover the pond surface. As the water lilies expand, excess floating plants can be removed. Note that water hyacinth can invade public waterways and is illegal in some states. Keep in mind that having some algae in the pond is normal.

A proper environment is needed for fish. Fish prefer cold water because it holds more oxygen. Do not overstock the pond with too many fish. Ideally, the proper number of fish can support themselves on natural food in the pond. This doesn't mean not to feed the fish. However, they should not be fed more than once a day and only as much food as they can eat in 5 minutes. Uneaten, nutrient-rich food acts as fertilizer for algae. Fish should be hungry enough to forage actively on natural food in the pond. In early spring and late fall, a low protein, high carbohydrate fish food should be fed. In the late spring to early fall, feed a high protein, low carbohydrate food. When the temperature reaches 40°F or below, do not feed the fish at all. Fish enter partial hibernation at 40°F.

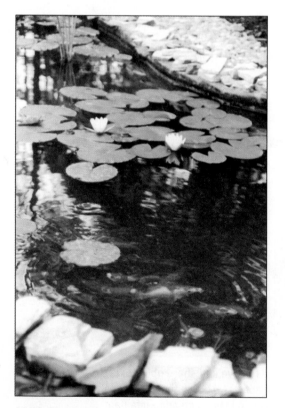

14-16. The proper number of fish can support themselves on natural food in the pond.

During hot weather, water may need to be added to the pond due to evaporation. If more than 25 percent of the pond volume is added, it may be necessary to test and re-treat the water. In the autumn, leaves and other debris need to be kept out of the pond. A dip net can be used to remove leaves or a cover net may be stretched over the surface to keep out leaves and debris. Whenever organic matter collecting on the bottom gets to be about an inch thick, drain and clean the pond. The pump should be checked and cleaned, on a regular schedule.

As temperatures cool in the fall, the water garden must be prepared for the coming winter. Depending on the geographic location, winter can be anything from icy cold to relatively balmy. The pond's surface should be lowered 6 inches to allow room for the water to expand due to freezing. The pump and any filters can be removed and cleaned or left running during the winter. If you choose to leave the pump running, it is important that it be raised to just below the surface of the water. Allowing the pump to circulate the water at lower depths is stressful to fish. If the pump is removed, a heater will be needed to keep the pond from totally freezing on the surface. A livestock tank heater or bird bath deicer can be purchased and used.

The fish will not freeze to death if a pond freezes over solid. However, they can smother. Debris and organic material on the bottom builds up methane and other gases that must be allowed to escape. A small surface opening will allow for proper oxygen and gas exchange. If a pond is allowed to freeze over solid, do not break the ice with a blunt object. The ensuing shock waves can be stressful or deadly to fish. Heating a pan of hot water, placing it on the ice, and allowing it to melt through can create the needed opening. Once spring arrives and the water temperature reaches 50°F, fish can be fed a high carbohydrate, low protein fish food. When the water temperature reaches 70°F, a high protein regular type fish food should be used.

Water garden winter preparation checklist: (1) discontinue feeding fish; (2) remove leaves and debris, cover pond with a net; (3) turn off moving water features such as waterfalls or fountains; (4) lower pond depth; (5) remove and clean pump and filters or raise pump level; (6) install a heater to prevent freezing over; (7) remove tropical plants before the first frost; (8) cut off hardy submersible plants and place on bottom; (9) store hardy marginal/bog plants.

14-17. This water garden has been prepared for the coming winter months.

Water plants can be grouped into three basic types—hardy submersibles, hardy marginal/bog plants, and tropical plants. Hardy means the ability to withstand cold temperatures. Different plant types need different preparations for winter protection. After the first frost, or when temperatures get down to 40°F, hardy submersibles should be cut off at the crown of the plant and placed on the bottom of the pond. Hardy marginal/bog plants need a dormant period. They may be placed in cold storage where the plants can go dormant without the container freezing solid. This type of environment may not be readily available. The other solution is planting them, container and all, with the top of the container at ground level in a planting bed. Tropical plants (non-hardy to zone 10) require indoor overwintering before the first frost. They can be submerged at the proper depth indoors in a fish aquarium. Some tropical plants such as umbrella palm and dwarf papyrus can be grown as houseplants. When spring arrives and water temperature in the pond reaches 70°F, tropical plants can be placed back in the water garden at their proper depth.

RESIDENTIAL IRRIGATION SYSTEMS

Water is essential for good plant growth. In many parts of the country, rain will naturally provide the necessary quantity of water. However, in other parts, there is not enough water for good plant growth. Irrigation can supplement and furnish adequate water to plants. Properly designed and properly installed irrigation systems coupled with educated homeowners can save a large amount of water runoff and waste. There are cities and towns that now require municipal approval or licensing prior to installing a lawn or landscape irrigation system. The landscape designer should check with the local municipality for approval or permits.

Individuals with water wells should assess the rate of flow produced by the well in deciding if to establish an irrigation system and, if so, the size of system that the well will support. The rate of flow of a well is measured in gallons per minute (GPM). The use of irrigation water combined with other water demand on the well should not exceed its GPM productivity. For example, if a well has a 20 GPM capacity, the combined water demand for irrigation and other uses cannot be greater than 20 GPM for any extended time.

14-18. Proper irrigation can supplement available water for good plant growth.

DESIGNING AN IRRIGATION SYSTEM

To ensure a complete and proper irrigation system design, a set procedure must be followed. The steps are (1) obtain site information, (2) determine the irrigation requirement, (3) determine water capacity and pressure, (4) select sprinklers and spacing ranges, (5) circuit the sprinklers into valve groups, (6) size pipe and valves and calculate total system pressure loss, (7) locate controllers and size wiring, and (8) prepare the final irrigation plan.

Site Information and Irrigation Requirements

The local climate is the main factor that will influence how much water will need to be applied for good plant growth. Evapotranspiration (ET) describes the loss of water from plant tissue, the soil, and the soil surface. The ET rate is affected by relative humidity, solar radiation, day length, air temperature, and wind velocity. Therefore, on a sunny, dry, windy, summer day plants will use larger quantities of water.

Most irrigation water is clean enough for human consumption. However, in some parts of the country waste water is used for irrigation. Some sprinkler manufacturers install a different colored sprinkler head on golf courses and other large turf areas where waste water is used for irrigation. This is to remind people that the irrigation water is not fit for human consumption.

> **TIP:** Check with the local water company to find out what the maximum water flow is in g.p.m. (gallons per minute) for the irrigation site.

Water Capacity and Pressure

The irrigation designer needs to know the flow in gallons per minute (gpm) available to the system and the working pressure (psi) at the point-of-connection. **Point-of-connection** is the location where the irrigation line is connected to the household water supply. Static water pressure refers to the pounds per square inch (psi) of pressure in a closed system with no water moving. The static water pressure can be determined by using a direct pressure gauge reading or can be obtained from the water company. The water meter size is usually stamped or cast into the meter itself. The service line material (copper or galvanized), length, and size needs to be known in order to calculate pipe flow loss and working pressure. The line may be a different size than the meter.

Three calculations should be made and the most restrictive value be used as flow for the irrigation system. The pressure loss through a water meter should not exceed 10 percent of the minimum static pressure on the main side. The maximum flow through the meter for irrigation should not exceed 75 percent of the maximum safe flow of the meter. A water meter flow loss chart will be needed for these calculations. The velocity of flow in an irrigation system should not exceed 5 feet per second. Use a flow chart to determine the correct irrigation pipe size.

Selecting Sprinklers

There are a number of different types of sprinklers and irrigation devices. The main types are spray head sprinklers, rotating sprinklers, bubblers, and drip irrigation devices. The size and shape of the areas to be irrigated and the types of plant material determines what type of sprinkler head will be used. Available water pressure and flow, local environmental conditions, soil type, and sprinkler grouping are other limiting factors. The goal is to select the type of heads that will cover the area properly using the least number of sprinklers.

Spray head sprinklers generally emit single or double sheets or fans of water in a fixed pattern. Examples include shrub spray heads, pop-up spray heads, and surface spray heads. **Pop-up rotating sprinklers** have a single or pair of nozzles that raise and revolve to distribute water. In a large, open lawn area, rotary pop-ups can irrigate vast areas with substantially fewer heads than if spray heads were used. Higher operating pressure is needed for rotating heads. A **drip irrigation device** produces a short throw, zero radius, or ultra-low volume water distribution. **Bubblers** and drip systems can irrigate a specific area without overthrow onto other plants or landscape features. A radius of 2 to 5 feet coverage is common with drip irrigation devices. This technique is used in parts of the country where irrigation water supplies are limited.

Sprinkler compatibility is important when circuiting sprinkler heads into groups that will be controlled by the same valve. Avoid mixing different types of sprinkler heads together on the same valve whenever possible. Different heads have different operating pressures and usually require widely varying operating times. Full-circle sprinkler heads water a complete circular area. Part-circle sprinkler heads distribute water on areas less than 360 degrees. Half-circle heads are used along a driveway, patio, property line, or house.

14-19. The well-designed head (right) will pop-up above plant material. The poor design (left) will not operate properly. (Courtesy, Rain Bird)

There are two major types of sprinkler spacing patterns. Depending on the area to irrigate, various combinations and adaptations of these two patterns will be used. The triangular pattern is used where the area to be irrigated has irregular boundaries or borders and only full circle heads are used. The triangular pattern will use fewer heads and is a more efficient sprinkler pattern. The spacing between sprinkler heads in a single row is called "S" (spacing), and the distance between irrigation rows is called "L" (lateral). Large areas, such as golf course fairways, use the triangular sprinkler pattern.

The square pattern will best irrigate areas with defined straight boundaries and corners. Home lawns commonly are rectangular in shape and usually have a square sprinkler spacing pattern. Square spacing uses both half-circle and full-circle sprinkler heads. More sprinklers will be needed to water a given area of turf when this pattern

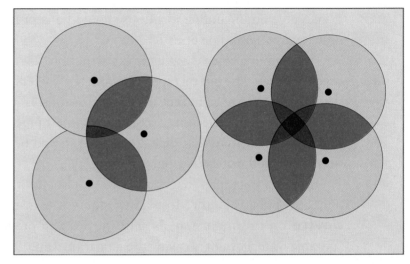

14-20. Triangular (left) and square (right) sprinkler spacing patterns.

is used. The very center of the square pattern may be under-watered and the turf may show signs of water stress.

The precipitation rate of the selected heads should be calculated to determine if the rate will apply enough water during operating times and that the rate does not exceed the soil's absorption rate. The average precipitation rate is expressed in inches per hour. The formula is:

$$\text{Precipitation Rate} = \frac{96.3 \times \text{gpm}}{S \times L}$$

Where: 96.3 is a constant which incorporates inches per square foot per hour, gpm is the total gallons per minute applied to an area by the sprinklers, S is the spacing in feet between sprinklers, and L is the spacing in feet between rows of sprinklers.

Sprinkler Circuits, Valves, Piping

Sprinkler circuits are established by adding the gallons per minute (gpm) of similar heads in each area. Each circuit (valve group) cannot exceed the system flow limit estab-

TIP: Before installing irrigation lines, call a utility locating service 48 hours in advance of digging and have all underground utilities located.

lished in step 3, determined water capacity and pressure. If the total is exceeded, an additional valve group will need to be added.

The designer will now need to locate the valves, mainlines, and lateral piping. Valves should be easily accessible for operation and service, and located where they will not interfere with normal traffic patterns. They should be located in the center of a sprinkler group to balance the flow and size of lateral pipe. Valve boxes are available for below ground installation. Valve and mainline locations should be kept in mind when circuiting sprinklers and drawing in lateral pipe lines.

The mainline pipe is heavier in construction, has constant pressure, and supplies water to several valves. The lateral pipe runs from the valve to the sprinkler heads. The flow through the valve should not produce a loss greater than 10 percent of the static pressure available. The valve should be the same size as the largest pipe in the lateral it serves or no more than one size smaller than that pipe. The valve should not be larger than the pipe in the lateral, unless a high flow results from a split lateral.

Irrigation water can "backflow" through irrigation pipes into the water supply system and endanger public health. Most states require the installation of a **backflow prevention device** on irrigation systems. This device will prevent contamination of drinking water (potable water) by not allowing the irrigation water to flow backwards into the water supply.

14-21. Installing a sprinkler system involves trenching, placing pipe, using a backflow prevention device (top right), and positioning underground nozzles. (Courtesy, Jasper S. Lee)

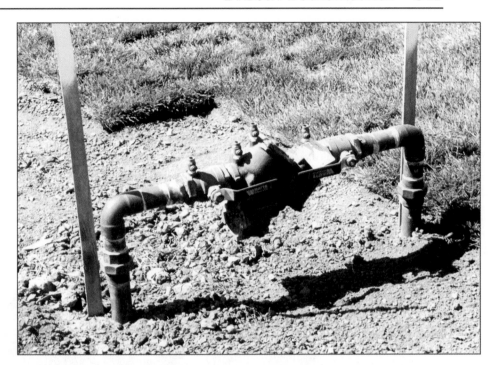

14-22. A backflow prevention device is designed to eliminate the movement of irrigation water back into its potable water system source.

Controllers and Wiring

Irrigation water is controlled using solenoid valves. ***Solenoid valves*** turn water on and off with electricity which allows remote clocks to time cycles. ***Irrigation controllers*** regulate and electrically control these valves in a sprinkler system. They have a day-of-the-week clock to select which day water is applied, a twenty-four-hour clock to control the time of day sprinklers operate, and a station clock to control the time each valve is turned on and off. Irrigation water valves operate on a low voltage (24 volts) system. A ground fault circuit interrupter (GFCI) must be used on the 120-volt electrical circuit supplying the irrigation controller.

TIP: The control wire for most home irrigation systems is 12-gauge while large commercial irrigation systems usually require 10-gauge wire.

The term ***station*** describes a single electric switch in an irrigation controller. It turns on or off a solenoid valve which controls water flow to a single sprinkler circuit. Small controllers used in residential irrigation systems may have four to six separate stations. Between the controller and the solenoid valve that feeds the sprinklers, a network of valve low voltage control wires exists. Each valve is hooked up with two wires, a control or power wire and common or ground wire. It is important that wiring be properly sized.

Preparing the System Plan

The final irrigation system plan is a diagram representing what the irrigation system should look like after installation. It will be used by the irrigation contractor as the system is installed. It should be drawn to scale with detailed explanations, a legend explaining the symbols, and indicate any major elevation changes. It will show all water and utility locations. The advantage to completing the final irrigation plan is the designer can ensure that complete coverage of the area to be irrigated has been achieved. The plan should also contain any notes for specific requirements which must be met.

TIP: Many cities require a licenced plumber to install an irrigation system. However, some cities only require a plumber to install the backflow prevention device.

14-23. An irrigation design showing spray patterns and head placements. (Courtesy, LANDCADD Division, Eagle Point Software)

REVIEWING

MAIN IDEAS

Landscape managers are discovering that outdoor lighting can enhance plantings and make turf, walkways, and gardens more visually pleasing at night. Besides providing beauty, safety, and security, lighting reinforces the image that property is well maintained. Many landscape contractors recommend low-voltage outdoor lighting systems because they operate on 24 volts instead of the standard high-voltage. Technological advances in low-voltage lighting have allowed manufactures to offer products equal in quality, if not better, than many high-voltage lights of just 10 years ago.

Always use as few lights as possible in the landscape. Good lighting can accent trees, shrubs, and flowers. Safety and security are other reasons for lighting the landscape. Install a ground fault circuit interrupter on all outdoor lighting equipment.

Water features provide the landscape with magic. Water features can be a formal fountain or a gentle brook flowing through the backyard. The sound of splashing water can mask noise made by nearby automobiles. Landscape pools are usually 18 inches deep. Heaters may be needed for fish ponds in colder climates.

Underground sprinkler systems are popular in many parts of the country. These systems have timers that electrically turn on water valves in the irrigation system. Small sprinkler heads cover 4 to 12 foot diameter circles, while large heads can wet circles over 15 feet in diameter.

QUESTIONS

Answer the following questions using correct spelling and complete sentences.

1. What are three reasons for lighting a landscape?

2. Define the term night-landscaping.

3. Name 10 major night-lighting techniques.

4. What is the difference between high- and low-voltage lighting systems?

5. What is a ground fault circuit interrupter?

6. Why are water features important in the home landscape?

7. Name the five steps used when installing a pool with a liner.

8. Why may it be necessary to install a filtration system on a reflecting pond?

9. What are the major parts of an automatic irrigation system?

10. What is the purpose of a backflow prevention device in an irrigation system?

CHAPTER SELF-CHECK

Match the term with the correct definition. Place the correct letter in the blank provided.

a. ground fault circuit interrupter   c. path lighting   e. spotlighting
b. solenoid valve   d. preformed pool   f. silhouette lighting

_____1. Landscape pools made from plastic or fiberglass, ready to install in the home landscape

_____2. A special electrical device that disconnects electricity to outdoor lights if an electrical short develops

_____3. Lighting for walks and steps for safety considerations

_____4. Direct attention to specific plants or statues with landscape lamps

_____5. Electric valves that turn on sprinklers to irrigate turf

_____6. To shine a light behind a plant on a wall or other vertical surface to create an interesting pattern

EXPLORING

1. Talk with a local landscape contractor about pool and pond installation. Observe a pool or pond that is in operation. Determine the routine maintenance requirements. Prepare a report on your findings.

2. Visit several commercial buildings that use night-lighting. Describe the type of lighting system. Determine the electrical use of such systems and establish an estimated cost of operation for a year.

3. Visit a home landscape that has a water garden. Take pictures and describe the water feature.

PART THREE

Landscape Maintenance

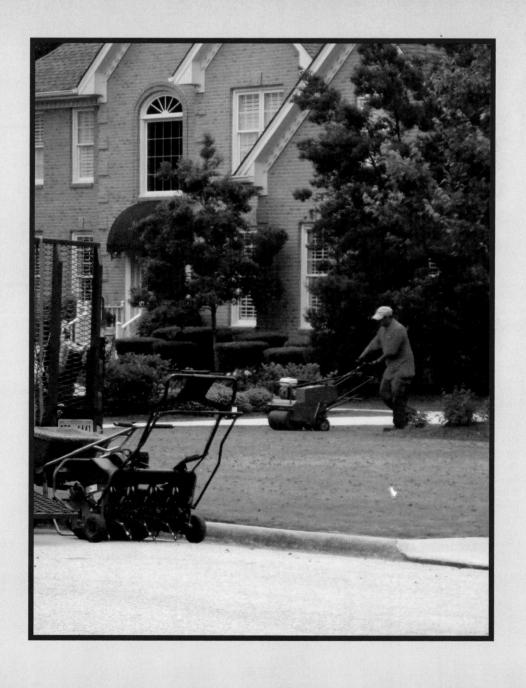

CHAPTER 15

Watering, Fertilizing, and Mulching Woody Plants

OBJECTIVES

1 Describe how woody plant biology influences maintenance practices.

2 Explain recommended watering practices for woody landscape plants.

3 Explain how woody landscape plants are fertilized.

4 Describe the use of mulch in the landscape.

TERMS

broadcasting
chlorosis
desiccation
dry fertilizer
fertilizer capsule
fertilizer spike
inorganic mulch

microirrigation
mulching
organic mulch
respiration
root watering needle
root zone
soaker hose

soil watering needle
soluble fertilizer
sprinkler
xeriscaping
water bag
wilting

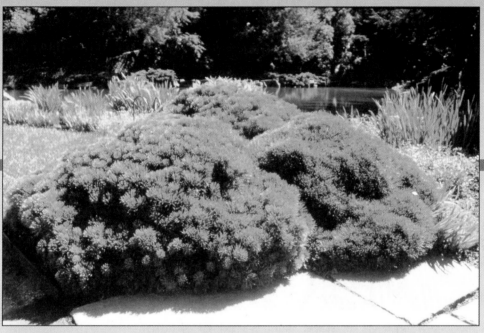

15-1. Healthy, woody landscape plants require little care. The foreground shrubs are Swiss Mountain Pine, *Pinus mugo* var. mugo. (Courtesy, University of Illinois Cooperative Extension Service)

DOES landscaping end with the installation of a landscape? The answer to that is an obvious no. Landscape plants are living organisms, and they require some care until they become established. If the plants die, the customer will be unhappy. A customer may demand that the dead plants be replaced.

If you are a smart landscaper, you will take the time to properly install the plants to reduce losses. You will probably check the plants occasionally as a follow-up procedure. In addition, you will leave instructions with the customer about how to care for the new plants. The question is how do you care for woody plants?

BIOLOGY AND WOODY PLANT CARE

15-2. Healthy plants contribute beauty to the landscape. Shown is a Hick's yew, *Taxus x media* 'Hicksii,' hedge; Flowering Crabapples, *Malus species*; and Austrian Pine, *Pinus nigra* var. nigra.

The health of woody landscape plants is worth maintaining for many reasons. One reason is it takes effort to install woody plants in the new landscape. Plants that die, particularly, well-established plants, are not easily replaced. Another reason is healthy plants are attractive plants. We appreciate the beauty of trees, shrubs, ground covers, and vines. Because these plants are expected to provide beauty in the landscape for many years, their health must be considered. Also, as plants' ornamental qualities increase with growth and maturity, they contribute to the home's real estate value.

An understanding of woody plant biology is necessary to properly care for plants in the landscape. Woody plants are part of nature. In nature, they have adapted to specific climatic and growing conditions. Water and nutrients for plant growth and health are obtained through natural processes. Most water becomes available for plant use through precipitation. Nutrients are obtained from the mineral matter in soil and from the decay of organic materials.

In the landscape, woody landscape plants are often subjected to adverse growing conditions not found in nature. Compacted soils, poor soil drainage, poor quality soil, and restricted areas for root growth, place stress on plants. Highway salts, air pollution, and competition from turfgrasses are other conditions that place stress on woody landscape plants.

TIP: One way to ensure healthy plants is to select plant species that do well in conditions offered by the site.

Plant selection can lead to problems. Selecting species that are best suited will help ensure health and vitality of woody landscape plants. Some plants are frequently used because they have high ornamental value, such as fall color, showiness of flowers, and growth habit. The selection often is not based on whether the plant is adapted to the growing conditions in the landscape. Placed in a stressful situation for which they are not well adapted, they often suffer, decline, and die.

Additional stress is placed on landscape plants during the transplanting process. Nursery plants, other than those grown in containers, are dug from the ground causing severe damage to the root systems. Some trees might lose up to 95 percent of their feeder roots in the process. The trees are stored in holding areas before planting. Then, they may be planted under conditions unlike the ones in which they were growing. Their exposure to wind and rain is changed and the soil type is probably different from the type in which their roots were growing.

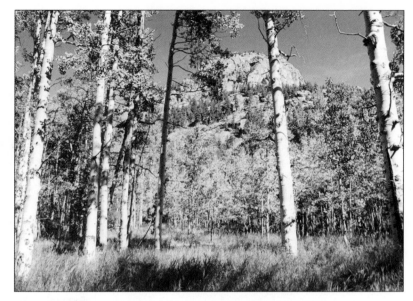

15-3. Woody plants are adapted to climatic and growing conditions in nature that differ from conditions in the artificial landscape.

One way to ensure healthy plants is to select plant species that do well in conditions offered by the site. Second, plants become established and grow more vigorously if the site

15-4. Balled and burlapped plants may lose up to 95 percent of their feeder roots during the transplanting process.

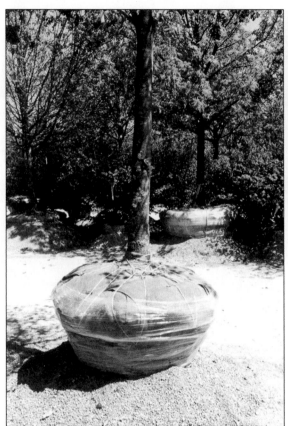

15-5. Trees might be stored in holding areas for months before planting which adds stress on the plant.

15-6. Healthy plants, such as this Wayfaringtree Viburnum, *Viburnum lantana*, are able to defend themselves from disease and insect pests. (Courtesy, University of Illinois Cooperative Extension Service)

has been well prepared before planting. Site preparation includes amending the soil or improving the drainage of water when necessary.

Stress affecting the health of woody landscape plants can sometimes be reduced with proper watering and fertilizing. Healthy plants are better able to defend themselves against diseases and insects than less vigorous plants. A good analogy is people and colds or flu. Most people catch a cold or flu when their immune systems are weakened. Perhaps, they have not gotten enough rest, they have not been eating a good diet, or they were improperly dressed in poor weather. These types of situations weaken their systems. The result is they are less able to fight off infectious organisms. The same is true with plants. Diseases more easily infect and insects are attracted to weakened plants.

Energy and Woody Plant Life

Energy for plant life is produced through photosynthesis. The energy is in the form of sugar, or glucose. Live cells in the plant require a constant supply of energy to live and function. When an abundance of sugars are produced, woody plants convert the sugars into starches and oils. The starches and oils are held in reserve and converted back to sugars when needed. The level of stored energy in a tree influences its growth rate, reproduction, and defense capabilities. Woody plants with high energy reserves tend to be healthy plants.

It should be noted that the energy demands of woody plants differ through the five key periods of its growth life. The five periods are youth, development of leaves, high-sugar producing, storage of energy, and dormancy.

15-7. Woody plants used energy stored in the previous growing season to produce leaves in the spring. Shown is bottlebrush buckeye, *Aesculus parvifolia*.

1. *Youth or juvenile period.* A young woody plant has living cells throughout the plant. Photosynthesis must produce all of the energy demanded by the individual cells. When the plant is young, the energy produced is directed toward vegetative growth. The energy demands increase as the cells multiply and the woody plant grows.

2. *Development of leaves period.* In the spring, woody plants form new leaves in which photosynthesis and the production of sugars will occur. During this period, woody plants use much of the energy, stored during the previous growing season, to produce the leaves. Disease or injury at the time of leaf development places great stress on the plant. Also, if leaves need to be replaced in the spring the plant must draw more deeply from its energy reserves.

15-8. The two periods in a woody plant's growth cycle when energy reserves are at their lowest are in the spring when leaves and flowers are developing and in the fall when roots are being formed. (The tree on the far left of the left photograph is an Eastern redbud, *Cercis canadensis*. The tree to its right is a Flowering crabapple, *Malus* sp. The tree in the right photograph is an Amur maple, *Acer ginnala*.)

The development of leaves is one of two periods in a woody plant's growth cycle when energy reserves are low. The other period of low energy is in the fall when leaves drop. While the leaves drop, much of the energy goes to the formation of roots. At both times, optimal water levels are critical. Irrigation is advised in times of drought to reduce the stress on the plants.

3. *High-sugar producing period.* Photosynthetic activity is at its highest for six to eight weeks after the leaves have fully developed (late spring to early summer). The abundance of energy spurs new growth. Ninety percent of a woody plant's annual growth occurs during this time. Hence, plants benefit from favorable water and nutrient levels.

15-9. The leaves of this bottlebrush buckeye, *Aesculus parvifolia,* reached their peak sugar producing period when this photo was taken in late spring to early summer.

4. *Storage of energy period.* After the leaves have become fully mature (midsummer), the woody plant converts much of its energy being produced into starches and oils. The stored energy is essential as it improves a woody plant's ability to defend itself from disease.

5. *Dormancy period.* Energy stored throughout the summer and early fall provides the woody plant with reserves to get through the winter.

An understanding of woody plant biology and how the production of energy promotes healthy plants is important in determining proper care. Knowing what conditions cause plant stress is critical. This is similar to medical practice, where doctors identify the problem before prescribing a treatment. Most of the time woody plants are fine without any treatments. In fact, many landscape plants have been "nurtured to death" by people with good intentions.

Treatments by people to promote vigor and healthy growth of established plants include three common practices. They are watering, fertilizing, and mulching. The timing of water or fertilizer applications is usually more important than the applications themselves. Timing may make the difference in the life or death of woody plants. Applications, if needed, must be based on the plant's stage of growth and growing conditions rather than the timetable of the landscaper or homeowner.

15-10. Most woody landscape plants are fine without supplemental water or fertilizer.

WATERING

Water is the basis of life. Hydrogen in water is a key nutrient in the photosynthetic process. Water is the carrier of dissolved nutrients from the soil into the roots. Water also sustains plant cells and keeps them turgid. Life processes in plants shut down when water is unavailable. That means, photosynthesis stops and energy production is halted. Obviously, stress to landscape plants will occur if water is scarce.

Newly transplanted landscape plants and firmly established landscape plants call for different watering practices. Newly transplanted trees and shrubs need special attention. They lose many of their roots in the transplanting process. It may take recently planted landscape plants three to six years to overcome the damage to their root systems. Until the plants recover, they need to be provided an adequate supply of water. On the other hand, large established trees and shrubs only need additional water in extreme drought conditions. Established

15-11. This young Red Sunset Red Maple, *Acer rubrum 'Red Sunset',* is showing severe signs of drought and will likely die unless it receives water.

trees and shrubs have extensive root systems that can pull water up through the soil from lower levels.

Xeriscaping

Xeriscaping is a term used to describe landscape practices involving water conservation. The term is derived from the Greek word xeros, which means dry. The practice is most common in parts of the country where rainfall is scarce. It will likely become more important as demands for water increase as population expands.

Xeriscaping involves seven fundamental principles for landscape planning and maintenance.

1. Planning is the most important step to a successful xeriscape. The design should group plants of similar water needs.

2. Limit turf areas as they require great amounts of water.

3. Select plants that are tolerant of dry conditions.

4. Analyze the soil for necessary improvements such as improved drainage and water holding capacity.

5. If irrigation is used, choose efficient systems such as drip irrigation or micro-irrigation systems.

6. Use mulches to reduce water evaporation from the soil, minimize weed growth, and keep the soil cool.

7. Conserve water in maintenance practices including weeding, pruning, and careful scheduling of irrigation.

15-12. These Arizona landscapes show xeriscape practices. The plants selected tolerate dry conditions. Gravel mulch is used extensively instead of turf, and rocks are placed to create interest.

FACTORS AFFECTING WATERING

Weather is one factor that influences how often woody plants need to be watered. Cloudy, rainy, cool conditions reduce the need for water. Sunny, hot, windy conditions increase the demands for water. Landscapers and gardeners must monitor weather conditions to determine the need for watering.

Another factor affecting watering practices is the soil type. Water drains from sandy soils quickly; whereas, heavy clay soils hold water. Know the type of soil in which the plants are planted. Trees and shrubs growing in porous, sandy soil require more frequent watering than those in silty or clay soils.

A third factor is the plant. It is important to know the growing conditions to which landscape plants are adapted. Some plants are tolerant of dry conditions. Other plants perform well in wet soil conditions. Most plants, however, prefer moist, well-drained soils. Moist, well-drained soils have a balance of water and air in the pore spaces.

WHEN TO WATER

Observation skills and experience help people in determining when and if plants need additional

TIP: A general rule for watering established woody landscape plants is to thoroughly soak the soil every two to three weeks during periods of drought.

15-13. The Common Hackberry, *Celtis occidentalis*, is very tolerant of drought conditions.

15-14. The leaves of this Miss Kim lilac curl in response to a lack of water.

water. The first plant symptom of insufficient water is wilting. Wilting is the drooping of a plant due to a lack of firmness in the plant tissues. Other early symptoms include a loss of color or dullness to the leaves and curling of the leaves. If lack of water becomes severe, leaf tissues die and leaves can appear scorched. Leaves on some plants turn yellow and drop prematurely.

Care must be taken because the symptoms for excessive dryness are the same as too much soil moisture. Stress symptoms appear during drought when there is no water available for the plant to absorb. In the case of too much soil moisture, most plants will show symptoms similar to those under drought conditions. Roots of plants die if the soil is saturated or waterlogged for long periods. This is because roots need oxygen. The oxygen is used in respiration. **Respiration** is the chemical process in which cells, including root cells, convert sugars into energy. Saturated soils have very poor air exchange with the atmosphere. If the root cells lack oxygen, they are subject to rot. The plant is then unable to absorb the water it needs. It is best to allow soil to approach drying before watering. As the soil dries, oxygen replaces water in the soil pores.

One concern with newly planted trees in construction sites is the compaction of the soil from heavy equipment. This is a problem particularly with clay soils. The hole for the plant is dug. The plant is planted. Because the soil is so compacted, water does not drain from the hole. Unaware of the problem, the homeowner or landscaper waters the plant. The hole fills with water; the roots rot, and the plant dies. In these cases, it is important to provide drainage for the plants before planting. Two possible solutions to this problem include breaking through the hard-packed soil to allow drainage or installing drain tile.

15-15. These Common Horsechestnut, *Aesculus hippocastanum*, leaves are scorched due to a summer drought.

15-16. This photograph shows a tree being watered by letting the water trickle from the end of a garden hose. (Water should be applied so that it soaks deep into the root zone of the tree.)

A general rule for watering established landscape plants is to thoroughly soak the soil every two to three weeks during periods of drought. It is best to physically check the soil first to see if it is moist. This check involves digging 4 to 6 inches into the ground and feeling the soil. A dry feel would indicate a need to water. Newly planted plants need to be watered on a regular basis during the first few years after transplanting.

A general rule for watering established woody landscape plants is to thoroughly soak the soil every two to three weeks during periods of drought. It is best to physically check the soil first to see if it is moist. This

15-17. Sprinklers are sometimes used to water woody landscape plants but with limited success. (The amount of water applied is often inadequate to soak deep into the root zone.) (Courtesy, University of Illinois Cooperative Extension Service)

check involves digging 4 to 6 inches into the ground and feeling the soil. A dry feel would indicate a need to water. Newly planted plants need to be watered on a regular basis during the first few years after transplanting.

In cold regions of the country, it is advisable to water landscape plants before the ground freezes. Available water in the soil in the winter helps to reduce damage caused by **desiccation**, water loss from tissues resulting in tissue death.

HOW TO WATER

The key to watering is getting the water into the soil where the roots can absorb it. Water slowly so it will soak the soil rather than run off the surface. To avoid runoff, it helps to build a soil saucer around the plants to hold water. Popular methods of watering include sprinkling, soaker hoses, watering bags, micro-irrigation systems, and soil needles. It is often enough to simply let water trickle out of the end of a hose until the soil around a plant is well moistened.

15-18. The bag around this newly transplanted tree is filled with water.

Sprinklers—Sprinklers water a large area. They are particularly useful in watering ground covers. If sprinklers are used, provide at least 1 inch of water at each watering. In average soils, 1 inch of water will soak the soil to a depth of 6–8 inches. The amount applied can be measured by placing a coffee can under the sprinkler and checking it periodically. Quite a bit of water is lost through evaporation when sprinklers are used.

Soaker hoses—Soaker hoses can be snaked through a landscape planting and hidden from sight with mulch. Rubber soaker hoses ooze water to provide a slow application.

Watering bags—Watering bags are useful for newly transplanted trees located where watering is not easily done. Tiny holes in the bag allow the water to slowly seep into the ground.

Microirrigation—Microirrigation is a closed system characterized by low operating pressure and small orifice size. It has become popular particularly in areas that have a low annual rainfall. Calculations to determine the amount of water for each plant require the soil type and plant size. Special emitters and tubing deliver the prescribed amount of water to each plant. Once set up, this method of watering is efficient. Little water is lost to runoff or evaporation.

Soil watering needle—Soil watering needles supply water directly to the root zone of the plants. The needle is inserted a number of times around the tree or shrub to ensure thorough watering.

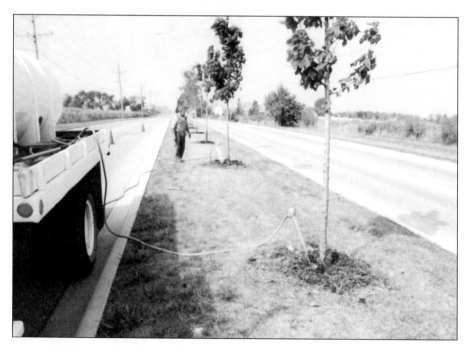

15-19. This landscape technician is using a root watering needle to pump water directly to the root zone of the tree. The same equipment is used to apply soluble fertilizers.

FERTILIZING

Most trees and shrubs never need to be fertilized. They extract the nutrients they need from the soil. However, due to housing construction practices and landscape maintenance, fertilizers are sometimes very beneficial. Developers often leave housing sites with an abundance of subsoil low in fertility. These types of soils have low organic matter content. Fertility levels in landscape soils are not improved with high-maintenance landscapes. The natural process of nutrients being released into the soil by decaying plant parts is prevented with the removal of leaves, twigs, and grass clippings.

Woody landscape plants show signs of stress that can be reduced with fertilizer applications. Some signs to look for are growth slower than normal, twig dieback, earlier than normal fall color, and heavy seed set. An application of general purpose fertilizer can boost the energy production in the plant.

15-20. Plant litter that could provide nutrients to the soil through decay is often removed.

Sometimes, nutrient deficiencies occur. Nutrient deficiencies are often related to the pH of the soil. Extremes of pH in soils restrict the ability of some plants to absorb micronutrients. For example, pin oaks, *Quercus palustris*, develop chlorosis when grown in alkaline soils. **Chlorosis** is a yellowing of the leaves caused by the absence of chlorophyll. Iron deficiency is commonly associated with the chlorosis of pin oaks. The deficiency appears in pin oaks grown in high pH soils even if the soil is full of iron.

15-21. One symptom of stress is earlier than normal fall coloration. Shown is Sugar maple, *Acer saccharum*.

15-22. It is possible that watering and fertilizing could have saved this Norway maple, *Acer platanoides*. It was damaged by building construction.

WHEN TO FERTILIZE

The best times to fertilize are in the spring of the year as the buds begin to swell and in the fall as the leaves drop. Spring applications provide the plants with nutrients when energy reserves are at their lowest. Nutrients applied in the fall are absorbed and stored until growth begins the following spring. Avoid fertilizer applications after mid-July as the nutrients encourage new growth at a time when the plants are naturally slowing in preparation for winter. Late season growth is soft and easily damaged by cold temperatures. Woody plants in need of fertilizers respond best if fertilized every three to four years.

Newly planted trees should not be given fertilizers. They are in the process of redeveloping their root systems. Soluble salts from the fertilizer can damage the young roots. It is recommended that only established landscape plants showing signs of stress receive fertilizer applications.

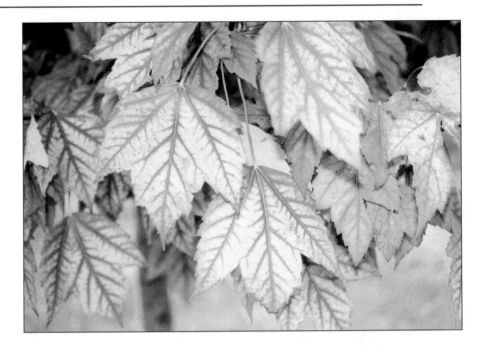

15-23. The leaves of this Red maple, *Acer rubrum*, show signs of chlorosis due to a micronutrient deficiency.

HOW TO FERTILIZE

One important key to fertilizing is to deliver the fertilizer to the root zone. The **root zone** is the area in which roots are growing. Most tree roots are found in the top 2 feet of soil and extend one and a half times the width of the tree. The majority of small feeder roots, on which a tree depends for absorption of nutrients and water, are located in the top 12 to 15 inches of soil. Up to 60 percent of these feeder roots are outside the drip line of the tree.

Fertilizer can be applied to woody landscape plants in several ways. Dry fertilizer can be placed in the root zone. Soluble fertilizer is injected into the root zone. Dry fertilizer is broadcast over the ground. Soluble fertilizer is sprayed onto the foliage. Solid fertilizer capsules are placed in the trunk of a tree.

Dry Fertilizer in Holes

TIP: One important key to fertilizing is to deliver the fertilizer to the root zone.

The method of using dry fertilizer involves placing dry fertilizer in the root zone of the plant. **Dry fertilizers** are most often sold in granular form. In this method, a series of holes 2 to 3 inches in diameter are made in the soil using an auger or punch bar. These holes are located under the drip line of the tree and 3 feet beyond the drip line. No holes are made closer than three feet to the trunk of the tree to avoid damaging major roots. The holes should be 2 feet apart and 12 to 15 inches deep. A large tree will require many holes so fertilizer is evenly distributed. The fertilizer is measured and placed in the holes. The holes are filled with water, then sealed with soil. This fertilizing method is time consuming and labor intensive.

The recommended amount of fertilizer depends on the size of the tree. Trees with diameters less than 6 inches should receive 5 pounds of 10-6-4 or 10-10-10 fertilizer for each inch. Trees larger than 6 inches in diameter should receive 10 pounds for each inch of diameter. These recommendations equal about 2 cups of fertilizer per hole.

Dry fertilizer is also available in the market as fertilizer spikes. **Fertilizer spikes** consist of hardened fertilizer. Nutrients are slowly released into the soil. The spikes are hammered into the soil around the tree to be fertilized. One advantage is they cut the labor of digging holes. However, they are difficult to place below the surface of the soil, and they tend to be expensive.

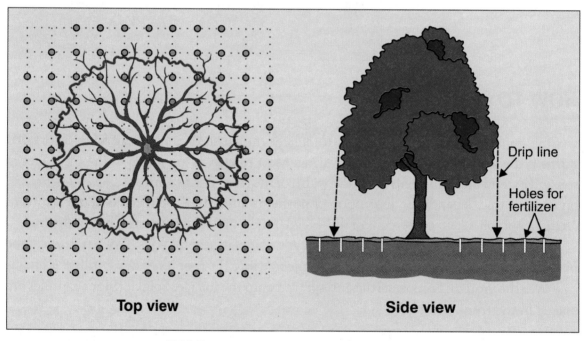

Top view   **Side view**

Drip line

Holes for fertilizer

15-24. Proper placement of holes for dry fertilizer.

Soluble Fertilizer Injections

Soluble fertilizers can be in pumped into the ground around woody plants. **Soluble fertilizers** dissolve readily in water. The soil needle is pushed into the ground. A hydraulic pump then forces the solution held in the tank through the needle into the root zone. A recommended rate of application calls for 30 pounds of 20-20-20 soluble fertilizer in 200 gallons of water. This method has advantages over dry fertilizers. The distribution of nutrients is more uniform, the nutrients are available to the plant immediately, the plant receives a good watering, and it requires less labor. Disadvantages are the equipment is relatively expensive, it can be difficult to push the needle into heavy clay soils, and soluble fertilizers leach or wash through the soil more quickly.

Broadcast of Fertilizer

Shrubs and ground cover plants are most often fertilized by broadcasting. **Broadcasting** involves the wide distribution of material on the surface of the soil. The fertilizer dissolves and slowly works its way into the soil. Two to four pounds of 5-10-10 or 10-10-10 fertilizer per 100 square feet is recommended. The fertilizer should be applied when the foliage is dry and then watered immediately.

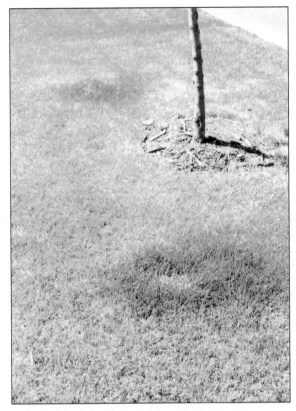

15-25. The owner of this tree used dry fertilizer spikes. They are shallow causing the death of grass above and rapid turf growth around the spike.

15-26. Shown is a soil needle used to inject soluble fertilizers into the root zone.

Soluble Fertilizers Sprayed onto Foliage

Foliage sprays using soluble fertilizers are effective when the leaves are young and during dry spells. The fertilizer nutrients are absorbed through the leaf tissues. Nutrients are quickly put to use in the leaves. Whereas, this method has some use with smaller landscape plants, it is impractical on the large scale.

Solid Fertilizer Implanted in Trunks

The method of inserting solid **fertilizer capsules** in the trunk of trees is primarily used for trees suffering from micronutrient deficiencies. Soil pH cannot be changed without damage to the roots, so the micronutrients are implanted in the tree. Holes are drilled in the trunk and the capsules are placed just under the bark. The nutrients dissolve in the sap and move up the tree. The major disadvantage of this method is it allows entry for disease and insect pests.

MULCHING

TIP: Mulch reduces water loss, prevents weed growth, and keeps soil temperatures uniform.

Mulching is the practice of spreading a material over the surface of the soil. Mulch reduces water loss, prevents weed growth, and keeps soil temperatures uniform. Quality mulches also contribute to an attractive landscape setting.

15-27. Mulching around trees helps prevent lawnmower damage to the trunk in addition to the other advantages discussed.

15-28. The crushed limestone mulch in this landscape is blinding and it raises the soil pH to levels harmful to plants. (Courtesy, University of Illinois Cooperative Extension Service)

In the case of organic mulches, the soil tilth can be improved as the mulch decays. The overall effect of mulches on landscape plants is very beneficial.

SELECTING MULCHES

There are two major types of mulches. ***Organic mulches*** originate from plant material. Examples include wood chips, shredded wood bark, pecan hulls, and pine needles. ***Inorganic mulches*** have their source from materials that never were living. Some inorganic mulches are marble stones, volcanic rock, and river gravel. The availability of mulches varies from one region of the country to another.

Select mulches carefully. Choose mulches that are easily obtained, easy to apply, and inexpensive. Also, it is best to use mulches that complement the site and region in which the landscape is

Table 15-1. Advantages and Disadvantages of Mulches

Advantages of Mulches
1. Suppress weed growth
2. Maintain uniform soil temperature
3. Increase water-holding capacity of sandy soils
4. Increase aeration of heavy clay soils
5. Prevent and reduce surface erosion and soil compaction
6. Improve soil tilth
7. Reduce evaporation of soil moisture
8. Create a desirable appearance
9. Promote root growth in the upper 2" of soil
10. Release nutrients for plant growth by increasing the breakdown of organic matter

Disadvantages of Mulches
1. Mulches cannot suppress large weeds
2. Some mulches are flammable
3. Rodents and insects may live or overwinter in mulch
4. Mulches may introduce certain plant diseases
5. Some mulches reduce nitrogen levels in the soil
6. Mulches encourage slug and snail populations
7. Mulches can prevent water from penetrating the soil
8. Mulches can be difficult to handle

located. Wood chips look natural in areas where woodlands are common. Wood chips look out of place in an arid region. For the same reason, volcanic rock appears at home in a rocky area or where volcanoes are found, not in a prairie or woodland area.

Because some mulches can change soil pH, they need to be used with caution. Crushed limestone or marble raises the pH of soil over time. This can be a particular problem if the soil pH is already high. Pine needles have the opposite effect. They are acid and lower soil pH.

APPLYING MULCHES

Before spreading mulch over the soil, many landscapers install landscape fabric (discussed in Chapter 10). The landscape fabric is helpful in reducing weed growth. Some landscapers apply the mulch directly over the soil. In each case, the mulch should be applied to a depth of 3 to 4 inches.

Table 15-2. Calculating Amounts of Mulch

CUBIC YARDS OF MULCH NEEDED	
Specified Depth	Multiply area to be covered (sq. ft.) by:
2"	.006
3"	.009
4"	.012

15-29. Spread mulch 3 to 4 inches deep.

Table 15-3. Mulches and Their Characteristics

Name	Positive	Negative	Uses
Cocoabean hulls	• attractive dark brown color • absorb solar heat and warm the soil	• develop mold when wet • light—may blow away	• in planting beds
Crushed corncobs	• good weed inhibitor • retains soil moisture	• reduces nitrogen level in soil • difficult for water to penetrate	• vegetable garden • annual and perennial flower beds
Decorative wood chips	• long lasting • available in various sizes	• may be expensive • not a good source of organic matter	• planting beds
Grass clippings	• readily available • source of nutrients for the soil	• form a mat • get moldy when wet • rot when spread thick	• vegetable gardens
Gravel chips, crushed stone	• permanent covering • dark colors absorb solar heat and warm the soil	• does not suppress weeds • expensive • heavy	• highlight landscape features
Leaves	• add essential nutrients to the soil • readily available	• some types pack flat • can become soggy	• perennial beds • vegetable gardens
Peanut hulls	• light weight • decompose quickly adding organic matter to the soil	• may develop mold when wet	• good mulch for tomato plants • annual and perennial flower beds
Pine needles	• light weight • weed free • easy to handle • absorb little moisture	• unattractive to worms • coarse in appearance	• good mulch for broadleaf evergreens
River gravel	• permanent cover • absorb solar heat and warm the soil • attractive appearance • available in different sizes	• expensive • does not suppress weeds • heavy	• highlight landscape features • planting beds
Shredded bark	• long lasting • allows moisture to penetrate	• can be stringy and difficult to handle	• planting beds

REVIEWING

MAIN IDEAS

Healthy plants are better able to defend themselves against disease and insect pests than plants weakened for one reason or another. Healthy plants also are more attractive and add value to the landscape appearance. Most woody landscape plants, if well established, require little care. Most plant care practices should be directed to newly installed plants and to plants under stress.

In determining care for woody plants, it helps to have an understanding of woody plant biology. The need for water and fertilizer is influenced by plant life cycles and the weather. In spring, when the leaves are developing and, in the fall, when roots are developing, plants have their lowest levels of energy reserves. Those plants under stress at these periods benefit from watering and fertilizer applications. Watering is also important at other times when drought conditions prevail.

Watering is one of three common treatments given to woody landscape plants to ensure good health. Before watering, determine if the soil is dry. If water is needed, soak the soil thoroughly. Soakings are recommended every two to three weeks during drought conditions. Watering methods include sprinkling, soaker hoses, watering bags, microirrigation systems, soil watering/feeding needles, and simply letting water trickle out of the end of a hose.

Fertilizer applications can give a plant a boost by providing nutrients. If needed, fertilize woody plants in the spring as the leaves unfold or in the fall when the plant goes dormant. Methods of fertilizing woody plants include dry fertilizer placed in the root zone, soluble fertilizer injected into the root zone, dry fertilizer broadcast over the ground, soluble fertilizer sprayed onto foliage, and solid fertilizer capsules placed in the trunk of a tree.

Mulching is a third practice beneficial to woody landscape plants. Mulches reduce water loss, prevent weed growth, keep soil temperatures uniform, improve soil tilth, and contribute to an attractive landscape setting. Organic mulches originating from living material and inorganic mulches with origins from nonliving material are used. When selecting mulch, choose one that appears native to the area in which the house is located.

QUESTIONS

Answer the following questions using correct spelling and complete sentences.

1. Why is it important to maintain healthy landscape plants?

2. How does the biology of woody plant materials influence plant care?

3. What role does stress play in plant health?

4. When are the energy reserves the lowest in the life cycles of woody plants?

5. What factors affect watering practices?

6. What methods are used to water woody landscape plants?

7. When is fertilizer beneficial to woody plants?

8. What are the major methods of fertilizing woody plants?

9. Why are mulches beneficial to plants?

10. How should mulches be applied?

CHAPTER SELF-CHECK

Match the term with the correct definition. Write the letter by the term in the blank provided.

a. wilting
b. desiccation
c. soaker hose
d. microirrigation
e. chlorosis
f. respiration
g. soluble fertilizer
h. organic mulch
i. soil watering needle
j. mulching

_____1. A yellowing of the leaves caused by the absence of chlorophyll

_____2. The drooping of a plant due to a lack of firmness in the plant tissues

_____3. Originate from plant material

_____4. The chemical process in which cells convert sugars into energy

_____5. Made of rubber, oozes water

_____6. Water loss from tissues resulting in tissue death

_____7. The practice of spreading a material over the surface of the soil

_____8. Supply water directly to the root zone of the plants

_____9. Emitters and tubing deliver the prescribed amount of water to each plant

_____10. Dissolve readily in water before use

EXPLORING

1. Volunteer to care for the woody plants in your yard, a relative's yard, or a neighbor's yard. Apply the knowledge you learned in this chapter to plants in the landscape.

2. Observe your neighborhood. Do any of the landscape plants you see show signs of stress? Based on what you have learned, would water or fertilizer applications help to relieve the stress? Prepare a report on your observations. You may use a digital camera and use it to prepare images for an electronic visual presentation.

3. Make plant care a part of your supervised experience. Keep records of the time devoted to plant care and/or the income earned. Use these experiences to advance in FFA degrees of membership.

Pruning Woody Landscape Plants

TERMS

arboriculture
arborist
branch bark ridge
callus
candle stage
chain saw
collar
compartmentalization
dead zone
drop-crotch pruning
hand pruner

heading back
heading cut
hedge shear
leader
loppers
pruning
pruning saw
rejuvenation pruning
renewal pruning
rootstock
scaffold branch

scion
shearing
subordination
sucker
thinning cut
U-shaped crotch
urban forester
V-shaped crotch
watersprout

16-1. Pruning can play a major role in the health and beauty of a plant, such as the tree shown here.

A LARGE limb splits from a tree and smashes a brand new car parked in the driveway underneath. The vigorous growth of shrubs out over a paved walk force people to walk on the grass. One spring, white flowers appear on a pink flowering dogwood. These occurrences have happened. They are also undesirable. Each of these situations could have been avoided with proper pruning.

Pruning is a major landscape maintenance activity. Landscapers must be well trained in approved techniques in order to prune woody landscape plants properly. The why, what, when, and how of pruning woody landscape plants is the subject of this chapter.

WHY PRUNE?

Maintenance of woody ornamental plants in the landscape involves pruning. **Pruning** is the term used for the selective removal or reduction of certain plant parts. Pruning practices range from the removal of huge tree limbs to pinching off growing tips. Proper pruning contributes to maintaining the desired appearance of ornamental plants. Improper pruning techniques can produce unsightly plants. It can also cause injury to the plant.

It helps to first identify and understand the reasons for pruning. There are multiple reasons for pruning woody plants. Some of those include:

16-2. Damage to this Silver Maple, *Acer saccharinum*, caused by a weak framework of branches could have been avoided with proper pruning.

- Developing a strong framework of branches that resist breakage and provide an attractive appearance

- Restricting the size of the plant, often necessary when plant materials are selected without regard to the plants' mature size

- Repairing damaged limbs

- Improving flowering of trees and shrubs

- Removing diseased or insect infested limbs, thereby reducing spread of the pest

- Directing growth

- Maintaining desired cultivars

- Opening the crown to allow light and wind to pass

- Maintaining safe conditions for humans

- Improve quality of fruit on fruiting trees, shrubs, and vines

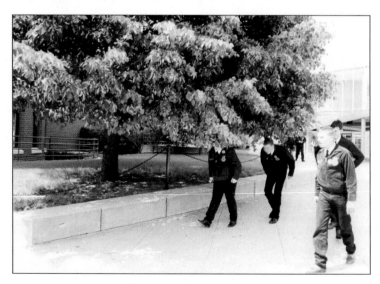

16-3. Pruning of this Littleleaf Linden, *Tilia cordata*, would make pedestrian traffic easier and safer.

HOW TO PRUNE TREES

Before any cuts are made, ask, why should I prune this plant? Then, be sure your cuts contribute to the pruning goals you have established. Always consider the results of the cuts before the cuts are made. View the structure of the plant from a distance before any cuts are made. Between cuts, step away from the plant to see if the desired growth pattern of the plant is being maintained.

TIP: The best time to start pruning trees is when they are young.

Different types of woody landscape plants respond to different methods of pruning. However, some rules apply to all materials:

1. Make cuts that cause the least amount of damage to the plant.

2. Begin pruning practices when the plant is young.

3. In most cases, prune after the plant has flowered.

4. Safely use sharp tools suitable for the job.

BRANCHING FRAMEWORK

The best time to start pruning trees is when they are young. A strong, well-balanced branching structure can be developed at a young stage of growth. Well-balanced trees have a single, strong

16-4. This Littleleaf Linden, *Tilia cordata*, has a strong leader.

16-5. The limbs on this American Sycamore, *Platanus occidentalis*, have U-shaped crotches and thus, are very strong.

16-6. Co-leaders on this Sugar Maple, *Acer saccharum,* have formed a weak V-shaped union. Disease has entered the tree at the union.

leader. A *leader* is a central branch that dominates over other branches on the tree. It leads the growth of the tree. Sometimes, trees develop co-leaders. These are not attractive and they usually result in weak V-shaped crotches.

Subordination can be used to develop a strong leader. *Subordination* involves cuts made that slow the growth of a branch. Removing lateral branches and/or reducing the length of the parent branch cause the branch to become subordinate or less dominant.

Subordination is used with all size trees, but is perhaps most useful in situations that involve multiple leaders on a small tree. Trees with multiple leaders are prone to structural problems as they age. The solution is to identify the best of the leaders and prune the others. The pruned branches will grow more slowly than the un-cut branch selected to be the leader. The un-cut branch will emerge as the dominant leader, while the others will become major limbs of the tree.

Secondary branches, or *scaffold branches*, grow laterally from the trunk. The greatest weakness of a tree's branching structure occurs at the point of attachment of scaffold branches. Branches that exhibit a 45- to 90-degree angle of attachment, or a *U-shaped crotch*,

16-7. The dark included bark is visible on this Norway maple, *Acer platinoides*. Allowed to develop the limb became a safety hazard and split in calm weather.

are structurally strong. Where the angle of attachment is sharp and a **V-shaped crotch** develops, the joint is weak. This is because the bark is crushed between the branches as the tree grows and expands. The bark becomes included, and the branches do not fuse. Trees with V-shaped crotches are prone to split from the force of wind or the weight of ice and snow. Prune limbs that show V-shaped crotches while the tree is young.

Watersprouts and Suckers

Remove watersprouts that detract from the appearance of the tree. **Watersprouts** are soft, green shoots that typically grow vertically from existing branches. They seldom flower. Watersprouts often occur following severe pruning. A common result of watersprout growth is crossing branches.

Suckers are soft, green shoots that develop at the base of the tree. Watersprouts and suckers offer no ornamental value. If allowed to grow they create an unsightly appearance. Removal of

16-8. A comparison of U-shaped (left) and V-shaped (right) crotches.

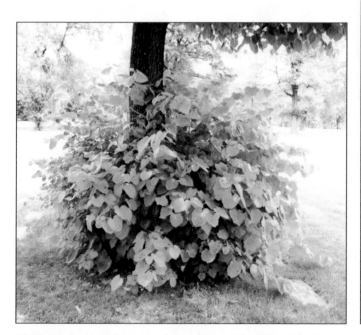

16-10. Suckers are fast-growing shoots originating at the base of a plant. Shown is an American Linden, *Tilia americana*.

16-9. Watersprouts are fast-growing vertical shoots that sprout from branches.

16-11. This photograph shows a graft union. Suckers from the rootstock should be removed if they sprout.

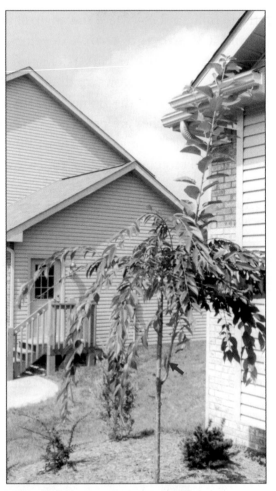

16-12. The vertical shoot below the graft union of this weeping flowering cherry, *Prunus subhirtella 'Pendula'*, should be removed as it detracts from the ornamental value of the tree.

suckers is particularly important when a cultivar is being grown. Cultivars are propagated by grafting. The grafting process involves the union of a **scion**, or top growth, to a **rootstock**, or root system. The rootstock of the plant does not have the same qualities as the scion. If suckers from the rootstock are allowed to grow, they will interfere with the desired ornamental effect of the scion. Some plants that exhibit this problem are flowering crabapples, cherries, and flowering dogwoods.

Crossing Branches

Study the branching structure to determine if branches are crossing one another. Crossing branches are unattractive. More important, the friction of limbs rubbing on one another may open wounds. These wounds allow entry of disease and insect pests. Regular removal of branches growing back toward the center of the tree eliminates most crossing branches. It is best to look for these when the tree is young. On trees where the crossing branches have grown large, remove the less important of the two branches.

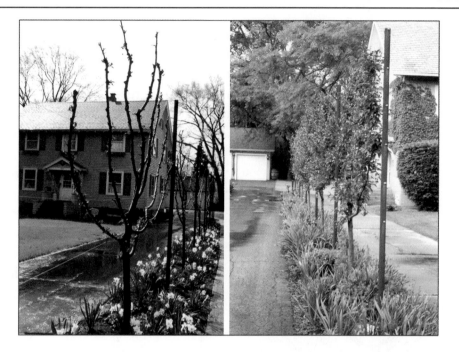

16-13. These crabapples have been pruned and trained to serve as a narrow screen between two driveways. The photos are taken at the same location from different angles and different times of the year.

Diseased or Dead Wood

Look for and remove dead or diseased wood from the tree. The same recommendation goes for broken branches. Dead wood left in the tree prevents the tree from healing. Dead wood and broken branches can also be safety hazards to those underneath. Cutting out diseased wood removes a source of disease that could spread to other limbs or other trees.

Pruning Newly Transplanted Trees

Transplanting places new trees under tremendous stress. This is particularly true with balled and burlapped trees that have lost a great majority of their roots in the digging process. Some trees never recover and die. The key to survival is the tree's ability to develop a new root system. Energy is required to regenerate new roots. The energy is in the form of sugar produced in the leaves of a tree. Some energy is also stored in the branches of a tree

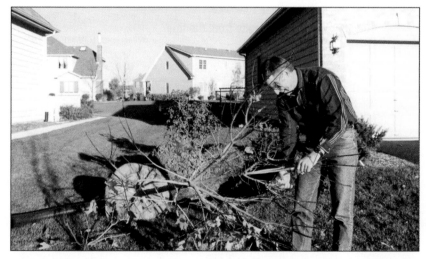

16-14. Limit pruning to dead wood, diseased wood, and co-leaders when a tree is first planted.

TIP: When pruning trees, never remove more than one-third of the crown.

as starch. When needed, it is converted back to sugar for the production of roots. Severe pruning of the crown at the time of planting adds to the stress. Removing limbs means the loss of energy-producing leaves and stored starches. Because the root development hinges on the production of sugars, it is best to remove as little of the crown as possible at the time of planting and for the first year after planting.

Removal of over 15 percent of the crown at the time of transplanting slows tree growth for several years. Concentrate on removing only the limbs that call for the most urgent attention. Co-dominant leaders, dead wood, diseased wood, and V-shaped crotches should be removed or corrected at the time of transplanting. This ensures that as many leaves as possible are left on the tree to produce energy.

Two to four years after planting, prune the tree again. During this second pruning, remove crossing branches, limbs that have died back, and some of the lower branches. Avoid removing all the lower branches. Removal of the lower branches over a longer period contributes to the development of a strong, healthy trunk. Choose to keep branches that will develop with U-shaped crotches.

Prune the tree again five to seven years after planting. The amount to prune at this time is minimal. Remove the remainder of the unwanted lower limbs. Also, remove dead wood, crossing branches, suckers, and watersprouts.

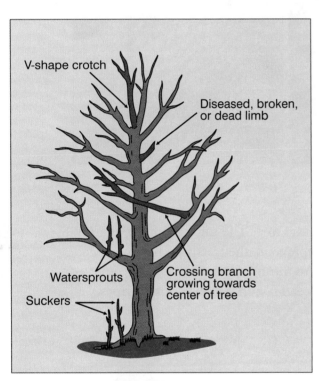

16-15. Prune obvious faults from the tree.

Labels on figure: V-shape crotch; Diseased, broken, or dead limb; Watersprouts; Suckers; Crossing branch growing towards center of tree

Compartmentalization

Trees can close their wounds. It is not the way our wounds heal, such as when we skin a knee. Rather, trees produce chemicals that inhibit decay caused by fungi and bacteria. The wound is sealed by these chemicals. This formation of a chemical barrier is called **compartmentalization**.

The concept of compartmentalization is fairly simple. When a tree is injured, all the wood present at the time of the injury could become subject to decay. Wood produced after the injury is walled off from infection by the tree's defensive chemicals. The new wood is protected from decay by the chemical barrier.

A good example of compartmentalization involves a hollow tree. At some time, wood-rotting fungi found entrance through a wound. Perhaps a branch broke in a storm. The wood present at the time of the injury became subject to fungal decay. Wood formed after the injury was protected by the tree's defenses. As the decay advanced, the old wood rotted, but the new wood was disease free. The new wood remained to provide support for the tree.

At the base of every branch there is a branch bark ridge and a collar. The **branch bark ridge** is a raised line of bark that forms on the upper side of where the branch joins the trunk. The **collar** is swollen trunk tissue surrounding the base of the branch. These structures have the ability to manufacture chemicals that inhibit the spread of decay in the trunk. In nature, decay that has entered a branch spreads until it reaches the chemical zone at the base of the branch. The branch eventually falls off the tree. Then, the tree forms a **callus**, or protective growth of tissue, over the wound. It is important to recognize this natural defense mechanism. Never remove the branch bark ridge and the collar during pruning because those are the tissues that defend the tree from infection and decay.

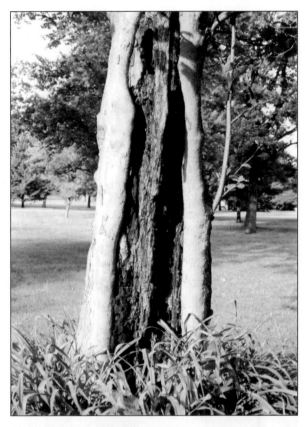

16-16. Decay has been compartmentalized in this American Sycamore, *Platanus occidentalis*.

The physical closure of the wound with callus protects the tree from disease and insect infestation. As the callus grows, it slowly covers the wound. The rate of this growth depends on the tree species, the energy reserves of the tree, and the wound itself. The threat of disease and insect infestation is reduced with the closure of the wound. Knowledge of how trees close a wound can be applied to pruning practices. Remove limbs in a way that will help the tree mend itself.

TIP: Never remove the branch bark ridge and the collar during pruning since those are the tissues that defend the tree from infection and decay.

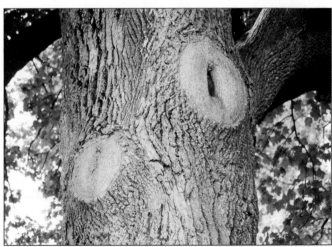

16-17. Callus tissue forms over these old wounds.

WHICH PRUNING CUT TO USE

There are three basic types of cuts used when pruning trees. They include drop-crotch cuts, thinning cuts, and heading cuts.

Drop-Crotch Cuts

The **drop-crotch pruning** method is effectively used to shorten tree limbs and to reduce the size of a tree. Drop-crotch pruning is a good way to direct the growth of a tree. It is commonly used to develop a good framework of branches in young trees. Drop-crotch cuts are the only accepted pruning technique for reducing the height or width of a tree.

Drop-crotch pruning involves cutting the leader limb back to a lateral branch. The lateral branch just below the cut should be at least one-third the diameter of the leader. This means that the branch remaining after the cut is smaller in diameter than the one removed. Drop-crotch pruning effectively reduces the length of the limb while maintaining a natural appearance to the tree. The tree can also seal off the wound that is created from the cut.

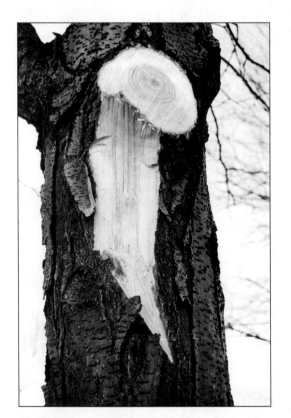

16-18. An improperly pruned limb has stripped bark from the tree.

Thinning Cuts

A **thinning cut** is a cut that removes a branch from the parent stem or trunk. Thinning cuts do not reduce the size of a tree. Rather, they are used to open up the canopy to more light. This pruning method is most commonly used with mature trees.

Heading Cuts

Heading cuts are cuts made between nodes on the stem to promote branching or to direct growth. Heading cuts are often used in nursery situations with young trees. Because the stems are small in diameter, the tree compartmentalizes them quickly. Heading cuts should be restricted to one- to two-year old branches. Heading of large diameter wood causes decay of the wood.

Removing Large Limbs

Safety is the number one consideration in pruning large limbs. The weight of large limbs ranges from hundreds to thousands of pounds. That same weight, which can injure the person pruning the branch, can also damage the tree if not removed properly. Improper removal of large limbs leaves wounds that close slowly, giving more time for diseases and insects to enter the tree.

Safe removal of large limbs is done with a series of cuts. Heavy limbs have a tendency to strip bark from the trunk as they fall. To avoid stripping of bark, remove the bulk of the limb before making the final cut. First, make an undercut about one-third of the way through the limb, 1 foot away from the trunk. Second, cut the upper side of the limb about 1 inch from the undercut. If this upper cut is closer to the tree than the undercut, the branch will swing toward the tree before it drops. If the upper cut is outside the undercut, the branch drops straight down. The third and final cut involves the removal of the remaining stub. It is advisable to make an undercut before the final removal if the stub is large.

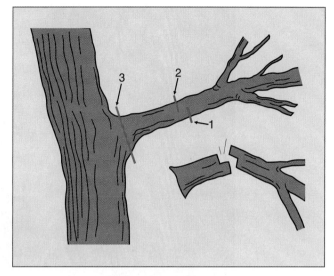

16-19. Use three cuts to remove most limbs.

In making the final cut, the landscaper is left with three choices. The final cut can be flush with the trunk, thus removing the collar and branch bark ridge. It can be made to leave a stub vulnerable to diseases and insects. Or the proper cut can be made. The proper cut is one made as close to the collar and branch bark ridge as possible without causing damage to those tissues. A well-made cut in time will display a doughnut shape growth of callus tissue.

After the final cut is made, leave the wound exposed. For many years, the popular belief was the wound should be sealed with tar, asphalt pruning paint, or shellac. They are not needed.

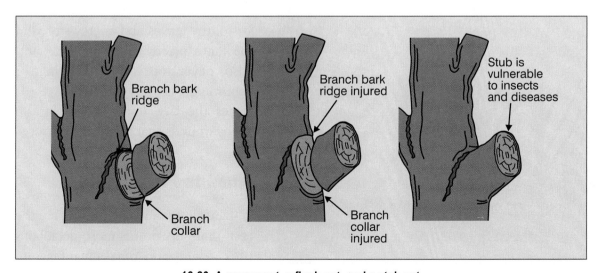

16-20. A proper cut, a flush cut, and a stub cut.

16-21. The proper cut keeps the branch bark ridge and collar intact. Note the wound is not sealed.

16-22. This well-made cut in time will display a doughnut shape growth of callus tissue. (Courtesy, Hendricksen the Care of Trees)

Studies have shown that sealers can actually promote decay by keeping the wounds moist. Moist conditions favor bacteria and fungi growth.

16-23. Topping of trees is both unsightly and unhealthy.

When pruning trees, never remove more than one-third of the crown. The loss of the leaves and energy stored in the limbs places stress on the plant. Also, never top a tree. Topping, or dehorning, is very unattractive. It places the tree under stress. It also opens wounds that might never close.

When to Prune Trees

Late winter and early spring are the best times to prune most deciduous trees. There are some advantages to pruning trees when they are dormant.

It is much easier to see the branching structure of a tree when the leaves are absent. The limbs are much lighter without the leaves. Also, cuts made in late winter or early spring have a full growing season in which to heal. A disadvantage is it is more difficult to identify dead or diseased branches when the tree is dormant.

Some trees respond best to pruning when the plant is actively growing. Maples, birches, elms, and dogwoods ooze sap from wounds if they are pruned in late winter or early spring. Although the sap is unsightly, it causes no damage to the tree. Prune these plants in midsummer when the sap is not flowing. The time of year when ornamental trees flower is another factor to consider before pruning. Trees that flower in the spring formed their flower buds the previous fall. Pruning in late winter or early spring removes the flower buds with the limbs. Therefore, it is best to prune a tree, such as a Flowering Dogwood, *Cornus florida*, after it has finished flowering in the spring so the flowers can be fully appreciated.

Tree Specialists

Removal of large limbs or entire trees requires care not only from a safety standpoint, but for the health of the tree. Professional tree care specialists, **arborists**, are the best qualified to tackle difficult pruning jobs. Arborists are trained in the culture of trees, **arboriculture**. Training in arboriculture includes plant identification, identification and diagnosis of tree diseases and pests, prescription of treatments, and safe removal of trees and tree limbs. A related profession is that of a forester. The type of forester who works with ornamental trees in city settings is an **urban forester**. The demand for urban foresters has increased as city populations have grown and inhabitants call for city greening.

16-24. Late winter or early spring is the best time to prune most trees.

16-25. Arborists are often called upon to remove large trees.

HOW TO PRUNE DECIDUOUS SHRUBS

16-26. Urban foresters are shown pruning dead wood and directing tree growth away from utility

Proper pruning of shrubs in the landscape ensures many years of pleasure. Pruning helps keep shrubs vigorous and ornamental. Keep a few general rules in mind when pruning deciduous shrubs. In most cases, prune shrubs after they have flowered. Learn the shrub's natural habit of growth, its mature size, when it flowers, and on which year's growth flower buds are formed. Also, start pruning practices while the plant is young to develop a strong framework of branches. Several pruning techniques are used to prune deciduous shrubs. They are renewal pruning, rejuvenation, heading back, and shearing.

TIP: In most cases, prune shrubs after they have flowered.

RENEWAL PRUNING

Renewal pruning is defined as the selective removal of older plant stems. By removing the older stems, new growth is encouraged, the plant size is maintained, and flowering is promoted. Cut the stems at ground level. Always choose which stems are to be cut carefully. This will help to ensure the natural shape of the plant is maintained. Annual spring pruning continues a steady production of new shoots. Some shrubs that respond well to renewal pruning are:

Lilac (*Syringa* species)
Lemoine Deutzia (*Deutzia x lemoinei*)
Mockorange (*Philadelphus* species)
Weigela (*Weigela* species)
Forsythias (*Forsythia* species)
Arrowwood Viburnum (*Viburnum dentatum*)
St. Johnswort (*Hypericum* species)
Redosier Dogwood (*Cornus stolonifera*)

REJUVENATION PRUNING

Rejuvenation pruning is a method of pruning deciduous shrubs that involves the complete removal of all the stems to 4 to 6 inch stubs. The best time to prune a shrub in this manner is in late winter or early spring. Energy stored in the root system produces new stems in the spring. Shrubs that respond well to rejuvenation pruning include:

> Anthony Waterer Spirea (*Spirea x bumaldi* 'Anthony Waterer')
> Glossy Abelia (*Abelia x grandiflora*)
> Honeysuckle (*Lonicera* species)
> Beautybush (*Kolkwitzia amabilis*)
> Privet (*Ligustrum* species)
> Slender Deutzia (*Deutzia gracilis*)

HEADING BACK

Heading back involves the shortening of individual stems using heading cuts. Reasons for heading back are to remove dead or diseased wood and to restrict the size of the

16-27. Renewal pruning is the selective removal of older plant stems.

16-28. Rejuvenation pruning involves the complete removal of all the stems to 4 to 6 inch stubs.

16-29. This Dwarf Winged Euonymus, *Euonymus alatus* 'Compactus', is sprouting after rejuvenation pruning.

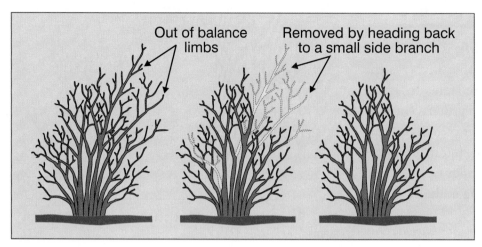

16-30. Heading back involves cuts made back to the parent stem rather than to the ground.

stem. Cuts are made back to the parent stem rather than to the ground, as is the practice with renewal pruning.

SHEARING

The practice of shearing shrubs should be reserved for clipped hedges and formal gardens. **Shearing** effectively reduces the total leaf surface a plant has to produce energy. As a result, the plant is placed under stress. From an ornamental standpoint, individual shrubs pruned tightly into geometric shapes draw the attention of the viewer. In the public area, the unnatural shapes divert attention from the house.

If a hedge is desired, shear the shrubs to be wider at the base than at the top. This allows light to reach all the leaves. Hedges pruned wider or the same width at the top as the bottom

16-31. Shear hedges to be wider at the base than at the top to allow light to reach all the leaves.

16-32. This yew (*Taxus x media* 'Hicksii') hedge is sheared wider at the base to maintain leaf growth to the ground.

tend to have open growth at the bottom. This is because thick leaf growth occurs only when sufficient light is provided. It is also advisable to allow the hedge to grow slightly each year to maintain a good coverage of new leaves. A few plants that make good hedges are privet (*Ligustrum* species), honeysuckle (*Lonicera* species), spirea (*Spirea* species), and Alpine currant (*Ribes alpinum*).

HOW TO PRUNE EVERGREEN SHRUBS

Different evergreens respond to different pruning methods. When to prune evergreens also varies with the species.

Arborvitae—These evergreens are easily maintained by heading back limbs with hand-held pruners. Prune arborvitae in the spring. Avoid severe pruning that exposes the dead zone. The **dead zone** is the region in the center of the plant that, when exposed to light, seldom produces new shoots.

Firs—Annual pruning in early summer, to shorten the leader and lateral shoots, promotes dense growth. Severe pruning of shoots back to three-year-old wood is tolerated.

Junipers—It is best to prune junipers using the heading back method in spring. Be careful not to cut into the dead zone of the plant as junipers do not produce new growth on old wood. It is important to start a pruning program while the plants are young to avoid overgrown situations that cannot be corrected.

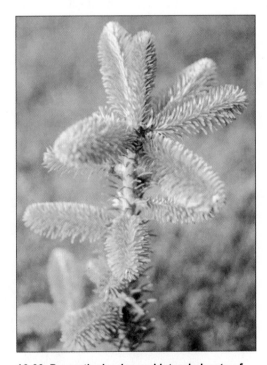

16-33. Prune the leader and lateral shoots of firs in early summer to produce dense growth. Shown is Fraser Fir, *Abies fraseri*.

16-34. Prune junipers using the heading back method in spring.

16-35. This juniper was pruned to expose the dead zone. It will not produce dense green growth again.

Pines—Prune pines when they are in the **candle stage** of growth. New growth on pines resembles candles. Cut the terminal candles leaving 8 to 12 inch stubs. Prune lateral candles to be 2 to 4 inches shorter than the terminal candles. Pines do not respond well to heavy pruning into old wood.

Spruce—Light pruning in early summer is best. Cut leaders leaving at least three buds on the remaining stub. Lateral shoots must be 1 to 2 inches shorter than the leader.

Yews—Yews respond very well to pruning. This characteristic makes yews a popular choice for clipped hedges. Prune yews in spring and again in early summer. The technique most often used is heading back. Yews also tolerate severe pruning, even when up to 50 percent of the plant is removed.

Terminal cut
8- to 12-inches

2- to 4-inches
shorter than
terminal cut

16-36. Prune pines to create a thick, compact appearance.

16-37. A scissors-style hand pruner is used to prune pines in the candle stage.

16-38. Yews respond very well to shearing.

BROADLEAF EVERGREENS

Broadleaf evergreens, such as rhododendron (*Rhododendron* species), holly (*Ilex* species), boxwood (*Buxus* species), and Japanese skimmia (*Skimmia japonica*), require very little pruning. Light heading back is recommended to maintain dense plants. Prune rhododendrons after they have flowered. Remove faded flowers and pinch back new growth. Boxwood, holly, and skimmia are used as clipped hedges. They tolerate shearing.

16-39. Remove faded flowers and pinch back new growth on rhododendrons to maintain dense growth.

PRUNING TOOLS

16-40. Scissors-style hand pruner (lower left), hedge shear (upper left), and a loppers (right).

There are a number of tools used for pruning purposes. For small branches, a **hand pruner** or a **lopper** will be sufficient. There are two styles of hand pruners and loppers. The scissors style is the recommended style as they slice the stem. The anvil design is less effective as it crushes the stem as it cuts. Larger limbs may require the use of a pruning saw or a chain saw. **Pruning saws** have large teeth with wider spacing than carpenter's saws. The large teeth ease the cutting effort and speed the cut. **Chain saws** are gas powered or electric and have a continuous cutting chain. They are extremely dangerous if used improperly. Pole saws and pole pruners are specialty tools with long handles that allow the person to reach high limbs from the ground. **Hedge shears** may be hand operated, electric, or gas powered clippers used to trim hedges and shape shrubs in formal gardens.

Keep safety in mind when selecting and using pruning tools. Select tools that are sharp. Sharp tools are easier to use, safer, and leave a smooth cut. Determine the cut to be made. Then, pick the tool that will do the job with the least amount of effort. For instance, a hand pruner is appropriate for removing small branches, but is a poor selection for the removal of a 2-inch limb. When using

TIP: Keep safety in mind when selecting and using pruning tools.

16-41. A pruning saw.

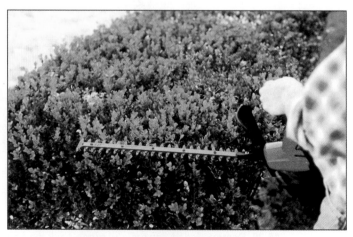

16-42. An electric-powered hedge shear.

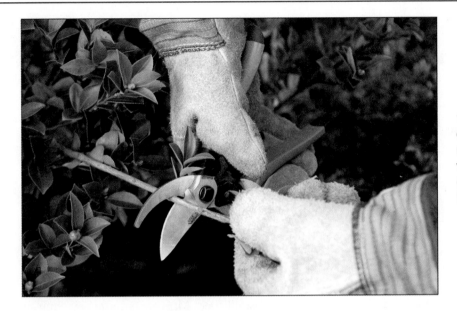

16-43. Proper and safe use of a hand pruner is needed to gain a good cut when pruning a shrub. (Courtesy, Education Images, Inc.).

power tools, wear goggles to protect your eyes. Hard hats and ear plugs are additional safety precautions to employ when operating a chain saw.

Pruning tree branches with a chain saw requires careful thought and constant attention. Determine which branches need to be removed and follow these guidelines:

- Study each branch before cutting.

- Accelerate the saw before you start cutting.

- Move your feet only when the chain completely stops turning.

- Do not cut with the upper tip of the guide bar.

- If the saw blade becomes pinched, shut the saw off before removing it.

It is recommended that individuals receive training from a well-qualified instructor on the safe use of chain saws before putting those skills to practice.

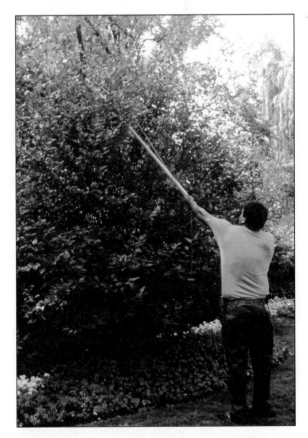

16-44. This person is using a pole pruner to trim a tree. (Courtesy, Illinois Landscape Contractors Association)

REVIEWING

MAIN IDEAS

Pruning is the selective removal or reduction of certain plant parts. It is a practice used in landscape maintenance of woody plants. Proper pruning promotes healthy and attractive growth. There are many reasons to prune landscape plants. Pruning is done to develop a strong framework of branches, restrict growth, direct growth, repair damage, remove disease, improve flowering, and provide a safe landscape.

Begin pruning trees while they are young to develop a strong branching structure. Identify certain faults when pruning trees. Establish a strong leader if more than one is evident. Prune diseased or dead wood. Remove crossing branches, watersprouts, and suckers. Consider the removal of limbs with V-shaped crotches as they are weak and prone to splitting. U-shaped crotches are much stronger. Perform a limited amount of pruning on newly transplanted trees. New trees need as many leaves as possible to produce food that will help the tree become established. Most trees can receive minor pruning throughout the year, but the best time is late winter or early spring.

Deciduous shrubs are pruned several ways. One method, known as renewal pruning, involves the removal of the older stems at ground level. Renewal pruning encourages new growth, maintains the plant size, and promotes flowering. Rejuvenation pruning is a method in which all the stems are cut to 4 to 6 inch stubs. New shoots develop the following growing season. A third method is heading back. Heading back is the reduction of stems back to the parent stem. A fourth alternative is shearing. Shearing is used for formal hedges. Different shrub species respond differently to various pruning methods.

Evergreen woody plants usually do not require a great deal of pruning. It is important to know that various evergreens respond to different pruning methods. The best time of the year to prune evergreens also varies with the species. Broadleaf evergreens also require little pruning. Heading back is the most common method of pruning broadleaf evergreens.

Select the proper tool for the pruning job. The selection of tools includes hand pruners, loppers, hand saws, chain saws, pole pruners, pole saws, and hedge shears. Choose the tool that requires the least amount of effort, yet makes a clean cut. Sharp tools are safer, easier to use, and leave a smoother cut than dull tools.

QUESTIONS

Answer the following questions using correct spelling and complete sentences.

1. Why are woody landscape plants pruned?
2. What are some general rules that apply to all materials pruned?
3. How do watersprouts, suckers, and crossing branches differ?
4. What faults should be addressed first when pruning trees?
5. What special attention do newly transplanted trees require? Why?
6. How are large limbs removed safely?

7. How does a tree defend itself from decay and heal its wounds?

8. When is the best time to prune deciduous trees? Why?

9. What are the major methods of pruning deciduous shrubs? Explain each.

10. What tools are used for pruning woody landscape plants?

CHAPTER SELF-CHECK

Match the term with the correct definition. Write the letter by the term in the blank provided.

a. compartmentalization
b. rejuvenation
c. dead zone
d. V-shape crotch
e. collar
f. sucker
g. leader
h. watersprout
i. arboriculture
j. heading back

_____ 1. Swollen trunk tissue surrounding the base of the branch

_____ 2. Soft, green shoots that develop at the base of the tree

_____ 3. A central branch that dominates over other branches on the tree

_____ 4. The culture of trees

_____ 5. Involves the shortening of individual stems

_____ 6. Soft, green shoots that grow vertically from existing branches

_____ 7. A weak attachment of the branch to the trunk due to the sharp angle

_____ 8. The region in the center of an evergreen plant that when exposed to light seldom produces new shoots

_____ 9. A wound sealed off from decay by a chemical barrier

_____ 10. Method of pruning deciduous shrubs involving the complete removal of all stems to 4- to 6-inch stems

EXPLORING

1. Take a walk in the neighborhood. Look for woody landscape plants that have been pruned. Decide for yourself based on what you learned in this chapter if proper pruning was practiced. Are you surprised with what you found? Did you see plants in need of pruning?

2. Visit a local arborist or urban forester. Find out what they like about their job. What are some challenges they have experienced while pruning trees?

3. Volunteer to prune the plants in your yard, in a neighbor's yard, or for a relative. Identify the plants to be pruned and determine the best time and method of pruning. Be sure to perform your work with direction from an individual who is well qualified in plant pruning.

CHAPTER 17

Maintaining Turfgrass Areas

OBJECTIVES

1 Describe turf fertilization.

2 Describe mowing practices with turf.

3 Identify and describe turf maintenance practices, including irrigation, dethatching, aerating, and rolling.

4 Explain weed management practices.

5 Explain turf disease management practices.

TERMS

aerifier
environmental stress
fertilizer analysis
herbicide
nutrient ratio

photosynthesis
postemergence
preemergence
rhizome
soil pH

stolon
thatch
tines
turfgrass maintenance

17-1. Careful management has eliminated weeds from the private area of this landscape. (Courtesy, Jasper S. Lee)

DOES the turf in a lawn, athletic field, or other location have a vibrant green color and appear to be healthy? It should have these qualities. If not, the turf is suffering from the lack of appropriate care. Once an appropriate turf species has been established, proper fertilization, watering, and pest management will yield big results in terms of appearance.

Turf maintenance involves using appropriate grass management practices to maintain an attractive and healthy turfgrass. These management practices will keep the turf at the desired level of quality. It is common to find that some managers either skip or apply these practices at the wrong time of the year. Good turfgrass management techniques and practices are presented in this chapter.

FERTILIZING TURFGRASS

Proper fertilization is essential in turfgrass maintenance. Turfgrass maintenance is keeping a stand of turfgrass in an attractive and healthy condition. This maintenance involves using appropriate turfgrass management practices to keep the turf at the desired level of quality.

SOIL AND NUTRIENTS

Plants must have certain nutrients to grow. Soil testing should be used to determine the soil pH and any nutrient deficiencies. Fertilizer, agricultural lime, sulfur, and other materials may be required to improve the soil for the needs of the turf plants.

Soil pH is a measure of the amount of alkalinity or acidity in the soil. It is based on the hydrogen ion concentration in the soil. Chemists use a 14-point scale to explain pH. A pH above 7.0 indicates that the soil is alkaline or basic. Most soils have a pH range between 4.0 and 8.5. Soil with a pH below 7.0 is acidic. Most turfgrass plants grow best when the soil pH is between 6.0 and 7.0, or slightly acidic.

Changing the soil pH is best done at the time the new lawn is established. It is very difficult to adjust the pH up or down after turfgrass is growing. A more complete discussion on soil pH is contained in Chapter 9. Fertilizer applied to established turf in the spring and fall will encourage good turfgrass growth. Additional applications may be needed throughout

17-2. A soil sample is being placed in a bag for sending to a lab for analysis. (Courtesy, Education Images, Inc.)

17-3. Sports turf requires more frequent fertilizer applications each year to keep the grass plants vigorous.

the growing season to help the grass plants survive stress and recover from disease and insect damage.

Sports turf, such as ball fields and golf courses, will naturally require more frequent fertilizer applications to keep the grass plants vigorous and to help them recover from damage. Turf plants are better able to survive hot summer weather if they have sufficient nutrients. Most turfgrass plants will grow best when they receive regular nitrogen, phosphorus, and potassium fertilizer applications. Today nitrogen, phosphorus, and potassium are commonly called the big-3 in the turf industry.

Grass plants use more nitrogen than any other nutrient. Nitrogen not only stimulates shoot and root growth but it also is a major component in the chlorophyll molecule. Chlorophyll molecules are at the heart of photosynthesis and also give grass leaves their dark green color. **Photosynthesis** is the process that green plants use to convert light energy into chemical energy. Plants combine carbon dioxide and water, in the presence of chlorophyll, into sugar and oxygen molecules. If the turf has a yellow-green leaf color, nitrogen can green-up the grass. Nitrogen will also stimulate shoot growth and increase mowing.

Turf plants use phosphorus in the high-energy bonds of plant cells and to help the plant release energy for improved growth. Germinating grass seeds need large quantities of phosphorus to develop good root systems. Potassium, also called potash, ranks just behind nitrogen in the amount needed by plants. It is important in plant respiration and also helps increase the plant's tolerance to environmental stress. Cold temperatures, high temperatures, drought, heavy foot traffic, and disease problems are all examples of **environmental stress** that can damage turfgrass plants.

TIP:	Use an inexpensive soil test kit to determine the pH and nutrient content of the soil.

Iron is a micronutrient that helps turfgrass leaves develop a dark-green color. This element may not be deficient in the soil, but when the pH is above 7.0 little if any iron is available for plant use. The long-term solution to this problem is adding sulfur to lower the soil pH. However, applying a fertilizer containing iron can quickly turn yellow-green grass into dark-green grass.

TIP:	Apply a fertilizer containing iron to improve turfgrass color without increasing plant growth and mowing frequency.

Fertilizer must be uniformly distributed over the turf area. Poor fertilizer application can stripe a lawn. Yellow stripes in a green lawn usually indicate an uneven application or missed areas in the application of nitrogen fertilizer. Drop-type and rotary-type spreaders are used to make uniform fertilizer applications. These machines must be calibrated to put out the right amount. Too much fertilizer is wasteful and could burn the grass plants. Not enough fertilizer fails to produce the desired growth results.

FERTILIZING ESTABLISHED TURF

Turfgrass growing in the cool humid region needs fertilizer applied four times a year—early spring, late spring, early fall, and late fall. Most landscapers in this region do not apply fertilizer between Memorial Day and Labor Day. Tall fescue and Zoysiagrass growing in the transition zone should have three fertilizer applications—March, May, and September. Turf managers in the warm humid region apply turf fertilizers each month to ensure that the grass is actively growing. Because these turfgrass plants grow best in hot weather, more fertilizer is applied during the summer months. In the arid region, most landscapers apply little if any fertilizer to lawns.

Turfgrasses will start growing two to three weeks earlier in the spring if fertilizer is applied in late winter. Not only does early fertilization speed spring green-up, but it also helps the cool season grasses heal from past injuries. Many homeowners want the greenest lawn in the neighborhood and spread fertilizer on their lawn to make it look extra green. Fertilizer, especially nitrogen, can green-up a lawn but it will also stimulate the grass plant growth and increase frequency of mowing.

Fertilization during late spring will provide the turfgrass with the nutrient reserves necessary to survive the hot summer growing season. An early fall fertilization will stimulate the production of new tillers, rhizomes, and roots for the following year. This fertilization will also help maintain a vigorous, green turf until late fall or early winter. Fertilizing at this time can also improve early spring green-up of the grass.

17-4. A rotary-type spreader with application calibration for uniform application of fertilizer to selected turf areas. (Courtesy, Education Images, Inc.)

FERTILIZER COMPOSITION

Maintenance fertilizers should be high in nitrogen, but also have moderate amounts of phosphate and potash. There are three major groups of nitrogen fertilizers: natural, soluble, and insoluble. Turf managers use fertilizer cost and desired grass response to decide which fertilizer to apply on each site.

Naturally or organically occurring nitrogen sources are slow-release and usually come from manure. Milorganite® is sold by the Milwaukee Sewage Disposal Plant and is commonly used by landscapers and golf course superintendents in the midwest to provide a natural nitrogen source. Natural fertilizers must be eaten by microscopic soil organisms which then release a form of nitrogen that turfgrass plants can use. Thus, natural nitrogen fertilizers do not turn grass green overnight, but will provide a slow and constant supply of nutrients for several months. It is also difficult to burn grass plants with the natural organic nitrogen fertilizers. In the past few years, there has been a renewed interest in the use of natural turf fertilizers.

The following are soluble or fast release nitrogen sources: ammonium nitrate (ammonium cal. nitrogen) and urea ($CO(NH_2)_2$). These nitrogen sources give grass plants a quick growth spurt lasting only two or three weeks. These soluble nitrogen sources can green-up a lawn literally overnight, but if over-applied may burn the grass leaves. Golf courses may dissolve small quantities of soluble nitrogen in water and spray this mixture to provide a quick feeding. Frequent light applications of nitrogen fertilizers are called spoon-feeding turf.

Insoluble or slow-release fertilizers are also called synthetic nitrogen fertilizers because they are manufactured at an industrial fertilizer plant. These fertilizers provide a uniform and sustained flow of nutrients for 6 to 8 weeks. Slow-release nitrogen sources are: sulfur-coated urea (SCU), methylene urea, urea-formaldehyde (urea form), and isobutylidenediurea (IBDU). Today, most landscapers and golf course superintendents use one of the above forms of slow-release nitrogen when fertilizing turfgrass.

By law all fertilizer materials must have the fertilizer analysis printed on the bag or label. ***Fertilizer analysis*** is the composition of the active ingredients in the formulation. The numbers represent the percent of nitrogen, phosphorus, and potassium in the bag or container. The first number is always the percent of nitrogen, the second is the percent of phosphorus, and the third is the percent of potassium. Therefore, a bag of fertilizer with the analysis 32-4-8 contains: 32% nitrogen, 4% phosphorus, and 8% potassium.

17-5. The numbers on the fertilizer bag indicate the nutrient content.

The exact analysis of the mixed fertilizer is not crucial. It may have a guaranteed analysis of 15-3-6, 32-6-2, or some similar content and all will produce equal results if properly used. However, the relationship of each of the three nutrients to each other is very important. A good turf fertilizer will have five times as much nitrogen as phosphorus, and twice as much potassium as phosphorus. Therefore, a 30-6-12 bag of turf fertilizer will have a nutrient ratio of 5-1-2. The ***nutrient ratio*** shows the relationship of nitrogen, phosphorus, and potassium to each other.

Divide the smallest number on the bag into the other two numbers to calculate the nutrient ratio.

> **TIP:** A good turf fertilizer will have one-half of the nitrogen available in a slow release form. Read the label to confirm how much of the nitrogen is slow release.

Example: Find the nutrient ratio of 30-6-12. This calculation is similar to finding the lowest common denominator of fractions.

$$\frac{30}{6} = 5 \qquad \frac{6}{6} = 1 \qquad \frac{12}{6} = 2 \qquad \text{This fertilizer has the nutrient ratio of 5-1-2}$$

FERTILIZER RATE

The amount of fertilizer applied should be adjusted to the natural fertility of the soil, the length of the growing season, and the amount of foot traffic on the turf. Turfgrass growing on infertile or sandy soil needs extra fertilizer. The longer the growing season the more fertilizer needed by the grass plants. The more stress from foot traffic, the more fertilizer required to maintain good turfgrass growth.

> **TIP:** The common abbreviation for fertilizer rate is 1# a N/K.
>
> **Key to this abbreviation:**
>
> # sign = pounds
> "a" = actual
> upper case N = nitrogen
> upper case K = Kilo or 1,000 sq. ft.

Many turf experts recommend applying 0.5 to 0.75 pounds of actual nitrogen per 1,000 square feet per growing month. This computes to 3.5 to 5.25 pounds of actual nitrogen per season in the cool humid region (average 7 months growing season). While turf growing in the warm humid region will need 4.5 to 6.75 pounds of actual nitrogen per season (average 9 months growing season). The standard rate of application for a nitrogen fertilizer is 1 pound of actual nitrogen per 1,000 square feet per application.

When only a light application of fertilizer is required, the half rate, also called ½ X rate, equals one-half pound of actual nitrogen per 1,000 square feet (0.5 # a N/K). If the lawn needs extra fertilizer, then a double rate, also called 2X rate, equals 2.0 pounds of actual nitrogen per 1,000 square feet (2.0 # a N/K).

A common problem for a landscaper is determining how much fertilizer is needed to give the right amount of nitrogen to a specified lawn area. A fairly simple equation is helpful and is explained through the following example:

Sample problem:

The landscaper has been asked to provide a proposal for maintaining 16,000 square feet of turfgrass for a homeowner. A 50-pound bag of lawn fertilizer has an analysis of 32-6-12. How much fertilizer should be spread on the lawn if the rate of application is 1 pound of nitrogen per 1,000 square feet?

$$\frac{\text{1 pound actual nitrogen per 1,000 square feet}}{\text{percent nitrogen in fertilizer}} \times 100 = \text{pounds of fertilizer needed per 1,000 sq. ft.}$$

$$\frac{\text{1 pound actual nitrogen per 1,000 square feet}}{\text{32\% nitrogen}} \times 100 = 3.125 \text{ pounds of 32-6-12 fertilizer per 1,000 sq. ft.} \quad (3.125\#/\text{K})$$

$$\frac{\text{16,000 sq. ft.}}{\text{1,000 sq. ft/K}} = 16 \text{ K}$$

There are 16 one-thousand square foot areas (1,000 sq. ft.) in this lawn. Multiply 16 K times the fertilizer needed per K (1,000 sq. ft.) to calculate the total fertilizer required for the lawn.

16 K × 3.125 #/K = 50 # fertilizer or one bag of 32-6-12 spread on the 16,000 sq. ft. lawn.

Setting the Fertilizer Spreader

All fertilizers must be spread uniformly over the turfgrass surface because little if any fertilizer will move laterally in the soil. Failure to provide uniform distribution will produce a very irregular response of the grass. The missed areas will get no benefit from the fertilizer and will show up as yellow-green stripes or spots in the lawn.

Uniform spreading is also desirable to avoid over-stimulation of grass in some areas. If applied correctly, fertilizers should not burn the turfgrass. Read the label on the fertilizer bag and adjust the fertilizer spreader to apply the desired amount in a given area.

There are two major types of fertilizer spreaders. The drop-type or gravity spreader will provide a very accurate application of fertilizer. However, the application process will be slow because the spreader only covers a 24 to 36-inch wide strip. The rotary-type spreader will cover a 6 to 12 foot wide strip and give a uniform application. Most landscapers use the rotary-type spreader to quickly fertilize large areas.

TIP: Use the spreader wheel tracks as a guide to uniformly apply fertilizer.

MOWING

There are four major types of mowers in common use today—rotary, reel, flail, and sickle. Rotary mowers are the most popular with landscape maintenance firms and homeowners. Reel mowers provide a high quality cut but require careful maintenance to keep them operating. The flail mower provides a good cut with improved safety for both operators and other people around the mower. They are often used for cutting coarse or tall grass along highways or in parks where safety is critical. The sickle type mower provides a low quality cut of grass and is mainly used on very low maintenance areas, such as roadsides.

A rotary mower has one or more blades that turn parallel to the ground. The mowing height is adjusted by raising or lowering the wheels. A rotary mower may mulch the clippings or be equipped with a bag for collecting grass clippings. Self-propelled walk-behind mowers in sizes from 21 to 61 inches wide are popular with landscape maintenance firms. A reel mower has a set of spiral blades rotating on a horizontal shaft. They cut the turfgrass blades against a stationary bed knife. Mowing height is adjusted by setting the height of the front roller. The reel mower is used to cut Bermudagrass, Centipedegrass, and Zoysiagrass in the south. It is also used on the closely mowed turf found on golf course greens, tees, and fairways, both in the north and the south.

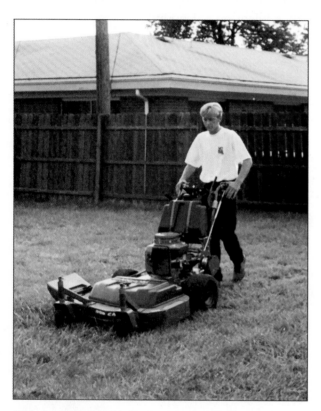

17-6. A walk-behind rotary mower used by lawn maintenance firms.

HEIGHT OF CUT

Table 17-1 provides recommended mowing heights for the various species of warm and cool season turfgrasses. Mowers for cool season grasses should be set to cut 2½ to 3 inches in height. Warm season grasses typically require 1- to 2- inch settings. Allowing the grass to grow taller induces a stemmy erect habit of growth, rather than the desired dense prostrate growth habit.

The general rule is to never remove more than 1/3 of the turfgrass leaf blade at a single mowing. For example, if the lawn will be cut regularly at 2" inches, set the mower at 2" and mow when the grass blades are 3 inches tall. Avoid mowing when the grass is wet. A sharp mower blade is very important. Dull mower blades can rip and shred grass blades instead of cutting them. This is especially a problem when mowing perennial ryegrass. Shredded grass blades also increase the potential entry sites for disease organisms to enter the turfgrass plant.

TIP: Stop mowing turfgrass in the fall when no clippings are caught in the mower bag.

During periods of rapid growth, turf may need mowing twice a week; at other times, once a week may be sufficient. In cooler dry seasons, frequency of mowing may be only once in three or six weeks. Continue mowing turf areas in the fall as long the plants continue growing. Disease development will increase if turf is left too tall in the late fall and throughout

Table 17-1. Turfgrass Mowing Heights and Recommended Type of Mower

Species	Propagation	Mowing height		Type of Mower
		Inches	**Centimeters**	
Warm Season Turfgrasses				
Bahiagrass	Seed	2–4	5.0–10	Rotary
Bermudagrass				
Common	Seed	1.5–3	3.8–7.5	Reel or Rotary
Improved	Sprigs	0.5–1.5	1.3–3.8	Reel
Carpetgrass	Seed or sprigs	1–2	2.5–5.0	Rotary
Centipedegrass	Seed, plugs, sprigs	1–2	2.5–5.0	Reel or Rotary
St. Augustinegrass	Plugs	1.5–3	3.8–7.6	Rotary
Zoysia tenuifloia	Plugs	1.5–2	3.8–5.0	Reel or Rotary
Transition Turfgrasses				
Zoysia japonica	Plugs	2–3	5.0–7.6	Reel or Rotary
Tall fescue	Seed	3–4	7.6–10	Rotary
Cool Season Turfgrasses				
Kentucky bluegrass	Seed	2.5–3	6.4–7.6	Rotary
Perennial ryegrass	Seed	2.5–3	6.4–7.6	Rotary
Fine fescue	Seed	2.5–3	6.4–7.6	Rotary
Tall fescue	Seed	3–4	7.6–10.0	Rotary
Creeping bentgrass	Seed	.25–1	.63–2.5	Reel
Blue gramagrass	Seed	2–3	5.0–7.6	Rotary
Buffalograss	Seed or plugs	2–3	5.0–7.6	Rotary

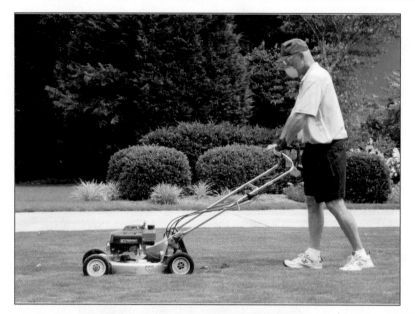

17-7. A self-propelled mower for small areas. (Note that proper mowing height is important when maintaining turfgrass areas.) (Courtesy, Hannah McKay, Education Images, Inc.)

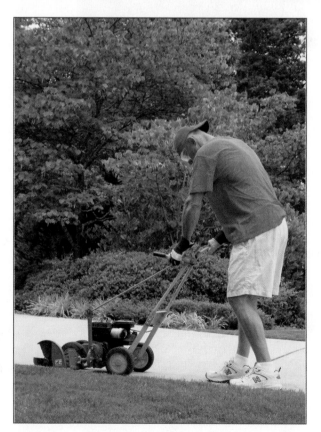

17-8. Edging is often needed along walks and driveways for a neat, well-kept appearance. (Courtesy, Hannah McKay, Education Images, Inc.)

the winter. Mowing turfgrass is a year round maintenance practice in some parts of the United States.

BAG OR MULCH CLIPPINGS

In the 1970s, lawn mower companies promoted using mowers that would bag the clippings. Many sales promotions at this time indicated that bagging grass clippings would prevent thatch accumulation. University research has since proven that grass clippings do not materially contribute to thatch buildup. Thatch prevention and control is discussed later in this chapter. A bagging mower may allow the homeowner to cut the lawn less often.

When the quantity of grass clippings produced by mowing does not readily sift down into the turf, it is best to bag the clippings. Excessive clippings are not only unsightly, but their continued presence on top of the grass is an invitation to turf diseases. Diseases prefer the high-humidity conditions found under this mat of clippings.

In the 1980s, a new and different style rotary mower, called the mulching mower, was introduced. These mowers do not have a bag to collect the clippings. Mulching mowers use specially engineered blades and decks that cut the grass into very small pieces. The clippings sift down through the grass to the soil and add to the soil's fertility. Grass clippings decompose rapidly and return about 25 percent of the nitrogen applied to the lawn back to the grass roots.

Millions of bags of grass clippings go to landfill dumps each year in this country. It is estimated that more than 25 percent of landfill waste is from landscape material. As the public became more concerned with the environment, the sale of mulching mowers increased in the 1990s.

Lawns must be mowed more frequently when using a mulching mower instead of a bagger. In the spring, when turfgrass plants are rapidly growing, the lawn may need mowing every 3 or 4 days. Because no time is spent emptying a bag full of clippings, mowing with a mulching mower takes less time. However, most homeowners think their lawn looks better right after mowing if a bagging mower is used instead of one that mulches.

WATERING TURF GRASS

In regions receiving less than 40 inches of annual rainfall, irrigation is essential for good turf maintenance. In humid regions, irrigation is desirable during periods of prolonged drought. A rain gauge should be installed to keep track of precipitation. The gauge should be set on a post in the open, and read after each rain. By keeping a record of rainfall, it is easy to assess the need for watering. After 7 to 10 days without rain, turfgrass plants start to wilt.

Water should be added only when needed. Lightly sprinkling turf in hot weather will benefit weeds more than the desirable turfgrasses. As a rule, water sufficiently to wet the soil to a depth of about 6 inches. Generally, 1 inch of water will soak the soil to a depth of 6 to 8 inches. Sprinklers will need to run one to two hours in one location to apply 1 inch of water on most home lawns.

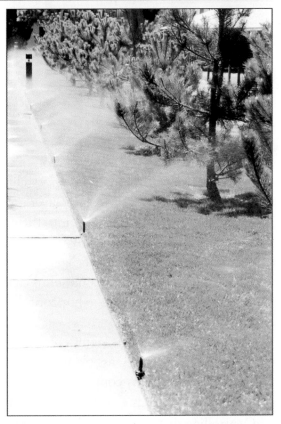

17-9. A well-designed automatic sprinkler system is designed to give complete coverage.

17-10. Home lawn irrigation controller.

The time of day for watering is not important except that it should be completed early enough in the day so the grass leaves can dry by nightfall. When grass leaves go into the night wet, an ideal environment develops for turfgrass leaf diseases. Claims that watering during the sunny part of the day will scald grass leaves are not valid. Any such scalding is probably caused by water-logging of the soil and the resulting death of roots where drainage is inadequate.

In many parts of the country, underground irrigation systems are installed to automatically water the turf and surrounding flower and landscape beds. These new irrigation systems accurately and uniformly apply water. Less water is wasted with these systems than with the old fashion hose-pull hand sprinklers.

THATCH MANAGEMENT

Thatch describes the accumulation of excess grass stems and roots in the turf. In the past, turf experts believed that bagging grass clippings would prevent thatch buildup. Most lawns develop problems when the thatch layer is over ½ inch thick. Water, fertilizer, and air cannot penetrate the thatch layer and get into the root zone where they are used by the grass roots. The part of the soil where turfgrass roots grow is called the root zone. Thatch is composed of grass stems and roots. Turfgrass plants have several different types of stems. Some turfgrasses develop horizontally growing underground stems called **rhizomes** which help the turf plants spread. Other turfgrass plants develop horizontally growing aboveground stems called **stolons** that also thicken the lawn.

The cells of all turfgrass stems contain a material called lignin. Lignin makes the cell walls strong, which keeps the grass plants erect. Because plant tissue that is high in lignin is slow to decompose, these stems contribute to thatch development. However, grass clippings do not contain lignin and do not contribute to thatch buildup.

Controlling thatch requires physically removing the excess plant growth and adopting maintenance practices to prevent additional thatch buildup. Power rakes or thatching machines can physically remove thatch from the lawn. All the thatch material must be removed from the lawn surface after thatching with a power rake. Most landscapers use hand rakes to pick up and remove the thatch brought to the surface with the power rake. Early spring or late summer is the time to remove thatch buildup with a power rake.

Another piece of power equipment called a core **aerifier** punches small holes in the turf's surface. The aerifier drives hollow tubes called **tines** into the soil and removes ½-inch diameter plugs of soil. Air can now penetrate into the thatch layer through these holes. Soil microbes need air to grow and will destroy the thatch material before it accumulates and causes problems. This technique prevents thatch accumulation. Chemical thatch removers have limited value in controlling thatch problems.

Excess grass growth from over fertilization creates the conditions for thatch accumulation. Applying less fertilizer will help prevent thatch problems. Thatch prevention is a lot easier than removing thatch from the lawn.

AERIFYING TURFGRASS SOIL

Aerifying turf can provide temporary improvement of compacted soil conditions in addition to preventing thatch accumulation. Heavy foot traffic on golf course putting greens and athletic fields can compact the soil. Compact soils will reduce water, fertilizer, and air penetration into the root zone of turfgrass. After the soil core is removed, holes 2 to 3 inches deep remain. Air, water, and fertilizer can penetrate the root zone through the holes.

The tines on the aerifier are usually spaced 6 to 8 inches apart. The more holes, the better the results from aerification. Use machines that have closely spaced tines or go over the turf area several times in different directions.

17-11. Using a core aerator can reduce thatch accumulation while improving soil aeration.

After aerification, the soil cores left on top of the lawn can be broken up and spread over the surface by dragging with a flexible steel mat. Aerify in early spring or late summer when turfgrass will quickly grow and cover the holes. Always aerify before applying fertilizer or limestone to the lawn.

ROLLING TURF AND LEAF REMOVAL

Rolling and leaf removal are two practices that may be needed with turf. When and how they are used will vary with the situation.

ROLLING

Rolling is used after seeding and sodding to establish good contact of the seed or sod with the soil. In regions where winter freezing and thawing occurs, the turf may appear rough in spring. There is a belief that spring rolling is necessary to create a smooth turf. Use a light water-filled roller to "replant" the grass plants. Repeated rolling when the soil is wet and soggy, particularly with a heavy roller, causes undesirable compaction of heavy-textured soils. Because grass roots will penetrate only into soil layers that are well aerated, spring rolling may restrict the new roots to the uppermost layers of soil.

The freezing and thawing of heavy soils is an effective natural means of producing a well-aerated soil. Unwise rolling in spring may nullify this natural aerifying process. The objective of sound turf maintenance should be to roll sparingly, if at all. Take full advantage of soil freezing to produce a soil structure favorable to grass roots. When absolutely necessary, a roller just heavy enough to press the crowns of the grass plants into the soil and smooth the soil surface may be used.

REMOVAL OF LEAVES

Leaves should be removed from under deciduous trees in autumn to pre-

17-12. Leaves should be removed to keep them from covering the grass and cutting off light.

vent them from covering the turf and cutting off light. It is also essential to remove leaves from newly seeded or renovated turf areas in order to allow development of the grass seedlings. Care in removing leaves is important to avoid injury to the grass plants. Leaf removal also improves the overall appearance of the landscape.

MANAGING WEEDS IN TURF

A good weed management strategy consists of three different techniques. (1) Natural competition making conditions more favorable for the desired grasses and less favorable for weed growth; (2) planting weed-free grass seed mixtures and preventing weed seed production in the turf; and (3) attacking weeds with herbicides at growth stages when the weeds are most vulnerable.

Nature controls certain types of vegetation by providing stiff competition from the desired plants and crowding out undesirable plants. Weeds will have difficulty gaining a foothold in dense healthy turf. An abundance of weeds in a lawn is evidence that conditions are not satisfactory for good turfgrass growth. Before applying herbicides, try to implement good turfgrass management practices and improve the overall growth of the desirable turfgrass.

17-13. This shows poor quality turf. What would you do to improve the turf? (Courtesy, Education Images, Inc.)

MOWING PRACTICES AND WEEDS

Most home lawns will have fewer weeds if the height of cut is raised to 2½ to 3 inches instead of the usual 1½ or 2 inches. Taller grass can better compete with weeds for water and nutrients. Mowing home lawns

TIP: Raising the cutting height from 2 inches to 3 inches can reduce weed problems in the home lawn.

17-14. A reel mower on a golf course fairway. (Courtesy, Education Images, Inc.)

17-15. Chemical methods can be used on turfgrass to control winter weeds. This shows henbit in a dormant Bermudagrass lawn before (top) and two weeks after spraying with a herbicide (bottom).

too short is one reason for weedy turf. Mowing the grass tall should be the rule, not the exception.

Adjust mowing height and frequency to prevent weeds from flowering and producing seed. These practices, combined with timely use of herbicides, constitute good weed control practice.

HERBICIDES

Herbicides are chemicals that kill or prevent weed growth. The herbicide label will specify the kinds of weeds managed, how to safely use the herbicide, and any special precautions. Herbicides are powerful compounds and may cause damage to desirable turf or other plants if improperly used. Always read the manufacturer's label and accompanying printed instructions and follow all recommendations.

Turfgrass weeds can be divided into three major groups—annual grass weeds, perennial grass weeds and broadleaf weeds. Different herbicides are used to control each group of lawn weeds. Correct weed identification is very important when selecting and applying weed control herbicides.

Annual grass weed seeds germinate in the spring. The plants grow and produce seeds in the summer and die in the fall. This cycle is repeated each year; therefore, these weeds are best controlled with herbicides that prevent the weed seeds from germinating. Crabgrass and dallisgrass are two very common annual grass weeds found in home lawns.

17-16. Two common summer annual weeds are cocklebur (left) and crabgrass (right).

Perennial grass weeds may go dormant in the fall but will not die. During the following spring, perennial grass weeds return to life and once again destroy the uniformity of the lawn. This group is more difficult to manage because they are genetically similar to desirable turfgrass plants. Quackgrass, nimblewill, and yellownut sedge are major perennial grass weeds.

The third group of lawn weeds is called broadleaf weeds. Weeds in this group do not have long narrow grass-like leaves. They have leaves with a netted vein structure. Dandelion, clover, buckhorn, and plantain belong to this large group of lawn weeds.

Herbicides may be applied to turf either before the weeds germinate and start growing or after the weeds start growing. **Preemergence** herbicides prevent certain weed seeds from germinating. They must be applied before the seed starts to germinate. Landscapers apply a preemergence herbicide also called crabgrass preventer in late winter to early spring to prevent crabgrass seed germination. Crabgrass seeds can start germinating in February in Florida, but will not germinate until late May in Minnesota. Timing of application is very important when using preemergence herbicides.

Crabgrass preventer herbicides are usually mixed with a fertilizer for ease of application. Not only will the turfgrass receive needed nutrients, but crabgrass seeds will be prevented from germinating. Common crabgrass preventer herbicides are—Balan® (Benefin), Betasan® (Bensulide), Dacthal® (DCPA), Ronstar® (Oxadiazon), Pre M® (Pendimethalin), Tupersan® (Siduron), and Princep® (Simazine).

Once weeds appear in the lawn, only postemergence herbicides will kill them. **Postemergence** herbicides are commonly used to control broadleaf weeds after they are present. These herbicides are absorbed by actively growing weeds. They kill the weeds but do not injure the desirable turfgrass plants. Treat turfgrass areas with postemergence herbicides when soil moisture is adequate and weeds are actively growing. The weeds are most vulnerable under these conditions. The technician should take appropriate care to prevent sprays from drifting onto flowers, shrubs, trees, and vegetables. Read the precautions on the herbicide package and protect susceptible plants. Common broadleaf herbicides are: MCPP (Mecoprop), Weedbgon® (2,4-D), Banvel-D® (Dicamba), and Turflon D® (Triclopyr + 2-4,D).

Today, many postemergence herbicides are mixed with water and sprayed on the lawn. Some companies mix these herbicides with turf fertilizers to make application easy for the home owner. Herbicides mixed with fertilizers need to be applied to moist leaves for the herbicide to adhere to the weed leaf. Read and follow label directions. After treatment, weed control may take from 3 to 10 days to complete. Do not re-treat for 14 days if weed control is not complete. Over treatment is dangerous and may damage desirable turf.

> **TIP:** Crabgrass seeds usually start to germinate at the same time forsythia and lilac shrubs start to flower. Apply crabgrass preventer herbicides before these shrubs flower.

> **TIP:** Tomatoes, roses, and grapes are very sensitive to postemergence herbicides. Use extreme caution when applying these herbicides near these plants.

Perennial grass weeds are the most difficult lawn weeds to control. Several special herbicides are available to control specific weeds. Apply either Manage® or Basagran® (Bentazon) to control actively growing yellownut sedge plants in the lawn. Yellownut sedge is not a true grass weed but belongs to the sedge group of plants. Since the early 1990s, new cultivars of tall fescue have been sold and planted in the cool humid and transition regions. However, in older lawns, common tall fescue grass is considered a major weed. The herbicide TFC® can be sprayed on the lawn and only the tall fescue weeds will die. Other perennial grass weeds can be controlled with spot applications of Roundup® (Glyphosate). Roundup herbicide is absorbed by green plant tissue. It will kill not only the weeds but any desirable grass that it is sprayed on. Always be careful when applying all herbicides on turfgrass.

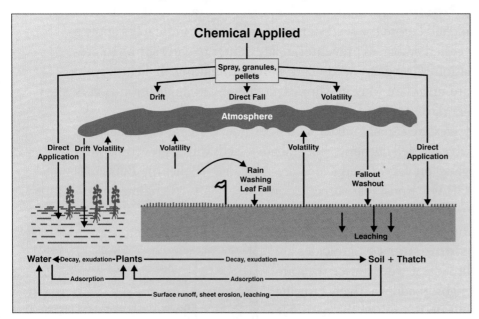

17-17. Fate of chemicals applied to turfgrass.

Seedling grasses are far more sensitive to herbicides than mature turf plants. It is important to apply herbicides well before any re-seeding of grass, so the herbicide may be dissipated before planting grass seed.

The pesticide manufacturers have calculated the most effective rates of application and the correct time of year to apply the herbicide. Read the entire label before using the pesticide and apply according to label directions. Follow all precautions listed to protect the environment. It is a violation of federal law to use a pesticide in a way not suggested on the label.

17-18. Spraying a herbicide on the turfgrass of a golf course fairway. (Courtesy, Eddie Seagle, Abraham Baldwin Agricultural College)

DISEASE IN TURFGRASS

Adopting sound management practices is a major step in managing disease in turfgrass. Although there are many turfgrass diseases, only a few are likely to cause serious problems.

The selection of grasses suited to the climatic region is important. Principles of soil management and proper use of fertilizers help the grass plants to develop resistance to disease and increase their ability to recover when invaded by an organism. Lawns planted with a mixture of several grass species will have fewer disease problems. Each turfgrass species has a different susceptibility and resistance to individual disease pathogens. Avoiding close cutting, removing clippings, and avoiding over-watering are all practices that help prevent diseases in turf.

Many diseases in turf are caused by different species of fungi. They are managed by following good practices in turf care. Properly use irrigation, as keeping turfgrass leaves wet promotes fungus growth. Clean equipment before moving from one lawn site to another. Apply fungicide at the appropriate rates. With new sod, only use sod from sources that are free of disease.

General information on plant diseases is covered in Chapter 18. A turf management expert should be consulted if a disease is suspected. Check with your local Extension Office for additional help in disease identification and management.

17-19. Some important turf diseases include Pink snow mold (top left), Leaf spot (top center), Dollar spot (top right), Powdery mildew (bottom left), Brown patch (bottom center), and Pythium blight (bottom right).

REVIEWING

MAIN IDEAS

Turfgrass maintenance is keeping a stand of turfgrass in an attractive and healthy condition using appropriate management practices.

Quality turfgrass needs regular fertilizer applications. Slow-release types of fertilizer provide several months of sustained nutrient feeding. Fertilizer should always be applied according to the manufacturer's recommendations. Either a drop-type or rotary-type fertilizer spreader can be used to apply the granular fertilizer to the lawn. Do not overlap the spreader pattern when applying fertilizer.

When natural rainfall does not supply adequate water for good grass growth, artificial irrigation must be used to keep the grass vigorous. Thatch must also be controlled to have a quality lawn. Power rakes or thatchers can remove part of the accumulated thatch from a lawn. Aerification punches small holes in the turf. The holes increase water and fertilizer penetration into the root zone. Both power thatching and aerifying should be done when the grass is actively growing, not when under stress.

Lawn weeds are divided into three groups; annual grass weeds, perennial grass weeds, and broadleaf weeds. Unwanted lawn weeds can be controlled by applying the correct herbicide at the proper time. Always read and follow all instructions on the pesticide label.

QUESTIONS

Answer the following questions using correct spelling and complete sentences.

1. What is turfgrass maintenance? What activities are involved?

2. How many pounds of actual nitrogen should be applied per 1,000 square feet of turf per growing month?

3. Why is aerifying turfgrass important?

4. What is thatch and how can it be prevented?

5. Why should lawns be aerified?

6. What is the difference between preemergence and postemergence herbicides?

7. Crabgrass belongs to what group of lawns weeds?

8. What herbicide will control yellownut sedge in a lawn?

9. Describe how the presence of excessive grass clippings can lead to disease in turfgrass.

10. Why do dull mower blades increase the possibility of disease in turfgrass?

CHAPTER SELF-CHECK

Match the term with the correct definition. Place the correct letter in the blank provided.

a. nitrogen   d. phosphorus   g. preemergence
b. 1 pound actual N e. 0.5 to 0.75   h. 1 inch
c. reel   f. rotary   i. stems

_____ 1. The number 6 on a bag of turf fertilizer with an analysis of 24-6-12 represents

_____ 2. The most important nutrient used by turfgrass is

_____ 3. The normal nitrogen rate of application is

_____ 4. Most turf experts recommend applying how much actual nitrogen each month during the growing season

_____ 5. What grass plant parts are slow to decompose and usually cause thatch to buildup in a lawn

_____ 6. Bermudagrass lawns are usually mowed with what kind of mower

_____ 7. Kentucky bluegrass lawns are usually mowed with what kind of mower

_____ 8. Crabgrass is best controlled with what group of herbicide

_____ 9. Actively growing turfgrass needs how much water each week

EXPLORING

1. Collect and identify 10 lawn weeds growing in your home lawn or school lawn.

2. Visit a golf course and talk with the superintendent about job skills necessary for employment.

3. Mow three different turfgrass plots at school, each at a different height, and evaluate the turf response.

CHAPTER 18

Managing Pests in the Landscape

1 Identify five major categories of pests.

2 Describe complete and incomplete metamorphosis of insects.

3 Explain the difference between selective and non-selective herbicides.

4 Discuss alternate pest management techniques.

5 Describe safety precautions necessary when handling and/or applying chemicals.

6 Explain Integrated Pest Management (IPM).

TERMS

aesthetic injury level
algae
bacteria
biological pest management
contact herbicide
cultural pest management
exoskeleton
fungi
fungicide
herbicide
host plant
insect

insecticide
integrated pest management (IPM)
larvae
Lethal Dose (LD_{50})
mechanical pest management
moss
nematicide
nematode
non-selective herbicide
nymph
parasite

pathogen
pheromone
pest
pesticide
plant disease
postemergent
preemergent
selective herbicide
systematic herbicide
viruses
weed

18-1. Carefully clean equipment to prevent the spread of pests from one site or job to another. (Courtesy, Education Images, Inc.)

PESTS in the landscape impact the health of the plants and their appearance. Plant pests can be managed by biological, mechanical, and chemical methods. An understanding of integrated pest management strategies is important for the future of our environment. Certification by a state agency will be required in order to purchase and apply most chemicals. Safety procedures must be followed when controlling pests in the landscape.

How can pest damage to plants be reduced? What precautions must be followed when applying chemicals to manage pests? Can pests be managed without using chemicals? What is IPM and why should this technique be considered? What type of personal safety protection should one wear when applying pesticides? The answers to these questions are important when managing pests in the landscape.

INSECTS AND RELATED PESTS

Ornamental plants are subject to damage by pests. Healthy plants can be attacked by insects and die. A ***pest*** is anything that causes injury or loss to a plant. Most pests are living organisms, either plant or animal. Pests damage plants by making them less productive, by affecting reproduction, or by destroying them. Fortunately, most pests can be controlled and losses reduced or eliminated. Pests can be put into five major categories—insects, diseases, weeds, nematodes, and rodents or other animals.

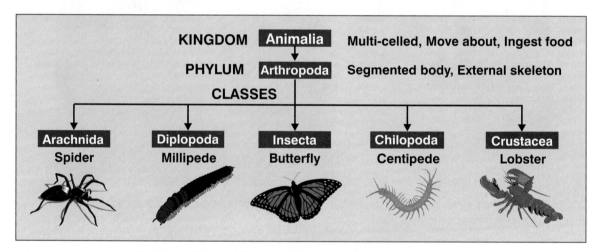

KINGDOM	**Animalia**	Multi-celled, Move about, Ingest food
PHYLUM	**Arthropoda**	Segmented body, External skeleton
CLASSES		

| **Arachnida** | **Diplopoda** | **Insecta** | **Chilopoda** | **Crustacea** |
| Spider | Millipede | Butterfly | Centipede | Lobster |

18-2. Scientific classification of insects and insect-related pests.

A ***host plant*** is one that provides a pest with food. Conditions must be right for pests to damage plants. The pest must be present to cause damage to the plant. Some plants are more likely to be damaged by pests than others. Many plants have a natural resistance to plant pests. Various pest management practices can be used to affect the environment and lessen or eliminate damage by pests.

True ***insects*** are animals with three distinct body sections (head, thorax, and abdomen), three pairs of legs, and one or two pairs of wings. Bugs with more than three pairs of legs are in the group called insect-related. Spiders and mites have four pairs of legs and two body sections. Hundred-legged bugs, called centipedes, have one pair

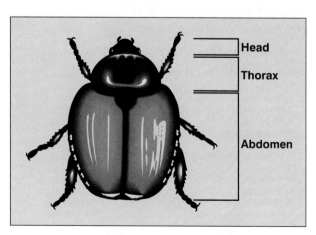

Head

Thorax

Abdomen

18-3. Parts of an adult insect.

of legs for each body section. Millipedes, commonly called thousand-legged bugs, have two pairs of legs per body section. Sowbugs and pillbugs have seven pairs of legs. Snails and slugs belong to the Crustacea group of animals.

There are more than 800,000 identified insect and insect-related animal species in the world. Less than 1,000 are pests of plants and people. Many different species are pests of ornamental plants and turf. In this chapter, the term insect will cover both true insects and insect-related organisms.

The insect body is cylindrical and segmented. It is made up of an external skeleton, called an **exoskeleton**, internal muscles, and organs. Insects breathe through pores on their sides called spiracles.

Insects are also divided by the kind of mouth parts, either chewing or sucking. Grubs, beetles, and caterpillars use chewing mouth parts to eat leaf, stem, and root structures. Aphids, scales, and leafhoppers insert an elongated beak (labrum) into the plant cell and suck out the cell contents.

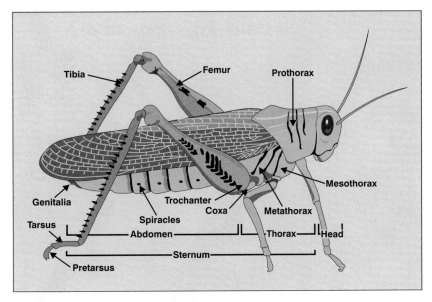

18-4. Major external parts of an insect.

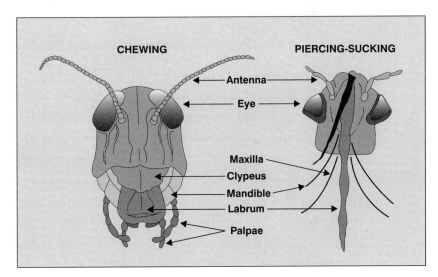

18-5. Mouthparts of a chewing and a piercing-sucking insect.

LIFE CYCLE

Insects can be divided into two major groups related to their stage of development or metamorphosis. Insects with life cycles that undergo four distinct stages (egg, larvae, pupae, and adult) belong to the complete metamorphosis group. Moths, butterflies, and beetles all

18-6. The life cycle of most insects is through complete or incomplete metamorphosis.

belong to this group. The insect egg develops into the **larvae**, which does not look any thing like the adult insect. Insects in the larvae stage cause the most damage to plants. A caterpillar is the larvae stage of a butterfly and moth. After feeding on plant tissue, the caterpillar goes into a resting stage called the pupae (cocoon stage). The adult butterfly emerges from the pupae stage and lays eggs to complete the life cycle.

Many other insects belong to a second group and go through incomplete metamorphosis. Insects in this group start as an egg but progress through a series of nymph stages. The **nymph** looks just like the adult insect but is much smaller. The nymph sheds its external skeleton four or five times. The stage between each shedding is called an instar. The nymph increases in size between each instar stage. Aphids, mole crickets, and chinch bugs are in this incomplete metamorphosis group.

Insects reproduce and go through several life cycles or generations each year. Aphids and red spiders can have ten complete generations each year. However, the periodic cicadas will take 13 to 18 years to complete one generation.

DAMAGE AND DETECTION

Some insects are beneficial, some are harmful, and others are simply a nuisance. Beneficial insects help plants grow. Beneficial insects improve the soil, help pollinate flowers, or

18-7. Tent caterpillar nest on a flowering crab apple tree.

destroy other harmful insects. Examples of beneficial insects that destroy insect pests include the lady beetle, the praying mantis, and the common green lacewing. Honey bees cross pollinate plants, by transferring pollen from one flower to another flower, while collecting nectar.

Many insects feed on plant tissue during the larvae and adult stage. The larvae stage of the Japanese beetle (grub) feeds on plant roots; while the adult stage (beetle) feeds on plant leaves. Insect feeding can reduce the quality and vigor of the host plant. Burrowing, nesting, and mound-building insects can indirectly damage plants. However, ants improve soil aeration and tilth.

Many ornamental and turf insects are nocturnal (night) feeders. Watch bird feeding patterns to help detect insects. Birds feeding in a lawn at dusk or sun-up indicate an infestation

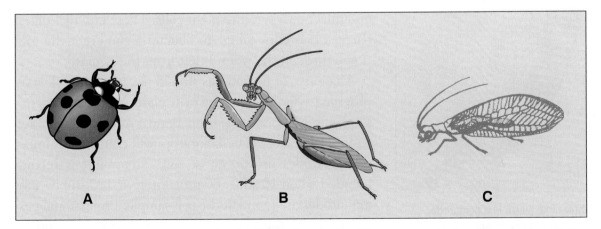

18-8. Some beneficial insects, (A) lady beetle, (B) praying mantis, (C) common green lacewing, attack and kill harmful insects.

18-9. Sticky pest traps are used to monitor insect populations.

18-10. This threadlike worm is a nematode, greatly enlarged with a microscope. They invade the roots of plants and reduce the host plant's vigor. (Courtesy, Frank Killebrew, Plant Pathologist, Mississippi State University)

of lawn insects. Use traps to detect and identify insects before starting control measures. Cut both ends from a coffee can and set the coffee can "tube" into a turf area suspected of harboring chinch buds or mole crickets. Fill the can with soapy water; wait 10 minutes; then, count the insects floating on the surface of the water. Treat the turf if more than three insects are found floating in the soapy water.

Cut and remove a sample of sod—1 inch thick × 1 square foot. Count the number of white grubs in the sample. Treat the lawn area when more than nine grubs are found in the sample. Several different beetle "traps" are sold and used to detect Japanese beetle populations. Place small, yellow, sticky 3 × 5 cards in a greenhouse to detect insect types and populations.

NEMATODES

Nematodes are very small threadlike animals. These microscopic organisms live in the soil and damage plant roots. Nematodes vary in size from 1/75 to 1/10 of an inch long. There are approximately 500,000 species of nematodes in the world, including 2,200 species that cause damage to plants. More than 20,000 nematodes can be found in 1 pint of soil. Nematodes feed by penetrating root cells with a hollow stylet mouth structure and inject enzymes into plant cells. These enzymes digest the cell contents. Fungi and bacteria can enter the root tissue through the wounds left from the nematode.

Diagnosis of nematodes should not be made solely on observed symptoms on the host plant. Accurate diagnosis requires laboratory testing. Send a soil sample to a soil testing laboratory. The laboratory will count the number of nematodes in 100 cc of soil. Treatment is recommended when 10 sting, 80 root-knot, or 100 stubby-root nematodes are found in the soil sample. Professional pesticide applicators using potent nematicide can control these soil-born organisms.

WEED PESTS

Unwanted plants can destroy the beauty of a well-landscaped yard and garden. Weeds detract from the overall appearance of the landscape. They can look different from desirable plants and compete for light, water, nutrients, and space. Weeds can reduce the vigor of landscape plants and turf.

CLASSIFICATION AND LIFE CYCLE

A **weed** is a plant growing out of place or an unwanted plant. Weeds may be classified as grassy (monocots), broadleaf (dicot), other (sedges or rushes), or moss and algae. The life cycle of the weed plant is very important in selecting a control measure. The life cycle includes germination of seeds, growth of plants, flowering, production of seeds, and finally death.

Summer annual weeds germinate in the spring, grow during the summer, produce flowers and seeds in the fall, and die at the first frost. Winter annual weeds germinate in the fall, grow that fall and winter, flower and produce seeds the next spring, and die in early summer. Perennial weed seeds can germinate in the spring, summer, or fall. These weeds grow for many years flowering and producing more seeds each year. The leaves and stems of many perennial weeds die in the fall but, new plants come from the strong healthy

18-11. A weed is a plant growing where it is not wanted or a plant out of place.

18-12. Common broadleaf lawn and garden weeds: (A) knotweed, (B) spotted spurge, (C) pennywort, (D) buckhorn, (E) broadleaf plantain, (F) dandelion, (G) mouse-ear chickweed, (H) common chickweed, and (I) henbit. (Courtesy, Amchem Products, Inc.)

roots that survive the cold winter temperatures. Accurate identification is the first step in any weed control program.

18-13. Moss growing may indicate this soil has a low pH.

MOSS AND ALGAE

Moss is a tangled green mat composed of thread-like growth that covers the soil surface. Shady areas with acidic, compact, poorly drained soil provide an excellent environment for moss growth and development. Control is achieved by maintaining vigorously-growing desirable plants and adjusting the above factors.

Algae are a group of small, primitive, filamentous, green plants that manufacture their own food. They form a thick, slimy, greenish scum on bare soil in poorly drained wet areas of the lawn. This scum can dry and form a tough black crust that prevents water penetration into the soil creating isolated dry spots in the turf. Provide good surface and subsurface drainage, avoid over-watering, aerify compact areas, and increase light penetration to reduce algae growth.

DISEASE

Plant diseases are abnormal conditions that interfere with the normal appearance, growth, and structure of a plant. Each disease has characteristic symptoms or signs. Some diseases attack the entire plant, while others attack leaves or roots. Plant diseases can be divided into two major groups called infectious and noninfectious diseases.

INFECTIOUS DISEASES

Parasites or pathogens cause infectious plant diseases. A **parasite** is usually a multi-celled organism that lives in or on other organisms. A **pathogen** is a biological agent or virus that can cause a disease. These organisms cannot manufacture their own food. They use the host plant tissue as a food source and disrupt its normal life. A microscope is often needed to see these organisms. Laboratory study is used to make accurate identification. For a disease to occur, a susceptible host, pathogen, and favorable environmental conditions must all be present. Plant pathogens are contagious and can be spread between plants usually by insects.

Diseases may be identified by the kind of damage done to the host plant. Symptoms of plant disease include: (1) rotting plant parts, particularly fruit; (2) yellow leaves called chlorotic; (3) wilting of plant leaves; (4) twisted leaves and/or stems; (5) buds, flowers, or fruits not developing or falling off; and (6) dead plants or plant parts called necrosis.

18-14. Pink snow mold turfgrass disease. The car keys are used for size comparison.

NONINFECTIOUS DISEASES

Noninfectious diseases are caused by elements in the plant's environment that are not right for good plant growth. Because plants vary in needs, their tolerance of poor environmental conditions varies. Some plants can live with a condition that will kill other plants.

Noninfectious diseases include the following: (1) weather, such as very cold or hot temperatures; (2) nutrient deficiencies, such as not enough potassium in the soil; (3) physical damage to plant parts, such as improper cultivation; (4) chemical injuries, such as incorrect applications of herbicides or insecticides; and (5) pollution injuries, such as smoke from car exhaust. Tissue analysis and soil testing may be needed to help identify these environmental diseases.

MAJOR ORGANISMS THAT CAUSE DISEASES

FUNGI

Fungi are small, one-celled, filamentous, spore-bearing organisms having no chlorophyll that grow on or in a plant. Fungi cause more plant diseases than all the other parasites.

"Fungus" is the singular form and "fungi" is the plural word form. Parasitic fungi can cause many different plant diseases, such as mildew, rusts, wilts, and smuts.

Fungi are spread by wind, water, insects, and people from plant to plant. Aphids, feeding on a diseased plant leaf, can spread the fungus organisms to healthy leaves. Pruning a diseased shrub can spread the pathogen to a healthy shrub if the pruning shears are not disinfected after pruning each shrub.

BACTERIA

Bacteria are small, one-celled organisms that have a primitive nucleus. Some bacteria are beneficial while others cause plant diseases. Bacteria often get into plants through cuts or breaks in the bark or epidermis. Some also enter through flowers and natural openings in the stem and leaves. Fireblight, common on flowering crab apples, is carried by honey bees from tree to tree during their nectar gathering flights. Blight, leaf spots, wilt, scab, and wetwood are other diseases caused by bacteria.

VIRUSES

Viruses are small infectious particles made of a core of nucleic acid surrounded by a protein sheath. The small size (approximately one-millionth of an inch) of a virus makes it visible only with an electron microscope. Viruses are obligate parasites; they reproduce only in living cells of the host. The most common plant attacked by the virus and the general symptoms are combined to name plant virus diseases. Examples include cucumber mosaic, aster yellows, and tomato ring spot. However, they can attack other plants besides the specific plants named.

18-15. Leaf spots caused by a mosaic virus disease.

RODENTS AND OTHER ANIMALS

Activity by small and large animals can damage plants. Animals can eat and destroy the stems, fruits, and leaves of ornamental plants. Birds, skunks, and raccoons disrupt the turf surface looking for grub-type insects. Mice, rabbits, and deer destroy the bark of many valuable trees and shrubs. Moles and voles destroy the roots of turfgrass by digging tunnels in search of earthworms and seeds. Other animals, such as dogs, urinate on turf and shrubs damaging or killing leaves.

If you are establishing a landscape in a location where pesky animals are found, select species of plants that the animals do not damage. For example, deer will not eat most holly plants. On the other hand, rabbits will attack hollies and destroy all small growth within their reach.

18-16. Some animal pests dig tunnels in the soil, which can damage the plant roots.

MANAGING PESTS

Many pest problems can be prevented. Good management practices will help to reduce other pest problems. The method selected must be right for the plant and the pest. Federal and state laws regulate the control practices that can be used.

There are four major ways of managing plant pests: (1) cultural practices, (2) biological methods, (3) mechanical methods, and (4) chemical methods. Genetic engineering is a new technique that utilizes biotechnology to make plants resistant to specific pests. It eliminates the need for control by eliminating the pest.

CULTURAL PEST PRACTICES

Cultural pest management is the use of cultural techniques (plant care practices) to control pests. The techniques include proper plant management programs, sanitation, and using resistant varieties. Good management programs improve the overall growth and development of the desirable plants in the landscape. Grow better plants by correctly mow-

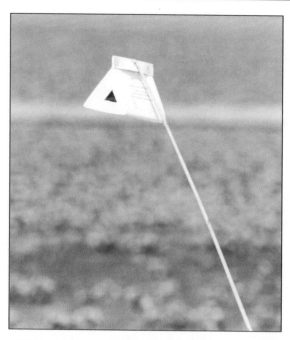

18-17. Insect traps contain pheromones that attract specific insects.

ing, irrigating, fertilizing, pruning, aerifying, and mulching. Environmental plant damage may be caused by chemical burns, animals, vandalism, summer drought, winter desiccation, ice, air pollution, or salt. Plant managers can develop corrective measures to eliminate the above cultural problems.

Insect traps containing chemical sex attractants, called pheromones, can lure insects into a trap for identification and proper disposal. Pheromones are substances secreted by insects or artificially developed in the laboratory. Plant breeding programs have developed many cultivars of turfgrass that have a natural immunity to common insects and diseases. Today, new cultivars of flowers, trees, and shrubs are available with natural resistances to insects and diseases and tolerances to conditions that lead to noninfectious diseases.

BIOLOGICAL PEST PRACTICES

Biological pest management is using living organisms that are predators to control plant pests. Biological management of insects includes nematodes feeding on mole crickets or bacterium that kill insects. Many beneficial insects feed on insect pests that damage ornamental plants.

18-18. Lady beetle feeding on aphids is an example of biological pest management. (Courtesy, Agricultural Research Service, USDA)

The lady beetles are well known for their role in controlling aphids on fruit trees. Predatory mites have been used to control other mites on flowering crab apple trees. Caution: Insecticides should not be used on plants to control insects if predator insects are present. The insecticide will kill the beneficial insects. Many gardeners like to have a few toads and turtles around to eat insects.

The bacterium *Bacillus thuringinensis* (often called Bt for short) can kill a variety of caterpillars and grubs that attack turf and other ornamental plants. It will take from several weeks to years for the biological organisms to build up sufficient populations to control plant pests. However, once this population is established, the natural forces should control the pests for many years.

Several major insect pests have been controlled by altering their reproductive process. Because some insects mate only once, a female that mates with a sterile (no sperm) male lays eggs that will not hatch. The male insects are raised in laboratories and sterilized. The sterile males are then released in an area with an insect pest problem. Research is underway to develop other new ways of using plants and animals to control plant pests.

MECHANICAL PEST MANAGEMENT

Mechanical pest management is using tools or equipment to reduce pest populations. The pests are destroyed or removed from the host plants. The following are examples of mechanical methods:

- Rototilling—Rototilling destroys some pests, particularly weeds in large landscape beds. However, hand pulling of a few weeds in small beds may be the best control technique. Tilling also brings some insects to the soil surface where birds can feed on them.
- Mowing—Mowing cuts off weed flowers and seeds. Not only does it partially destroy the weed, but it also destroys places where other insect and disease pests can hide.
- Mulching—Covering the ground with a layer of plastic, bark mulch, or other material prevents weed growth. Mulching is used in landscape beds that contain many ornamental plants.
- Picking— Remove insects from plants by picking them off. A few bag worms on evergreen trees can be removed by individual picking. Cut the branches of the tree to remove the tent caterpillar nests.

CHEMICAL PEST MANAGEMENT

A **pesticide** is a chemical used to reduce pest populations. The term pesticide means pest killer. Cide is the Latin term meaning to kill. Pesticides can be divided into the following major groups: **insecticides** kill insects, **fungicides** kill fungi, **herbicides** kill weeds, and **nematicides** kill nematodes.

18-19. Pine needle mulch used to control weeds in this flower bed.

Pesticides are complex compounds developed and tested in a laboratory. The use of a particular pesticide must be approved by various government agencies, such as the Environmental Protection Agency (EPA). Each pesticide has a label that describes conditions of use. A product should only be used according to the label. Pesticides can be hazardous to humans; handle with care. Pesticides vary in how they can be mixed with water, fertilizer, or other compounds to help apply them on the host plant. Wetting agents help disperse and spread the pesticide on waxy leaf surfaces.

18-20. Handle all insecticides with care.

Insecticides

Chemicals that kill insects or insect forms, such as larvae, are known as insecticides. Some substances used are very poisonous. The active ingredient in the insecticide does the killing. By law, the labels on containers must describe the amount and kind of active ingredient. Always follow the approved uses on insecticide labels.

Insecticides can be manufactured in several different formulations or forms—wettable powders, solutions, and granules. Each formulation is designed to work under certain conditions. Mix wettable powders and solutions with water and apply this liquid to plants. Apply dry pesticides, called granules, to the soil surface.

INSECTICIDES CLASSIFICATION

- Stomach poisons—Stomach poisons are eaten by the insects. The insecticide must be on the plant leaf when the pest eats the leaf. Stomach poisons work best on chewing insects, such as caterpillars, armyworms, and bagworms.

- Contact poisons—These poisons are absorbed through the insect's exoskeleton. To work, the insecticide must come in contact with the insect. Apply after insects begin damaging the plant. Use contact poisons for controlling sucking insects, such as aphids and scale insects.

- Systemic poisons—Systemic poisons are inside the plant tissue. Apply granules containing the systemic poison to the soil around the host plant. The roots will absorb the poison and translocate through the plant.

- Fumigants—Fumigants are insecticides in a gas form. The poison enters the insect's body through the respiratory system. Plow or rototill the soil and cover with a plastic sheet. The nematicide fumigant is injected into the soil after covering. Methyl bromide and chloropicrin (tear gas chemicals) are commonly used for fumigation. They will kill insects, nematodes, fungi, and weed seeds.

18-21. The soil under the plastic has been fumigated to kill insects and disease organisms prior to planting new turf.

Take care in handling and applying insecticides. They are dangerous! Humans should wear protective clothing and masks. Always wash skin and clothes after using insecticides. Read all insecticide labels before using. Remember that in using a pesticide you are releasing it into our environment. It can get into the air, water, and other natural resources.

An insect management program should include the following steps:

- Identify and monitor insect population.

- Determine the potential for damage/economic threshold.

- Assess environmental hazards.

- Decide on an integrated control measure.

- Use control measures.

- Evaluate results.

TIP: When opening paper bags that contain pesticides, always cut them open. Do not tear them. This reduces the danger of pesticide particles getting into the air and prevents spilling.

Nematicides

Chemicals used to manage nematodes are known as nematicides. Because the nematodes are in the soil, treatments must penetrate into the soil. Most nematicides are granular in form. Water the soil and wash the pesticides down to where the nematodes live.

Herbicides

Herbicide chemicals are used to destroy weeds in the landscape. *Herb* is the Latin word for plant. Thus, herbicides are really plant killers. Herbicides applied to the soil before weed seeds germinate are called **preemergent** (*pre* = before). They prevent weed seeds from germi-nating. Apply **postemergent** (*post* = after) herbicides to the leaves of the weed after they have germinated. This group of herbicides will destroy actively growing weeds. Remember that just as herbicide may destroy a weed, it may also destroy the desired plant. Always choose and use her-bicides according to the label.

TIP: Always spray pesticides on a calm day. Wind speeds of over 10 mph can cause spray parti-cles to drift onto non-target plants and areas.

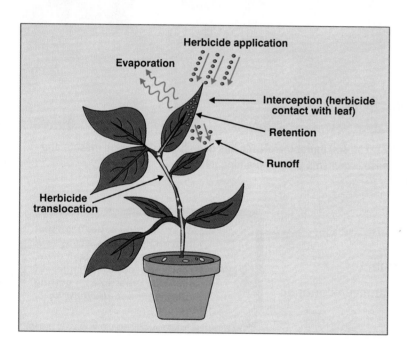

18-22. Herbicide uptake by plants.

Selective herbicides are chemicals used to kill only certain plant species. They are effective in controlling broadleaf weeds in a lawn without damaging the desirable turfgrass. **Non-selective herbicides** will kill all vegetation without regard to species. **Contact herbicides** kill only the portions of the plants that they contact. **Systemic herbicides** are absorbed into a plant's vascular and root system, destroying the entire plant.

The performance of herbicides depends upon temperature, rainfall, humidity, maturity of the weeds, soil characteristics, and the chemical concentration. Higher temperatures elevate metabolic rates in plants, thus speeding up the injurious effects of the herbicide. High humid-ity also increases herbicide uptake and action. Young plants are more susceptible to herbicide injury than old plants.

18-23. Apply granular preemergent herbicides to prevent weed seed germination.

Chemicals to Manage Plant Diseases

Many kinds of chemicals are used to manage plant diseases. The kind used depends on the disease problem. Accurate diagnosis of the disease is important. Apply protective chemicals before the disease attacks the plant. Curative chemicals are applied to plants after they have the disease.

Fungicides are used with plant diseases caused by fungi. The best fungicides are systemic in action. Fungicides move into the vascular system of a plant and reach all parts. Fungi are killed all over the plant. Fungicides that kill by contact must be sprayed directly on the growing fungi. Bactericides control plant diseases caused by bacteria. Spray the systemic bactericides on the plant leaves to prevent and/or cure diseases. For viral diseases, remove the infected plants from the landscape to prevent the further spread of the disease.

Wet, shady landscape sites promote the growth of moss and algae. Prevent their growth by improving soil drainage and pruning trees and shrubs to increase light penetration to the affected surface. Control existing moss and algae by mixing 2 ounces of copper sulfate in 5 gallons of water. Use a sprinkling can to apply this mixture to the moss or algae infected area.

SAFETY PRACTICES IN PEST MANAGEMENT

Many of the methods used to manage pests pose hazards to the user and to the environment. They can injure people and other animals. They can pollute the environment and contaminate water and food. Government laws have been passed to regulate the use of pesticides. Also, pesticides are approved for specific pests and host plant application.

> **TIP:** MSDS safety information on each chemical used must be available to all employees. This is true not only for pesticides but also for window cleaners and floor wax.

> **TIP:** Do not allow children around spray equipment or where pesticides are stored.

Federal laws require all businesses to have Materials Safety Data Sheet (MSDS) information to employees that come in contact with any chemicals in the workplace. MSDS are provided by the company that makes the chemicals. All pesticides are shipped with MSDS information so each business will be able to inform employees and maintain a file of these data sheets. Today, there are many computer databases available that contain this important information.

Pesticides are divided into three major groups and are given signal words to describe their toxicity or potential for harming humans. The signal word DANGER-POISON means the pesticide is highly toxic to humans. The signal word WARNING means moderately toxic, while CAUTION means low or slightly toxic. These signal words will be in large print on all pesticide labels. Read the entire pesticide label before using any pesticide.

Pesticide toxicity is given in milligrams of pesticide per kilogram of body weight that will kill 50 percent of a test population. This is called **Lethal Dose (LD$_{50}$)** which is pronounced as L D fifty. For example, one pesticide may have a LD$_{50}$ of 8 while another pesticide may have a LD$_{50}$ of 200. Only 8 milligrams of the first pesticide with the LD$_{50}$ of 8 would be needed to kill 50 percent of the test population while 200 milligrams from the second would be needed. The smaller the number the more toxic the pesticide is to humans!

UNDERSTANDING A PESTICIDE LABEL

The approved label on a pesticide product is a license to sell for the manufacturer. It is a way to control the distribution, storage, sale, use, and disposal of the product to the state or federal government. To the user, the label is a source of facts on how to use the pesticide correctly and legally. To physicians, the label is a source of information on proper treatment for injury. The pesticide label is the law.

Every manufacturer has a Brand, Trade, or Product Name for its pesticide. Different manufacturers use different names for products containing the same active ingredient. The Common Name of a pesticide is a shortened version of the complex chemical name. It is included in the Ingredient Statement on the label. Only Common Names which are approved by the U.S. Environmental Protection Agency (EPA) may be used in the Ingredient Statement. The Chemical Name is the complex name which identifies the chemical components and structure of the pesticide. The Chemical Name is listed in the Ingredient Statement along with the percentage amount of each ingredient. The type of pesticide and what it will successfully control is also listed, as well as the net contents. The contents are expressed in ounces or pounds for dry formulations, and as gallons, quarts, or pints for liquids. Liquid formulations may also list the pounds of active ingredient per gallon of product. Pesticides are available in a variety of formulations and each is used in its own way. A wettable powder is not the same as a dust.

chipco® Sevin® 80WSP

brand Carbaryl Insecticide

RHÔNE-POULENC

FOR COMMERICAL USE ONLY ... NOT FOR USE BY HOMEOWNERS

ACTIVE INGREDIENT:
Carbaryl (1-naphthyl N-methylcarbamate) .... 80% by wt.
INERT INGREDIENTS: .... 20% by wt.
E.P.A. Reg. No. 264-526   E.P.A. Est. No.

KEEP OUT OF REACH OF CHILDREN
WARNING   AVISO

Si usted no entiende la etiqueta, busque a alguien para que se la explique a usted en detalle.
(If you do not understand the label, find someone to explain it to you in detail.)

For <u>MEDICAL</u> And <u>TRANSPORTATION</u> Emergencies <u>ONLY</u> Call 24 Hours A Day 1-800-334-7577
For <u>PRODUCT</u> <u>USE</u> Information Call 1-800-334-9745

STATEMENT OF PRACTICAL TREATMENT

Carbaryl is an N-Methyl Carbamate Insecticide.

IF SWALLOWED: Never give anything by mouth to an unconscious or convulsing person. If conscious and not convulsing, drink 1 to 2 glasses of water and induce vomiting by touching the back of the throat with finger.

IF IN EYES: Flush eyes with plenty of water. Get medical attention if irritation persists.

IF ON SKIN: Wash thoroughly with soap and water.

IF INHALED: Move from contaminated atmosphere and call a physician.

GENERAL
Contact a physician immediately in all cases of suspected poisoning. Transport to a physician or hospital immediately and SHOW A COPY OF THIS LABEL TO THE PHYSICIAN.

ANTIDOTE STATEMENT
ATROPINE SULFATE IS HIGHLY EFFECTIVE AS AN ANTIDOTE. See NOTE TO PHYSICIAN.

NOTE TO PHYSICIAN
Carbaryl is a carbamate insecticide, which is a cholinesterase inhibitor. Overexposure to this substance may cause toxic signs and symptoms due to stimulation of the cholinergic nervous system. These effects of overexposure are spontaneously and rapidly reversible.

Specific treatment consists of parenteral atropine sulfate. Caution should be maintained to prevent over atropinization. Mild cases may be given 1 to 2 mg intramuscularly every 10 minutes until full atropinization has been achieved and repeated thereafter whenever symptoms reappear. Severe cases should be given 2 to 4 mg intravenously every 10 minutes until fully atropinized, then intramuscularly every 30 to 60 minutes to maintain the effect for at least 12 hours. Dosages for children should be appropriately reduced. Complete recovery from overexposure is to be expected within 24 hours.

Narcotics and other sedatives should not be used. Further, drugs like 2-PAM (pyridine-2-aldoxime methiodide) are NOT recommended.

To aid in confirmation of a diagnosis, urine samples should be obtained within 24 hours of exposure and immediately frozen. Analyses will be arranged by Rhône-Poulenc Ag Company.

Consultation on therapy can be obtained at all hours by calling Rhône-Poulenc emergency number 1-800-334-7577.

PRECAUTIONARY STATEMENTS

HAZARDS TO HUMANS (& DOMESTIC ANIMALS)
WARNING

MAY BE FATAL IF SWALLOWED. Avoid breathing of dust or spray mist. Do not take internally. Avoid contact with eyes, skin or clothing.

PERSONAL PROTECTIVE EQUIPMENT:

Applicators and other handlers must wear long-sleeved shirt and long pants, waterproof gloves, shoes plus socks and chemical-resistant headgear for overhead exposure.

Discard clothing and other absorbent materials that have been drenched or heavily contaminated with this product's concentrate. Do not reuse them. Follow manufacturer's instructions for cleaning and maintaining Personal Protective Equipment (PPE). If no such instructions for washables, use detergent and hot water. Keep and wash PPE separately from other laundry.

When handlers use closed systems, enclosed cabs, or aircraft in a manner that meets the requirements listed in the Worker Protection Standard (WPS) for agricultural pesticides [40 CFR 170.240 (d) (4-6)], the handler PPE requirements may be reduced or modified as specified in the WPS.

18-24. A sample pesticide label.

Signal Words and Symbols are used on the label as a clue in recognizing how potentially dangerous the product is to humans. The Signal Word must appear on the front in large letters immediately following "Keep Out of Reach of Children" which must appear on every pesticide label.

Signal words include:

- DANGER—indicates that the pesticide is highly toxic. Any product which is highly toxic orally, dermally, or through inhalation or causes severe eye and skin burning will be labeled "DANGER." In addition, all pesticides which are highly toxic orally, dermally, or through inhalation will carry the word POISON printed in red and will have the skull and crossbones symbol.

- WARNING—indicates that the pesticide is moderately toxic. Any pesticide which is moderately toxic orally, dermally, or through inhalation or causes moderate eye and skin irritation will be labeled "WARNING."

- CAUTION—signals that the product is slightly toxic. Any pesticide that is slightly toxic orally, dermally, or through inhalation or causes slight eye and skin irritation will be labeled "CAUTION."

Precautionary Statements are included on pesticide labels to help users decide the proper steps to take to protect the user, others, and domesticated animals that may be exposed. These statements are sometimes listed under the heading "Hazards to Humans and Domestic Animals."

Route of Entry Statements immediately follow the signal word, either on the front or side of the pesticide label. They indicate the route or routes of entry (mouth, skin, lungs) that must be particularly protected. Many pesticides are hazardous by more than one route. A single pesticide label may have several precautions listed.

Specific Action Statements follow the Route of Entry Statements. They tell the user the specific action that should be taken to prevent poisoning accidents. The statements are related to the toxicity of the pesticide (Signal Word) and the Route of Entry Statements. "Do not breathe vapors or mist" and "avoid contact with skin or clothing" are common Specific Action Statements.

Examples of Specific Action Statements:

- Protective Clothing and Equipment Statements—listed on many pesticide labels. Long-sleeved shirts, long-legged pants, and gloves should be worn when applying all pesticides.

- Statement of Practical Treatment—gives the recommended first aid treatment in case of accidental poisoning. All DANGER and some WARNING and CAUTION labels contain a note to physicians describing the appropriate medical procedures for poisoning. They may identify an antidote.

- Environmental Hazards Statements—warns of potential hazards to the environment. Special warning statements should be read very closely.

- Special Toxicity Statements—warn of potential hazards to wildlife, insects, or aquatic organisms. These statements help choose the safest pesticide for a particular situation.

- General Environmental Statements—appear on almost every pesticide label. They are reminders to use common sense to avoid contaminating the environment.

- Physical or Chemical Hazards Statements—indicate special fire, explosion, or chemical hazards the pesticide may pose.

- Classification Statements—indicate whether the Environmental Protection Agency (EPA) has classified the pesticide as "general" or "restricted use." This does not mean that the product has a low hazard level. Use the Signal Words and Precautionary Statements to judge the toxicity hazard of the pesticide.

- Reentry Statements—included on pesticide labels that have DANGER or WARNING signals. They tell how much time must pass before people can reenter a treated area without appropriate protective clothing and equipment. If no Reentry Statement appears on a label, sprays must be dry or dusts must be settled before reentering a treated area without protective clothing. This is the minimum legal reentry interval.

- Storage and Disposal Instructions—included for a pesticide and its container on all pesticide labels.

- Directions for Use—tell how to use the pesticide. It gives information about the pest the product claims to control; the crop, animal, or site it is intended to protect; the form in which the product should be applied; the proper equipment needed; how much to use; mixing directions; compatibility with other products; as well as where and when the product should be applied. Additional information may include the minimum number of days between application and the harvest of crops.

APPLYING PESTICIDES SAFELY

Understanding the proper use of pesticides is imperative to their effectiveness and to the safety of people. When applying pesticides, the user should wear the proper protective clothing and equipment that the label on the pesticide container recommends. The application equipment should be

TIP: When mixing pesticides, the minimum protective clothing articles are: rubber boots, rubber gloves, rubber apron, and goggles.

checked for leaking hoses or connections and plugged or dripping nozzles. Any defects or problems should be repaired or corrected before use. All people, pets, or livestock should be cleared from the area before application. Pesticides should be applied only on days with no breezes to minimize drift, preferably in the morning.

- **Goggles**
- **Respirator**
- **Long-sleeved shirt**
- **Sleeves over long rubber gloves**
- **Wide-brimmed hat**
- **Overalls**
- **Rubber band around cuff**
- **Rubber boots**

18-25. Wear protective clothing and equipment when applying pesticides.

TIP: The minimum protective clothing articles when applying pesticides are: hat, long sleeve shirt, long trousers, socks, and shoes.

Some safety guidelines when applying pesticides include:

- Use only approved pesticides—Government regulations allow the use of certain pesticides and prohibit the use of others. Follow the law!

- Read the label before application—Review specific warnings and precautions and other instructions before you begin.

- Use the pesticide with the lowest toxicity—Toxicity refers to how poisonous the pesticide is.

- Use the right equipment—The same sprayer should not be used for insecticides and herbicides because a residue can be left in the tank or other parts.

- Mix according to the directions on the pesticide label—If mixing is required, use the recommended proportions, measure carefully, and mix thoroughly in a well-ventilated area.

- Apply evenly—The pesticide should be sprayed uniformly with a minimum of overlap.

- Avoid vapor damage—Vaporization is the evaporation of an active ingredient during or after application and can occur when it is windy or when the temperature following application will reach 85°F.

- Clean up—Thoroughly clean all equipment inside and out following the pesticide label instructions; including any excess pesticide that cannot be used.

- Store properly—Pesticides should be stored in their original containers and be protected from temperature extremes.

- Know the correct emergency measures—Read the statement of practical treatment before you begin. It is a good idea to have emergency telephone numbers handy.

TIP: If clothing is contaminated during pesticide application, remove it and shower at once. The clothing should be laundered in hot water before it is worn again.

STORING PESTICIDES SAFELY

Proper storage of pesticides is important. Some reasons include protecting human health, preserving the environment, and maintaining chemical effectiveness. One should buy only the amount of pesticide that is needed for a particular job or for the current growing season. Smaller containers may be more expensive. However, they may be the best buy because they eliminate waste and the need for storage space.

If you need to store pesticides, always read the pesticide label for specific requirements. The chemical and the container must be maintained in good condition and disposed of properly.

When designing or designating a pesticide storage area, there are several considerations. The area should be easy to lock, well-ventilated, properly lighted, dry, and protected from extreme heat and freezing. The area should allow enough space so that the various types of chemicals can be separated. It should be enclosed in such a manner that leaks or spills can be easily contained and easily cleaned up. Storage areas must be designed so that there is no danger of chemicals being washed into local water supplies.

Use approved management techniques for storing pesticides safely. Some techniques include:

- Locate your storage area where clean-up materials, such as absorbents and water, are close at hand.

- Keep pesticides in their original containers with pesticide labels in place.
- Never store pesticides near food, medicine, or cleaning supplies.
- Do not store flammable materials with pesticides.
- Organize the materials so they are accessible and visible.
- Mark each container with the date of purchase.
- Routinely check containers for damage or leaks.
- Dispose of unwanted or outdated materials and containers according to the pesticide label recommendations.

INTEGRATED PEST MANAGEMENT (IPM)

Integrated pest management (IPM) uses cultural, biological, mechanical, and chemical techniques to limit pest populations with the least disruption to the environment. Integrated pest management is an ecologically based pest strategy that relies heavily on natural enemies and weather to control pest populations. Research has shown that no single measure works consistently over a long period in pest management. One reason is pests can

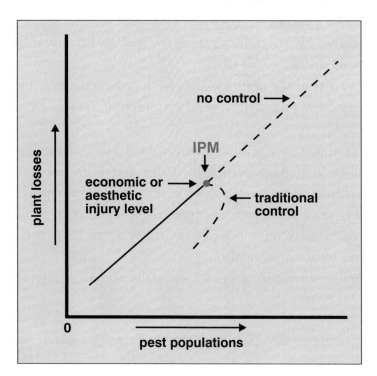

18-26. Growers strive to hold plant losses and pest populations at or below the aesthetic injury level.

develop a resistance to the pesticide. The goal of IPM is to keep pest populations below the **aesthetic injury level**. At this point, visible plant damage justifies using pest control techniques.

BASIC ELEMENTS OF AN IPM PROGRAM

- Knowledge and information needed to devise the system and make sound decisions
- Program for monitoring the ecosystem elements
- Pest densities at which control methods are put into action
- Techniques used to manipulate pest populations
- Agents and materials

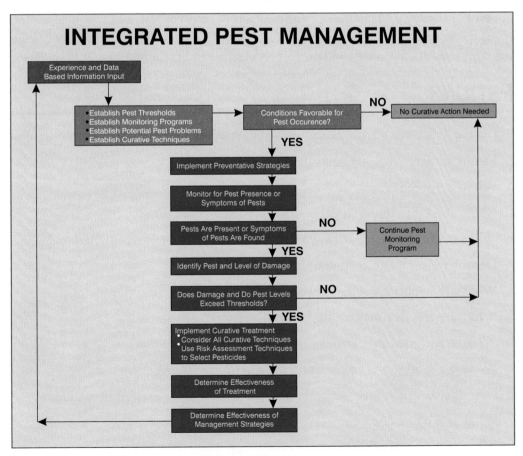

18-27. Integrated pest management (IPM) decision flowchart.

REVIEWING

MAIN IDEAS

The presence of pests in our environment impacts the quality and growth of ornamental plants. Five major groups of pests are: (1) insects and insect-related, (2) weeds, (3) diseases, (4) nematodes, (5) rodents and other animals.

A pest is anything that causes injury or loss to a plant. A host plant provides a pest with food. Insects feeding on a host plant can reduce the quality and vigor of the host plant. Weeds compete with ornamental plants for light, water, nutrients, and space. Plant diseases interfere with the normal appearance, growth, and structure of a plant.

Many pests are not harmful to the plants, but some can destroy entire communities of plants. Pests that attack plants can be found growing actively above and below the soil. Understanding the life cycle of each pest can help improve strategies and techniques to reduce pest populations so damage is minimized. An integrated pest management (IPM) approach uses a combination of measures to limit pest populations and involves biological, cultural, mechanical, and chemical techniques.

Always follow safety procedures when using pesticides. Read the pesticide label twice before applying any pesticides. People should protect themselves and the environment from damage.

QUESTIONS

Answer the following questions using correct spelling and complete sentences.

1. Define integrated pest management (IPM).

2. What is a weed?

3. Name three beneficial insects.

4. What is the difference between preemergent and postemergent herbicides?

5. Describe incomplete metamorphosis.

6. What are important safety practices to follow when using pesticides?

7. What are the five major categories of pests?

8. What is included in cultural pest management techniques?

9. What is the meaning of the term "aesthetic injury level"?

10. Describe the difference between a selective and nonselective herbicide.

11. What is a plant disease?

12. What is a pesticide?

CHAPTER SELF-CHECK

Match the term with the correct definition. Place the letter in the blank provided.

a. host
b. larvae
c. pesticide

d. preemergence
e. incomplete metamorphosis

f. nematode
g. pathogenic

_____1. Very small worm-like organisms that invade the roots of ornamental plants

_____2. The stage of insect life that causes the most damage to plants

_____3. Chemicals that will control most pests on ornamental plants

_____4. Cause infectious plant diseases

_____5. A plant that has insect or disease damage

_____6. Herbicide applied before weed seeds germinate

_____7. The nymph stage belongs to this insect life cycle.

EXPLORING

1. Collect and identify ten weeds from your home lawn and landscape planting beds. Prepare a display of your collection for the classroom. Devise a management plan to reduce the population of these pests. Prepare a report on your findings.

2. Collect and identify ten insects. Include at least two beneficial insects. Properly identify and display the insects.

3. Make an inventory of all the pesticides at your home or school. Review the labels on the products. List the intended pest(s), active ingredient, and toxicity level for each pesticide. Caution: Be sure to wear protective gloves and avoid inhaling pesticide products when handling containers.

CHAPTER 19

Calculating Landscape Maintenance Costs

OBJECTIVES

1 Identify the skills to be mastered by a landscape maintenance technician.

2 Describe how to estimate costs associated with landscape maintenance.

TERMS

computer spreadsheet
contingency costs
cost summation
estimate sheet

landscape maintenance
landscape maintenance
   technician
landscape service contract

landscape service proposal
overhead costs
profit

19-1. Turfgrass aeration is a seasonal or once-a-year landscape maintenance activity.(Courtesy, Eddie Seagle, Abraham Baldwin Agricultural College)

A COMMON landscape maintenance activity is the mowing of a turfgrass area. If you were in the maintenance business, how would you determine what to charge for mowing the area? Would you charge the same amount for every job? Would you base your price on what your competitors charge? What would you charge for related maintenance activities?

Pricing maintenance work can be challenging. It can be particularly challenging for those people who love the horticulture work but have not been educated in the business aspects of the industry. This chapter will focus on how you might determine the cost for maintenance work performed. It also shows an example of a landscape service proposal and a landscape service contract.

MAINTENANCE TECHNICIANS

Landscape maintenance is the continued efforts to preserve the existing landscape. Maintenance practices begin once the landscape has been installed. Landscape maintenance practices involve a wide range of activities. The *landscape maintenance technician*, the person trained in and given charge of maintaining a landscape, must be proficient in numerous maintenance skills.

Landscape maintenance technicians can learn maintenance skills through a variety of ways. Many begin their horticulture education at the high school level, and continue at a community college or a four-year university. Others begin at a community college or on the job. Education is essential for the technician due to the technical nature of the skills in

19-2. A landscape maintenance technician must be proficient in numerous maintenance skills.

which he or she must be proficient. Some states have certification exams to obtain a license to perform landscape maintenance jobs.

People who work in landscape maintenance must often have skills in a wide range of areas. However, some workers may only operate equipment, such as a mower. Some of the areas in which skills may be needed are listed below.

Determining the cost of maintaining landscapes really begins with an understanding of the types of jobs conducted in the maintenance end of the landscape industry. Some of the most common jobs or technical skills to be mastered by landscape maintenance technicians follow.

LANDSCAPE MAINTENANCE SKILLS

Safety—Safety should be the number one priority for landscape maintenance technicians. An understanding of the proper use of tools and safety procedures can greatly reduce the risk of injury on-the-job. Training in first aid is highly recommended. First aid training should include CPR, treatment for burns, proper care of cuts, frostbite, heat cramps, heat exhaustion, heat stroke, chemical injury, and impaled objects.

Reading a plan—Plan reading is one of the most important aspects of determining maintenance costs. The technician should be able to interpret the designer's intent in order to maintain the desired landscape. Also, linear and area measurements can be obtained from the plan and used to calculate maintenance costs.

Identifying and caring for plants—Landscape maintenance technicians need expertise in plant identification and care. Being able to correctly identify landscape plants allows the technician to administer proper care. It is also beneficial for the technician to understand specific cultural requirements of plants.

Grading and establishing turfgrass—Turfgrass is the most common ground cover used in landscapes. It often needs to be repaired or replaced due to damage or disease. Landscape maintenance technicians should be able to level and grade an area and plant sod, plugs, or seed. Specific skills related to turfgrass establishment are discussed in Chapter 11.

Identifying irrigation components—Irrigation systems have become common in landscape settings. Landscape maintenance technicians should have knowledge in the identification and function of the various irrigation system components. Such knowledge is useful in the maintenance and repair of those systems.

Programming irrigation controllers—Irrigation controllers are the key to automated irrigation systems. They allow precise watering timetables and water management. Understanding how to install and program controllers is essential when working with automated irrigation systems.

Repairing lateral lines and head adjustments—Lateral lines make up an essential part of irrigation systems. Lateral lines often require repair, cleaning, and testing. A technician should be knowledgeable in these skills. An understanding of how to repair and adjust sprinkler heads that distribute the water is also valuable.

Trucks and trailers—Landscape maintenance technicians should have a thorough understanding of safety, maintenance, and operation of trucks and trailers. Mastery of skills required by state licensing agencies is critical.

Transplanting woody plants—On occasion woody landscape plants need to be transplanted to the landscape to replace existing plants or to alter the landscape appearance. Knowledge of planting procedures and care for the newly planted plants discussed in Chapter 10 is important for landscape maintenance technicians.

Pruning techniques—A critical aspect of maintaining existing landscapes is the pruning of woody plants. Landscape maintenance technicians should understand reasons for pruning and pruning techniques discussed in Chapter 16.

Mowing turfgrass—An important facet of maintaining the landscape is the management of the turfgrass areas. Landscape maintenance technicians should be well versed in the safe use and maintenance of both walk behind and riding mowers. Skills pertaining to turf management and care are discussed in Chapter 17.

Aerating turfgrass—Aerators relieve soil compaction in turf areas. Landscape maintenance technicians should be able to operate and maintain these pieces of equipment.

Edging and trimming—Edging and trimming of turf areas provides a clean appearance to the landscape. Landscape maintenance technicians should be able to operate and maintain these pieces of equipment.

Using pesticides safely—It is critical that landscape maintenance technicians receive extensive training in the safe use and handling of pesticides. An important skill is the ability to mix and apply pesticides in accordance to the instructions on the label. Safe practices are explained in Chapter 18.

Fertilizing—Landscape plants may benefit from the application of fertilizers. Landscape maintenance technicians should be able to choose fertilizers for specific uses and calculate the exact amounts to be applied. Details on fertilizing landscape plants are covered in Chapters 15 and 17.

DETERMINING MAINTENANCE COSTS

Determining the cost of maintaining landscapes begins with an understanding of the types of jobs conducted in the maintenance end of the landscape industry. Some of the skills in estimating costs follow.

One of the first things to understand about costing landscape maintenance projects is nearly every company has a different method of reaching a final cost estimate. There is no standard used by the industry. However, from a business standpoint it is essential that landscapers determine a method to accurately price their services. Prices should provide a profit so the business stays viable. They should also be competitive to ensure a regular flow of customers. Finally, the work should be of high quality to maintain customer loyalty.

TIP: It is essential that landscapers determine a method to accurately price their services.

As with the pricing of landscape installation, an estimate sheet is a useful tool in calculating landscape maintenance costs. An **estimate sheet** is a form for calculating prices. It helps if the same form is used for each project. On the estimate sheet, identify the jobs to be completed, determine the size of the job, and estimate how many hours it will take workers to complete the project. Also, calculate the cost of labor and materials used to complete the job. The estimate sheet is for the landscaper only. Figures presented to the customer are placed on a proposal sheet or a contract.

Add overhead costs, contingency costs, and profit to the cost of labor and materials to obtain a grand total for the services to be provided. One procedure for establishing landscape maintenance costs is as follows:

1. List in detail the anticipated cost for both labor and materials. Use the actual wages the employees will be paid and the cost of the materials purchased.

2. The job cost is the cost of labor and materials required to complete a specific task or job. The same job could be completed a number of times during the year. An example is mowing the lawn. The job cost is multiplied by the number of times the job is performed annually to get a total annual cost.

3. **Overhead costs** are the general costs in running a business. Examples include mortgage or lease payments, legal fees, utilities, insurance, office expenses, trucks, trailers, and maintenance of equipment. To obtain the overhead costs multiply the total for labor and materials by 20 percent.

4. A **contingency cost** should be figured into all jobs. This cost accounts for theft of materials on the work site, mechanical breakdowns, rain outs, etc. The

contingency charge may vary from job to job. An accepted charge is to multiply the overhead plus labor and materials by 10 percent.

5. Add the labor, materials, overhead, and contingency charges to obtain a *cost summation*.

6. *Profit* is the amount of money the landscaper receives after deducting all costs of the project. The mark-up for profit is included on the estimate sheet. A fair mark-up for profit is 20 percent. Multiply the cost summation by 20 percent to determine the profit.

7. Total cost for the project is the addition of the summation costs and the profit.

Table 19-1. An Example Landscape Maintenance Estimate Sheet

LANDSCAPE MAINTENANCE ESTIMATE SHEET						
JOB NAME				DATE		
JOB LOCATION						
JOB DESCRIPTION						
Description	**Number of times done annually**	**Hours per visit**	**Labor cost ($15.00/hour)**	**Material costs**	**Job cost**	**Total annual cost**
Mowing and trimming 10,000 sq. ft.	30	2	$30.00	0	$30.00	$ 900.00
Fertilize turfgrass	3	1	$15.00	$50.00	$65.00	$ 195.00
Broadleaf weed control	2	1	$15.00	$20.00	$35.00	$ 70.00
Aerate turfgrass	1	2	$30.00	0	$30.00	$ 30.00
Prune woody plants	3	2	$30.00	0	$30.00	$ 90.00
Fall clean up	1	6	$90.00	0	$90.00	$ 90.00
			Subtotal annual costs (labor + materials)			$1,375.00
			Overhead costs (subtotal annual costs × 20%)			$ 275.00
			Contingency costs (subtotal annual costs + overhead × 10%)			$ 165.00
			Cost summation (subtotal annual costs + overhead + contingency)			$1,815.00
			Profit (cost summation × 20%)			$ 363.00
			TOTAL (cost summation + profit)			$2,178.00

When pricing landscape maintenance work, be aware that every job will be different from the others. Some properties are more difficult to maintain than others. For example, some properties might be hilly, while others are flat. Some lots may have numerous trees that take time to mow around. Pricing should reflect the difficulty of the job. Experience in the business will help in preparing accurate estimates for jobs with varied degrees of difficulty.

Using Computer Spreadsheets

Computer spreadsheet software is a useful tool that can be used to calculate landscape maintenance costs, prepare estimates, and keep records. A **computer spreadsheet** is an all-purpose computer program that is used for almost any task involving the organization of numbers based on columns and rows. Once the spreadsheet has been set up properly, it can be used over and over as a template with all of the calculations stored as formulas in place. A knowledge of how to enter formulas and formats for the particular software program being used is essential in setting it up properly. Some current computer spreadsheet programs include Excel, Lotus, and Paradox.

19-3. An example of a computer spreadsheet used to calculate landscape maintenance costs.

Landscape Service Proposal and Service Contract

Once the cost for the work has been determined, a landscape service proposal can be made. The **landscape service proposal** is a document prepared for the client where proposed services to be provided are identified. Only total costs are given to the client. The method used in calculating mark-ups on the estimate sheet is not discussed.

Should the proposal be accepted, a service contract is signed. The **landscape service contract** is a legal document binding the client and the landscaper. It is wise to have the contract prepared in advance to the meeting with the client. Then, if both parties reach an agreed upon price for the services, the deal can be sealed with the signing of the service contract.

AJB Landscapes, Inc.

February 28, 2009

LANDSCAPE SERVICE PROPOSAL

Weekly mowing and trimming throughout the growing season:

Mow the grass.
Trim edges.
Blow clippings from paved areas.

Fertilizer applications to the lawn:

Fertilize the lawn with premium fertilizer in May, June, and September.

Broadleaf weed control:

Apply broadleaf weed control in the spring and the fall.

Aerate the lawn:

Core cultivate the lawn in early spring.

Prune woody plants:

Prune woody plants twice during the year.
Remove branches from property.

Fall clean up:

Collect and remove fallen leaves and debris.

Total   **$2,178.00**

Respectfully submitted,

Figure 19-4. A landscape service proposal.

AJB Landscapes, Inc.

February 28, 2009

LANDSCAPE SERVICE CONTRACT

AJB Landscapes, Inc., agrees to provide landscape services specified on order number 32515 dated February 28, 2009, in the sum of $2,178.00.

— Two Thousand One Hundred Seventy-Eight and 00/100 dollars —

Payment is to be made as follows:

Twelve monthly payments of $181.50, with the first payment to accompany the signing of the contract.

AJB Landscapes, Inc., shall not be responsible for "Acts of God" or any other conditions beyond their direct control but otherwise guarantees all materials and services specified herein for a period of one year unless neglected by the purchasers.

Authorized Signature _____

AJB Landscapes, Inc.

Accepted _____

Date _____

Figure 19-5. A simple landscape service contract for work to be performed.

REVIEWING

MAIN IDEAS

Landscape maintenance involves the work of landscape maintenance technicians. To do maintenance work properly, the maintenance technician must be versatile in many tasks. Skills considered necessary for these technicians include safety; reading a plan; knowledge in identification and care of landscape plants; grading and establishing turfgrass; identifying, programming, and controllers and repairing irrigation systems; and operating trucks and trailers. Other skills to master are transplanting woody plants, pruning landscape plants, mowing turfgrass, aerating turfgrass, trimming and edging, using pesticides safely, and fertilizing landscape plants.

The landscaper should determine his or her cost of services to be performed. This is done before presenting the customer with a proposal or contract. An estimate sheet is very helpful in calculating costs. On the estimate sheet, the landscaper can determine his or her costs for labor and materials. Overhead costs, contingency costs, and profit can then be calculated based on the labor and materials. Computer spreadsheet software is a useful tool in calculating landscape maintenance prices.

QUESTIONS

Answer the following questions using correct spelling and complete sentences.

1. What are some skills a landscape maintenance technician should master?

2. What type of education is required of a landscape maintenance technician?

3. How is an estimate sheet used in calculating costs?

4. What are the costs to be calculated in order to reach the total cost? Explain each.

5. What are some factors that might cause one landscape project to be priced differently than another?

CHAPTER SELF-CHECK

Match the term with the correct definition. Write the letter by the term in the blank provided.

a. contingency costs

b. profit

c. landscape maintenance technician

d. overhead costs

e. cost summation

f. estimate sheet

_____1. The amount of money the landscaper receives after deducting all costs of the project.

_____2. This cost accounts for theft of materials on the work site, mechanical breakdowns, rain outs, etc., and should be figured into all jobs.

_____3. Person given charge of maintaining a landscape who is proficient in numerous maintenance skills.

_____4. General costs in running a business including: mortgage or lease payments, legal fees, utilities, insurance, office expenses, trucks, trailers, and maintenance of equipment.

_____5. The addition of the labor, materials, overhead, and contingency costs.

_____6. A form used for calculating prices.

EXPLORING

1. Visit a local landscape company that performs landscape maintenance services, and conduct an informal interview. Ask them how they got into the business. Ask them for recommendations on how to calculate prices.

2. Contact your local, state, and national professional landscape associations. Request information on the education needed to become a qualified landscape maintenance technician. Ask whether there is a landscape maintenance skills certification exam in your state.

3. Calculate the operating costs of grass cutting equipment. Assume a mower uses a half-gallon of gasoline per hour, how much would it use in an 8-hour day? What would the gasoline cost for a day?

Appendixes

Appendix A — Mathematical Conversion Chart

Equivalents	To Convert From:	To:	Multiply By:
1 sq. ft. = 144 sq. in.	sq. ft.	sq. in.	144
	sq. in.	sq. ft.	.006944
1 sq. yd. = 9 sq. ft.	sq. yd.	sq. ft.	9
	sq. ft.	sq. yd.	.111111
1 acre = 43,560 sq. ft.	acres	sq. ft.	43,560
	sq. ft.	acres	.0000229
1 cu. yd. = 27 cu. ft.	cu. yds.	cu. ft.	27
	cu. ft.	cu. yds.	.037037
1 cu. yd. gravel = $1\frac{1}{2}$ tons	cu. yds.	tons	1.5
	tons	cu. yds.	.666666
1 ton = 2,000 lbs.	tons	lbs.	2,000
	lbs.	tons	.0005
1 lb. = 16 oz. = 1 pint	lbs. or pints	oz.	16
	oz.	lbs. or pints	.0625
1 pt. = 2 cups	pts.	cups	2
	cups	prints	.5
1 qt. = 2 pints	qts.	pints	2
	pints	qts.	.5
1 gal. = 4 qts.	gal.	qts.	4
	qts.	gal.	.25

KEY FOR APPENDIX B

Use

A – Accent	G – Garden
B – Bed	GC – Ground Cover
Bg – Bedding	H – Hedge
Bk – Background	P – Potpourri
Br – Border	Ps – Poisonous
C – Container	S – Seeds
CF – Cut Flower	Sc – Screen
DS – Dried Seed	Sh – Shade
E – Edging	Sp – Specimen
F – Foundation	VS – Vine Screen

Texture

C – Coarse	MC – Medium Coarse
F – Fine	MF – Medium Fine
M – Medium	

Color

B – Blue	P – Pink
B-G – Blue Green	Pr – Purple
Bk-G – Black Green	R – Red
C – Crimson	Rs – Rose
G – Emerald Green	R-G – Red Green
Gr – Green	S – Silver
Gy – Gray	Sc – Scarlet
Gy-G – Gray Green	V – Violet
L – Lavender	W – White
Lc – Lilac	Y – Yellow
M – Multi	Y-G – Yellow Green
O – Orange	

Exposure

○ – Sun   ● – Shade   ◗ – Partial Shade

Appendix B — Plant Materials List

ANNUAL FLOWERS

Common Name	Botanical Name	Height	Spacing	Exposure	Color	Use
Ageratum	*Ageratum houstonianum*	6–20"	9–12"	○	B,P,W	G/E/CF
Alyssum, Sweet	*Lobularia maritima*	2–4"	5–10"	○ or ●	W,P,V	E/GC
Aster	*Callistephus chinensis*	12–24"	10–12"	○	W,Y,Pr	B/CF
Baby's Breath	*Gypsophila elegans*	12–18"	12"	○	P,W	B/Br/CF
Balsam	*Impatiens balsamina*	12–28"	8–12"	●	P,R,W,M	B/Br
Begonia	*Begonia semperflorens*	6–10"	8–12"	●	P,R,W	B/C
Candytuft	*Iberis sp.*	6–12"	8–12"	○	W,Lc	E/B/G/GC
Carnation	*Dianthus sp.*	12–24"	12–18"	○	R,Y,W	B/E/CF
Celosia (Cockscomb)	*Celosia argentea*	6–36"	8–12"	○	R,Y,O	B/Br/CF
Coleus	*Coleus blumei*	12–24"	12"	●	R,Y,P	E/B/C
Cornflower	*Centaurea cyanus*	12–36"	12–18"	○ or ◗	B,P,W,R	B/G/CF
Cosmos	*Cosmos bipinnatus*	24–48"	12–18"	○	R,Y,O,P,W	CF/Br
Dahlia	*Dahlia sp.*	12–40"	12–24"	○	R,Y,P,M	B/E/CF
Dianthus	(See Pink)					

(Continued)

435

Appendix B (Continued)

ANNUAL FLOWERS (Continued)						
Common Name	**Botanical Name**	**Height**	**Spacing**	**Exposure**	**Color**	**Use**
Dusty Miller	*Cineraria maritima*	8–24"	8–12"	○	Gy	B/Br
Forget-me-not	*Myosotis* sp.	6–12"	6–8"	○ or ●	P,B	E/B/CF
Four-o'clock	*Mirabilis jalapa*	20–36"	12–18"	○	R,Y,W	Br
Gaillardia	*Gaillardia pulchella*	12–30"	9–12"	○	R with Y	Br/CF
Geranium	*Pelargonium x hortorum*	6–30"	12–15"	○	P,R,W	Bg/C
Globe Amaranth	*Gomphrena globosa*	6–24"	6–12"	○	W,P,R,O	Br/B/CF
Hollyhock	*Alcea rosea*	18–72"	12–18"	○ or ◗	R,P,Y,W,L	Sc/Br
Impatiens	*I. walleriana*	6–15"	8–12"	●	R,P,W,M	B/C
Lantana	*Lantana* sp.	12–36"	2–15"	○	R,Y,B	B/C
Larkspur	*Delphinium* sp.	18–48"	12–18"	○	B,P,W,R	Sc/Br/CF
Lobelia	*Lobelia* sp.	3–6"	4–6"	◗	B,P,W	B/C
Lupine	*Lupinus* sp.	12–36"	8–12"	○	P,Y,W,M	B/CF
Marigold	*Tagetes* sp.	6–30"	6–12"	○	R,Y,P	B/E
Nasturtium	*Tropaeolum* sp.	12–15"	9–12"	○	M	B/E
Pansy	*Viola* sp.	6–8"	6–8"	○ or ◗	M	E/B/C/CF
Petunia	*Petunia x hybrida*	8–24"	12–15"	○	B,P,R,W	B/C
Phlox	*Phlox drummondi*	6–15"	6–15"	○	M	B/E
Pink	*Dianthus chinensis*	8–15"	6–12"	○	P,R,W,M	B/E
Poppy	*Papaver* sp.	18–36"	6–12"	○	R,Y,W	Br/B/CF
Rose Moss	*Portulaca grandiflora*	4–6"	6–12"	○	P,R,W,Y,Sc	B/E/G
Rudbeckia	*Rudbeckia* sp.	18–24"	18"	○	Y	B/Br
Salvia (Scarlet Sage)	*Salvia splendens*	10–36"	8–12"	○	R,W,Pr	B/Br
Snapdragon	*Antirrhinum majus*	10–36"	10–12"	○	M	B/Br/CF
Strawflower	*Helichrysum* sp.	12–36"	12–18"	○	R,Gr,W,Y,Pr	Br/CF
Sunflower, Common	*Helianthus* sp.	2–10'	2–4'	○	Y,O	Sc/B/S
Sweet Pea	*Lathyrus odoratus*	20–30"	8–12"	○	M	VS/B/Br
Verbena	*Verbena x hybrida*	9–18"	8–12"	○	R,W,P,B	B
Vinca (Periwinkle)	*Vinca rosea*	10–18"	8–12"	○	P,W,Cr	B
Zinnia	*Zinnia* sp.	6–48"	8–15"	○	M	B/Br/CF

(Continued)

Appendix B (Continued)

BIENNIAL FLOWERS							
Common Name	Botanical Name	Zone	Height	Spacing	Exposure	Color	Use
Canterbury Bells	Campanula medium	4	3–4'	18–24"	○ or ◗	Y,W,B,P	CF/Br
Daisy, English	Bellis perennis	4	4–8"	10–12"	○	R,W,B,P	E/G
Forget-me-not, Alpine	Myosotis sylvatica	3	8–24"	12–18"	●	B	B/Br
Foxglove	Digitalis purpurea	4	2–4'	18–24"	○ or ◗	P,Y,W,Pr	B/Br/Po
Hollyhock, Old Fashion	Alcea rosea	3	4–8'	12–18"	○	R,Y,P,W	Br
Honesty (Money Plant)	Lunaria annua	4	3'	18–24"	◗	B,W	G/DS
Pansy	Viola cornuta	4	6–8"	10–12"	○ or ◗	M	E/B/Br
Sweet William	Dianthus barbatus	4	12–20"	12–18"	○	R,W,P	E/Br/CF

PERENNIAL FLOWERS							
Common Name	Botanical Name	Zone	Height	Spacing	Exposure	Color	Use
Alyssum (Basket-of-Gold)	Aurinia saxatilis	4	12–15"	24"	○	Y	G/E/CF
Anchusa (Alkanet)	Anchusa azurea	3	1–4'	24"	◗	B	Br/CF
Anthemis	Anthemis tinctoria	4	30–36"	18–24"	○	Y,W	Br
Artemisia (Silver Mound)	Artemisia schmidtiana	3	8–12"	10–15"	○	Gy-Gr	B/E/Br
Aster, Hardy	Aster sp.	4	12–60"	36"	○	W	B/G/CF
Astilbe (False Spirea)	Astilbe x arendsii	4	15–40"	18–24"	●	R,W,P,Sc	Br
Baby's Breath	Gypsophila paniculata	4	2–3'	48"	●	W,P	Br/CF
Balloon Flower	Platycodon grandiflorus	3	20"	12–18"	○ or ◗	W,B,P	Br
Baptisia (False Indigo)	Baptisia australis	3	4–5'	3'	○ or ◗	W,Y,B	Br/GC
Bellflower	Campanula sp.	3	8–20"	12–24"	○ or ◗	B,W	Br/E
Bleeding Heart	Dicentra spectabilis	4	2–3'	1–3'	○ or ◗	W,P	G
Blue Fescue (Festuca)	Festuca ovina	4	8–12"	12–18"	○ or ◗	S-B	B/E/GC
Carnation	Dianthus caryophyllus	3	18–24"	12–15"	○	P,R,W,Y	B/Br/CF
Chinese Lantern	Physalis alkekengi	4	24"	36"	○	O	Br/Sp
Chrysanthemum	Chrysanthemum sp.	5	8–36"	12–30"	○	M	B/Br/E/C F
Columbine	Aquilegia sp.	3	30–36"	12–18"	○ or ◗	M	B/CF
Daisy, Painted	Chrysanthemum coccineum	4	12–24"	12–18"	○	M	Br/CF
Daisy, Shasta	Chrysanthemum maximum	4	15–36"	18–30"	○	W	B/CF
Daylily	Hemerocallis sp.	4	12–48"	24–36"	○ or ◗	P,R	B/G
Delphinium	Delphinium sp.	4	48–60"	24"	○	B,W,Pr	B/CF
Dianthus (Pink)	Dianthus sp.	3	3–24"	12"	○	P	Br/E/CF
Gaillardia (Blanket Flower)	G. x grandiflora	3	12–30"	24"	○	Y,Sc	Br/CF
Globeflower	Trollius europaeus	3	30"	8–10"	●	Y,O	B/CF
Globe Thistle	Echinops exaltatus	4	4'	24–36"	○	B	Br/CF
Hibiscus	Hibiscus sp.	5	3–8'	24"	○	R,W,P,Rs	Br/B/G
Iberis (Candytuft)	Iberis sempervirens	4	8–12"	12–18"	○	W	G/E/GC

(Continued)

Appendix B (Continued)

PERENNIAL FLOWERS (Continued)							
Common Name	**Botanical Name**	**Zone**	**Height**	**Spacing**	**Exposure**	**Color**	**Use**
Lavender	*Lavandula angustifolia*	5	12–36"	12–18"	○	Pr	Br/G/P
Liatris (Gayfeather)	*Liatris* sp.	3	18–72"	18"	○ or ◐	Rs, Pr	Br/CF
Lobelia (Cardinal Flower)	*Lobelia cardinalis*	6	24–30"	24"	◐	Sc	Br/B
Lupine	*Lupinus* sp.	4	3–5'	3'	○	R,P,W,O,Y	Br/CF
Lychnis (Maltese Cross)	*Lychnis* sp.	3	1–3'	18"	○ or ◐	R	Br
Peony	*Paeonia* sp.	3	18–36"	24–36"	○ or ◐	P,R,W	B/Br/CF
Phlox, Moss	*Phlox subulata*	3	4–5"	8"	○	R,P,W,B	Br
Phlox, Summer	*Phlox paniculata*	4	36"	18–24"	○	R,P,W,B	Br/CF
Poppy, Iceland	*Papaver nudicaule*	2	12–18"	24"	○	R,P,W	Br/CF
Poppy, Oriental	*Papaver orientale*	3	24–36"	24"	○	R,P,W,O	G/Br/CF
Potentilla (Cinquefoil)	*Potentilla* sp.	4	24–36"	24–36"	○	W,Y,O,P	B/Br
Primrose	*Primula* sp.	3	6–12"	10–12"	◐ or ●	R,P,W,Y,B	G/Br
Primrose, Evening	*Oenothera* sp.	3	12–18"	8"	○ or ◐	Y	G/Br
Red-hot Poker Plant (Torch Lily)	*Kniphofia* sp.	5	3–5'	18"	○	R,W,Y	Br/Sp
Rudbeckia (Coneflower)	*Rudbeckia* sp.	4	2–4'	24–30"	○	R,P,W	B/Br/CF
Salvia (Sage)	*Salvia* sp.	4	3–4'	18–24"	○	R	Br
Snow-in-Summer	*Cerastium tomentosum*	2	6–9"	24–36"	○	W	G/GC
Speedwell	*Veronica* sp.	3	6–36"	18"	○	Pr	Br/G/CF
Thrift	*Armeria maritima*	3	18–24"	12"	○	P	E/Br/CF
Virginia Bluebells	*Mertensia virginica*	4	12–24"	12–18"	◐ or ●	B	Br
Yarrow	*Achillea* sp.	3	6–36"	36"	○	R,Y,W,P	Br/CF

GROUND COVERS—Herbaceous Perennials							
Common Name	**Botanical Name**	**Zone**	**Height**	**Width**	**Exposure**	**Texture**	**Color**
Ajuga (Bugle Flower)	*Ajuga reptans*	4–8	4–6"	6–12"	◐	C	R-G
Crown Vetch	*Coronilla varia*	3	1–2'	18–24"	○	M	B-G
Lily-of-the-Valley	*Convallaria majalis*	2	6–12"	6–8"	●	MC	B-G
Phlox, Creeping	*Phlox subulata*	2	2–6"	8–12"	○	F	G
Plantain Lily, Fragrant	*Hosta plantaginea*	3	18–24"	2–3'	◐ or ●	C	B-G
Sedum, Red Creeping	*Sedum spurium*	3	6–8"	12–18"	○	F	G
Spurge, Japanese	*Pachysandra terminalis*	4	6–8"	10–16"	○ or ●	M	Y-G
Thyme, Creeping	*Thymus serpyllum*	1–3	1–4"	12–18"	○	F	G

(Continued)

Appendix B (Continued)

GROUND COVERS—Evergreens							
Common Name	**Botanical Name**	**Zone**	**Height**	**Width**	**Exposure**	**Texture**	**Color**
Barren-strawberry	*Waldsteinia ternata*	4	6–12"	12"	○ or ●	MC	G
Bearberry	*Arctostaphylos uva-ursi*	2–6	8–12"	spreads	○ or ◗	F	G
Bearberry, Cotoneaster	*Cotoneaster dammeri*	5–8	12–18"	3–6'	○ or ◗	F	G
Candytuft	*Iberis sempervirens*	4–8	6–12"	18–24"	○ or ◗	F	G
Ivy, Baltic	*Hedera helix 'Baltica'*	4–9	6–8"	8–12"	◗ or ●	M	Bk-G
Euonymus, Purple Wintercreeper	*Euonymus fortunei 'Coloratus'*	5	6"	12–24"	○ or ●	M	G
Juniper	(See Narrowleaf Evergreens)						
Lilyturf, Creeping	*Liriope spicata*	5	8–12"	12–18"	○ or ●	F	G
Mahonia, Creeping	*Mahonia repens*	5	10"	18–24"	○ or ◗	M–C	G
Pachistima, Canby	*Pachistima canbyi*	5	12"	12–24"	◗ or ●	MF	G
Periwinkle, Common (Myrtle)	*Vinca minor*	3	3–6"	9–18"	◗ or ●	MF	G
Spring Heath	*Erica carnea*	5	6–12"	24–36"	●	F	G
St. Johnswort, Aaronsbeard	*Hypericum calycinum*	5–8	12–18"	spreads	○ or ◗	MF	G

VINES							
Common Name	**Botanical Name**	**Zone**	**Height**	**Width**	**Exposure**	**Texture**	**Color**
Akebia, Fiveleaf	*Akebia quinata*	4–8	20–40'	spreads	○ or ●	MF	B-G
Bittersweet, American	*Celastrus scandens*	3–8	20'	spreads	○	M	G
Clematis, Hybrid	*Clematis x hybrida*	3–8	6–18'	4–10'	◗	M	B-G
Fig, Climbing	*Ficus pumila*	8–6	climbs	spreads	◗ or ●	MF	G
Honeysuckle, Trumpet	*Lonicera sempervirens*	4–8	10–20'	spreads	○ or ◗	M	B-G
Ivy, Boston	*Parthenocissus tricuspidata*	4–8	25–35'	spreads	○ or ●	MC	G
Ivy, English	*Hedera helix*	4–9	climbs	spreads	◗ or ●	M	Bk-G
Moneywort	*Lysimachia nummularia*	4	climbs	spreads	○ or ●	M	G
Morning-glory	*Ipomoea purpurea*	4	5–10'	spreads	○	M	G
Silvervine	*Polygonum aubertii*	4	25–30'	30–35'	○ or ●	M	G
Trumpet Vine	*Campsis radicans*	4–9	25–35'	6–8'	○ or ◗	M	G
Virginia Creeper	*Parthenocissus quinquefolia*	3–9	25–50'	spreads	○ or ●	M	G
Wisteria, Japanese	*Wisteria floribunda*	5	25–30'	spreads	○ or ◗	M	G

(Continued)

Appendix B (Continued)

			BULBS/TUBERS				
Common Name	**Botanical Name**	**Hardi-ness/Zone**	**Flower Time**	**Plant Time**	**Planting Depth**	**Spac-ing**	**Height**
Allium	*Allium* sp.	hardy/4	late spring	fall	4–8"	3–6"	4'
Amaryllis	*Amaryllis* sp.	tender/5	summer	spring	top to ground level	12"	2–3'
Anemone	*Anemone blanda*	†/5	very early spring	spring	4"	12"	8"
Begonia, Tuberous	*Begonia x tuberhybrida*	tender	summer	late spring	top to ground level	6–8"	7–14"
Caladium	*Caladium* sp.	tender	summer	late spring	1–4"	10–18"	15–20"
Calla Lily	*Zantedeschia* sp.	tender/9	summer	late spring	3"	12–15"	7–14"
Canna	*Canna* sp.	tender/7	summer	spring	3–4"	1–2'	24–36"
Crocus, Spring	*Crocus* sp.	hardy/4	very early spring	fall	4"	2"	2–6"
Daffodil	*Narcissus* sp.	hardy/4	mid-spring	fall	8"	6–8"	7–12"
Daffodil, Fall	*Stembergia* sp.	†/7	late summer	mid-summer	5"	3"	1'
Dahlia	*Dahlia* sp.	tender/8	summer	spring	4"	24–48"	40–48"
Eranthis	*Eranthis* sp.	hardy/4	spring	late summer	4½"	3–4"	3"
Gladiolus	*Gladiolus* sp.	tender/8	summer	spring	6"	4–6"	28–48"
Hyacinth	*Hyacinthus* sp.	hardy/4	mid-spring	fall	8"	6–8"	7–12"
Hyacinth, Grape	*Muscari* sp.	hardy/4	mid-spring	fall	4"	2–4"	1–4"
Hyacinth, Summer	*Caltonia* sp.	tender	summer	spring	4–6"	6–8"	1–6"
Iris, Bulb	*Iris reticulata*	hardy/4	summer	spring/fall	4"	12"	4–6"
Lily	*Lilium* sp.	hardy/3	summer	spring/fall	2–8"	12–18"	2–4'
Oxalis (Wood Sorrel)	*Oxalis* sp.	†/6	summer	fall	3"	6"	—
Ranunculus	*Ranunculus* sp.	†/3	summer	late spring	2"	12"	7–18"
Tulip	*Tulipa* sp.	hardy/4	mid–late spring	fall	8"	6–8"	7–20"

(Continued)

†Tender in northern zones and hardy in southern zones.

Appendix B (Continued)

NARROWLEAF EVERGREEN SHRUBS								
Common Name	**Botanical Name**	**Zone**	**Height**	**Width**	**Expo-sure**	**Use**	**Tex-ture**	**Color**
False Cypress	*Chamaecyparis* sp.							
Dwarf Hinoki	*C. obtusa* 'Nana'	4–8	3'	3–4'	◐ or ◗	Sp/G/F	M	Bk-G
Threadleaf	*C. pisifera* 'Filifera Nana'	4	6–8'	6–8'	◐	Sp/G	M	Bk-G
Juniper	*Juniperus* sp.							
Andorra	*J. horizontalis* 'Plumosa'	3	2'	8–10'	◐	GC	F	B-G
Blue Pacific	*J. conferta* 'Blue Pacific'	5–9	1'	6–9'	◐	GC	M	B-G
Blue Rug	*J. horizontalis* 'Wiltonii'	3	3–6"	6–8'	◐	GC	MF	B-G
Blue Star	*J. squamata* 'Blue Star'	4–7	2–3'	4–5'	◐	Sp/GC/B	M	Gy-G,B-G
Creeping	*J. horizontalis*	3	6–18"	4–8'	◐	B/GC	F	B-G
Compact Pfitzer	*J. chinensis* 'Pfitzeriana Compacta'	4	5–6'	5–6'	◐	F/G	MF	G-G
Dwarf Common	*J. communis* 'Depressa'	3	2–4'	6–8'	◐ or ◗	G/F	F	B-G
Japanese Garden	*J. procumbens*	5	18–24"	6–8'	◐	G/F	F	B-G
Sargent	*J. chinensis* 'Sargentii'	4	12–18'	8'	◐ or ◗	GC	F	B-G
Pine	*Pinus* sp.							
Dwarf White	*P. strobus* 'Nana'	3	4–6'	4–5'	◐ or ◗	G/Sp	MF	B-G
Mugo	*P. mugo* var. *mugo*	2–7	4–8'	12–20	◐ or ◗	G/F	M	G,Bk-G
Spruce	*Picea* sp.							
Bird's Nest	*P. abies* 'Nidiformis'	2	1–2'	3–5'	◐	Sp	M	G
Compact Colorado	*P. pungens* 'Compacta'	2	8–10'	10–12'	◐	F/Sp	M–C	Gy-G,B-G
Dwarf Alberta	*P. glauca* 'Conica'	2	3'	2'	◐ or ◗	G/F	M	G
Dwarf Globe Blue	*P. pungens* 'Glauca Globosa'	2	2–3'	3–4'	◐	Sp	M–C	Gy-G,B-G
Dwarf Norway	*P. abies* 'Pumila'	3	3–4'	4'	◐ or ◗	Sp	M	G
Yew	*Taxus* sp.							
Dense	*T. x media densiformis*	4	4–6'	4–6'	◐ or ●	F/G	M	Bk-G
Hicks	*T. x media* 'Hicksii'	5	4–6'	4–6'	◐	F/G/H	M	Bk-G
Japanese	*T. cuspidata* var. *nana*	4	5–6'	5–6'	◐ or ●	F/H/Sp	M	Bk-G
Spreading English	*T. baccata* 'Repandens'	6	2–3'	3–4'	◐ or ◗	F/GC	M	Bk-G
Tauton Anglojap	*T. x media* 'Tauton'	4	6–10'	8–10'	◐ or ●	F/G	M	Bk-G

(Continued)

Appendix B (Continued)

BROADLEAF EVERGREEN SHRUBS								
Common Name	**Botanical Name**	**Zone**	**Height**	**Width**	**Expo-sure**	**Use**	**Tex-ture**	**Color**
Aucuba, Japanese	*Aucuba japonica*	7–10	6–10'	7–9'	●	F/H	M	Bk-G
Barberry, Wintergreen	*Berberis julianae*	5–6	6–10'	4–6'	◑	Sp/H	MF	G
Boxwood	*Buxus* sp.							
Common	*B. sempervirens*	6	15–20'	12–18'	○ or ☽	F/H	MF	Bk-G
Littleleaf	*B microphylla*	5	3–4'	3–4'	○ or ☽	F/H/Br	MF	G
Camellia	*Camellia* sp.							
Japanese	*C. japonica*	7–9	10–15'	6–10'	☽	Sp	M–MC	G
Sasanqua	*C. sasanqua*	7	6–10'	5–8'	○ or ●	F/Br/Sp	M–MC	G
Daphne, Rose	*Daphne cneorum*	4–7	6–12"	2'	☽ or ●	G	MF	Gy-G
Euonymus, Bigleaf	*Euonymus* sp.							
Japanese	*E. japonica*	7–9	10–15'	4–6'	○ or ●	F/Br/Sp	M	Bk-G
Wintercreeper	*E. fortunei* var. 'Vegetus'	5–8	4–5'	4–5'	○ or ●	C/F/H	MF	G
Fatsia, Japanese	*Fatsia japonica*	7	6–10'	6–10'	●	G	C	G
Firethorn	*Pyracantha* sp.							
Formosa	*P. koidzumi*	8–10	8–12'	8–12'	○ or ☽	Br/Sp	M	G
Scarlet	*P. coccinea*	6–9	6–16'	6–16'	○ or ☽	Br/Sp	M	G
Gardenia, Cape Jasmine	*Gardenia jasminoides*	8–10	4–6'	4–6'	○ or ●	Br/Sp	M	G
Holly	*Ilex* sp.							
Chinese	*I. cornuta*	7–9	8–10'	8–12'	○ or ●	F/H/Sp	M–MC	G
Dwarf Burford	*I. cornuta* 'Dwarf Burford'	7–9	5–6'	5–6'	○ or ●	F/Sp	M–MC	G
Winterberry	*I. verticillata*	3–9	6–10'	6–10'	○ or ☽	Br	M	G
Laurel, Mountain	*Kalmia latifolia*	4–9	7–15'	7–15'	☽ or ●	F/G	M	G
Leucothoe, Drooping	*Leucothoe fontanesiana*	5–8	3–6'	3–6'	☽ or ●	F/Br	M	G
Nandina	*Nandina* sp.							
Dwarf Heavenly Bamboo	*N. domestica* 'Nana'	6–9	2–4'	2–4'	○ or ●	Br	M	B-G
Heavenly Bamboo	*N. domestica*	6–9	6–8'	4–5'	○ or ☽	F/Br	M	B-G
Oleander	*Nerium oleander*	8	8–10'	6–8'	○ or ☽	Br/Sc/Sp/Po	M	G
Oregongrapeholly	*Mahonia aquifolium*	4–8	3–6'	3–6'	☽ or ●	F/Br/Sp	M	G
Pieris, Japanese	*Pieris japonica*	5–8	9–10'	6–8'	☽ or ●	F/Sp	M	R-G,Bk-G
Privet	*Ligustrum* sp.							
Howard	*L. japonicum* 'Howard'	7–10	6–12'	6–8'	○ or ●	F/Br	M	Y-G
Japanese	*L. japonicum*	7–10	6–12'	6–8'	○ or ●	F/Sc/Sp	M	G

(Continued)

Appendix B (Continued)

BROADLEAF EVERGREEN SHRUBS (Continued)								
Common Name	**Botanical Name**	**Zone**	**Height**	**Width**	**Exposure**	**Use**	**Texture**	**Color**
Rhododendron	Rhododendron sp.							
Carolina	R. carolinianum	5–8	3–6'	3–6'	◐ or ◑	F/B/Br/Sp	M	G
Catawba	R. catawbiense	4–8	6–10'	5–8'	◑ or ●	F/B/Br/Sp	MC–C	G
Korean	R. mucronulatum	4–7	4–8'	4–8'	●	F/B/Br/Sp	MF	G
P.J.M.	R. P.J.M.	4	3–6'	3–6'	◐ or ◑	A/Sp/G/B	M	G
Wilson	R. x laetivirens	4	2–4'	4–6'	◐ or ◑	F/B/Br/Sp	MF	G
Skimmia Japanese	Skimmia japonica	7–8	3–4'	3–4'	◐ or ◑	F/H/G	M	G
Viburnum	Viburnum sp.							
Japanese	V. japonicum	8–9	10–15'	10–15'	◐	F/Sp/Sc	M	G
Laurustinus	V. tinus	9–10	6–12'	6–12'	◐ or ◑	F/Br/Sc	M	G
Leatherleaf	V. rhytidophyllum	5–8	10–15'	10–15'	● or ◑	F/Br	C	G
Wayfaringt ree	V. lantana	4–8	10–15'	10–15'	◐ or ◑	H/Sc/Br	M	G
Yucca	Yucca sp.							
Adam's Needle	Y. filamentosa	4	3'	3–4'	◐	A	C	G
Spanish Dagger	Y. gloriosa	6	6–8'	3–4'	◐	A	C	G
Spanish Bayonet	Y. aloifolia	7	8–12'	5–6'	◐ or ◑	A	C	G

DECIDUOUS SHRUBS								
Common Name	**Botanical Name**	**Zone**	**Height**	**Spread**	**Exposure**	**Use**	**Texture**	**Color**
Abelia, Glossy	Abelia x grandiflora	6	3–6'	3–6'	◐ or ◑	A/Br/F	MF	Bk-G
Azalea	Rhododendron sp.							
Exbury Hybrids	R. x exbury	5–7	8–12'	5–8'	◑	Sp/G/Br	M	G
Flame (Yellow)	R. calendulaceum	5	4–8'	4–8'	◐ or ◑	Br/Sp	M	G
Glenn Dale	R. x 'Glenn Dale'	6	4–5'	4–5'	◑	F/B/E	M	G
Karens	R. kaempferi var. karens	6	3–4'	3–5'	◑	F/B/E	M	G
Kurume Hybrids	R. x obtusum	6	4–6'	3–6'	◑	F/B/Br/G	M	G
Mollis Hybrids	R. x kosterianum	5–6	3–6'	3–5'	◐ or ●	F/B/Br/G	M	G
Royal	R. schlippenbachi	4–7	6–8'	6–8'	◐ or ◑	B/F/A	M	G
Barberry	Berberis sp.							
Crimson Pygmy	B. thunbergii 'Crimson Pygmy'	4	2'	2'	◐	A/Br	MF	R-G
Japanese	B. thunbergii	4	5–7'	4–7'	◐ or ◑	H/Br/Sp	MF	G
Mentor	B. x mentorensis	5	5–6'	4–5'	◐ or ◑	H/A/Sp/G	M	G
Blueberry, Highbush	Vaccinium corymbosum	4	6–12'	8–12'	◐ or ◑	Sp/H	M	B-G
Buckeye, Bottlebrush	Aesculus pariflora	5	8–12'	8–15'	◐ or ◑	Sp/Br	C	G

(Continued)

Appendix B (Continued)

DECIDUOUS SHRUBS (Continued)								
Common Name	**Botanical Name**	**Zone**	**Height**	**Spread**	**Expo-sure**	**Use**	**Tex-ture**	**Color**
Chokeberry	*Aronia* sp.							
Black	*A. melanocarpa*	5	3–5'	3+'	○ or ☽	Br	M	G
Red	*A. x arbutifolia*	5	6–10'	3–5'	○ or ☽	Br	M	G
Cotoneaster	*Cotoneaster* sp.							
Cranberry	*C. apiculatus*	5	2–3'	5–8'	○ or ☽	GC/F	F	G
Creeping	*C. adpressus*	5	1'	4–6'	○ or ☽	G	F	G
Many-Flowered	*C. divaricatus*	4–8	5–6'	6–8'	○ or ☽	H/Br/Sp	F	G
Rockspray	*C. horizontalis*	4	2–3'	5–8'	○ or ☽	GC/B/G	F	G
Spreading	*C. multiflorus*	3–7	8–12'	12–15'	○ or ☽	Sp	MF	Gy-G
Daphne, Fragrant	*Daphne odora*	7–9	3'	3'	○ or ☽	Sp	MF	G
Deutzia	*Deutzia* sp.							
Showy	*D. x magnifica*	5	6–10'	6–10'	○ or ☽	Sp/Bk	MF	G
Slender	*D. gracilis*	4–8	2–4'	3–4'	○ or ☽	B/G/Sp	MF	G
Dogwood	*Cornus* sp.							
Redosier	*C. sericea*	2–8	7–10'	10'	○ or ☽	H/Sc/Br	M	G
Tatarian	*C. alba*	2–7	8–10'	5–10'	○ or ☽	H/Sc/Br	M	G
Elaeagnus	*Elaeagnus* sp.							
Autumn Olive	*E. umbellata*	2–7	18'	18'	○	H/Sc	MF	Gy-G
Silver	*E. multiflora*	5–7	6–10'	6–10'	○	H/Sc/Sp	MF	Gy-G
Euonymus	*Euonymus* sp.							
Dwarf Winged	*E. alatus* 'Compactus'	3	6–8'	5–6'	○ or ●	H/B/Br	M	G
Winged (Burning Bush)	*E. alatus*	4–8	15–20'	15–20'	○ or ☽	H/Sc/Sp	M	G
Forsythia	*Forsythia* sp.							
Border	*F. x intermedia*	5	8–10'	8–10'	○ or ☽	H/Br/Sp	M	Y-G
Bronx	*F. viridissima* 'Bronx'	5	2'	2–4'	○ or ☽	B/A	M	G
Fothergilla	*Fothergilla* sp.							
Dwarf	*F. gardenii*	4–8	2–3'	3–4'	○ or ☽	Sp/F/G/Br	MC	G
Large	*F. major*	4–8	6–9'	6–8'	☽	G/Br	M	G
Hibiscus Rose-of-Sharon)	*Hibiscus syriacus*	6	8–12'	6–10'	○ or ☽	H/Br/Sp	M	G
Honeysuckle	*Lonicera* sp.							
Amur	*L. maacki*	2–8	12–15'	12–15'	○ or ☽	H/Sc/Sp	MC	Y-G
Clavey's Dwarf	*L. x xylosteoides* 'Clavey's Dwarf'	4–6	6'	4–6'	○ or ☽	H	M	Gy-G
Morrow	*L. morrowi*	4–6	6–10'	8–10'	○ or ☽	H/Sc/Sp	M	B-G
Tatarian	*L. tatarica*	3–8	9–12'	10–12"	○ or ☽	Sp/H	M	B-G
Winter Fragrant	*L. fragrantissima*	4–8	6–10'	6–10'	○ or ☽	H/Sc/Sp	M	B-G

(Continued)

Appendix B (Continued)

	DECIDUOUS SHRUBS (Continued)							
Common Name	**Botanical Name**	**Zone**	**Height**	**Spread**	**Expo-sure**	**Use**	**Tex-ture**	**Color**
Hydrangea	*Hydrangea* sp.							
Hills-of-Snow	*H. arborescens* 'Grandiflora'	4	4–8'	5–8'	○ or ◐	F/H/Br	C	G
Oak-Leaf	*H. quercifolia*	5	4–6'	3–5'	◐ or ●	Sp/Br	C	Gy-G
Peegee	*H. paniculata* 'Grandiflora'	3–8	10–15'	6–10'	○ or ◐	Sp	C	G
Lilac	*Syringa* sp.							
Common	*S. vulgaris*	3	8–20'	4–10'	○	Sp/H/Sc	M	G
Late	*S. villosa*	2–7	6–10'	4–10'	◐	Sp	M	G
Mockorange	*Philadelphus* sp.							
Minnesota Snowflake	*P. virginalis* 'Minnesota Snowflake'	4	8'	4–6'	○ or ◐	A/Br	M	G
Natchez	*P. x* 'Natchez'	5	8–10'	8–10'	○ or ◐	G/Br	M–MC	G
Prunus	*Prunus* sp.							
Dwarf Flowering Almond	*P. glandulosa*	4–8	4–5'	3–4'	○	Sp/A/Br	M	Y-G
Nanking Cherry	*P. tomentosa*	3	8–10'	10–15'	○	Br/Sp	M	G
Quince	*Chaenomeles* sp.							
Flowering	*C. speciosa*	5	6–10'	8–10'	○	Sp/Br	M	R-G
Japanese	*C. japonica*	4	3–4'	4'	○	Br/F	MF	G
Spirea	*Spiraea* sp.							
Anthony Waterer	*S. bumalda* 'Anthony Waterer'	5	3–4'	3–4'	○ or ◐	Sp	MF	R-G
Bridal-Wreath	*S. prunifolia*	5	5–8'	6–8'	○ or ◐	H/Sp/Br	MF	B-G
Snowmound	*S. nipponica* 'Snowmound'	4	3–6'	3–4'	○ or ◐	Sp/Br	MF	B-G
Vanhoutte	*S. x vanhouttei*	4	6–8'	8–10'	○ or ◐	Br/Sp	M	B-G
St. Johnswort, Shrubby	*Hypericum prolifium*	3–8	1–4'	1–4'	○ or ◐	Br/G	MF	B-G
Sumac, Fragrant	*Rhus aromatica*	3	2–6'	5–8'	○	F/GC	M	R-G
Sweetshrub, Common	*Calycanthus floridus*	4–9	6–9'	6–12'	○ or ●	Br/G	M	G
Viburnum	*Viburnum* sp.							
American Cranberrybush	*V. trilobum*	2	8–12'	8–12'	○ or ◐	Br/Sc	M	G
Arrowwood	*V. dentatum*	2–8	15'	15'	○ or ◐	Sp/Br	M	G
Compact American Cranberrybush	*V. trilobum* 'Compactum'	2	5–6'	5'	○ or ◐	H/Sc/G/Br	M	G
Doublefile	*V. plicatum* var. *tomentosum*	5–8	8–10'	9–12'	○ or ◐	A/Sp	M	G
Dwarf European Cranberrybush	*V. opulus* 'Nanum'	3	2'	2'	○ or ◐	A/Sp/G	M	G
European Cranberrybush	*V. opulus*	3–8	8–12'	10–15'	○ or ◐	Br/Sc/G	M	G
Fragrant Snowball	*V. x carlcephalum*	5	6–9'	6–8'	○ or ◐	Sp/Br	M	G
Koreanspice	*V. carlesii*	5	4–8'	5–8'	○ or ◐	B/Br	M	G
Linden	*V. dilatatum*	5–7	7–10'	5–7'	○ or ●	Sp/Br/Sc	M	G

(Continued)

Appendix B (Continued)

DECIDUOUS SHRUBS (Continued)								
Common Name	**Botanical Name**	**Zone**	**Height**	**Spread**	**Expo-sure**	**Use**	**Tex-ture**	**Color**
Weigela	*Weigela florida*	5	6–10'	9–12'	◐ or ◗	Sp/Br	C	G
Witchhazel, Vernal	*Hamamelis vernalis*	5	6–10'	6–10'	◐ or ◗	Sp/Br	M	G

FLOWERING TREES								
Common Name	**Botanical Name**	**Zone**	**Height**	**Spread**	**Expo-sure**	**Use**	**Tex-ture**	**Color**
Apricot, Japanese	*Prunus mume*	6–9	15–20'	15–20'	◐ or ◗	Sp/Sh/Br	M	G
Cherry	*Prunus* sp.							
Dwarf Japanese	*P. serrulata* 'Shogetsu'	5–6	10–18'	10–18'	◐	A/Br	M	G
Weeping	*P. subhirtella pendula*	5–6	20–30'	15–25'	◐	Sp	F	G
Crabapple	*Malus* sp.							
Carmine	*M. x atrosanquinea*	4	15–20'	15–20'	◐	Sp/Br	M	G
Japanese	*M. floribunda*	4	15–25'	30'	◐	Sp	F	G
Crapemyrtle	*Lagerstroemia indica*	7–9	15–25'	15–25'	◐	Sp	M–MF	G
Dogwood	*Cornus* sp.							
Cherokee Chief	*C. florida* 'Cherokee Chief'	5	20–30'	20–30'	◐ or ●	Sp	M	G
Pagoda	*C. alternifolia*	3–7	15–25'	20–35'	◗	Br	M	G
Pink	*C. florida var. rubra*	5	20–30'	20–30'	◐ or ●	Sp	M	G
White	*C. florida*	5	20–30'	20–30'	◐ or ●	Sp	M	G
Goldenchain Tree	*Laburnum x watereri*	5–7	10–15'	9–12'	◐ or ◗	A	MF	G
Hawthorn	*Crataegus* sp.							
Green	*C. viridis*	4	20–30'	20–30'	◐ or ◗	Sp/Sc	M–F	G
Washington	*C. phaenopyrum*	4	30'	20–25'	◐	Br	M–F	G
Magnolia	*Magnolia* sp.							
Big Leaf	*M. macrophylla*	5–8	30–40'	30–40'	◐ or ◗	Sp	C	G
Lily	*M. liliiflora*	5–8	10–12'	8–12'	◐ or ◗	F/Br/A	M–C	G
Saucer	*M. x soulangiana*	4–9	20–30'	20–30'	◐ or ◗	Sp	MC	G
Star	*M. stellata*	4–8	15–20'	10–15'	◐	Sp	M	G
Mimosa (Silk Tree)	*Albizia julibrissin*	5–7	25–35'	18–25'	◐	Sp	F	Y-G
Pear, Bradford Callery	*Pyrus calleryana* 'Bradford'	5	30–40'	20–35'	◐	Sp/Br	MF	G
Plum, Purple Leaf	*Prunus cerasifera* 'Newport'	5	15–30'	15–30'	◐	A/Sp/Br	M	G
Redbud, Eastern	*Cercis canadensis*	5	20–25'	15–30'	◐ or ●	Sp	MC	B-G
Serviceberry, Downy	*Amelanchier arborea*	4–9	15–25	15–20'	◐ or ●	G/Br	MF	G

(Continued)

Appendix B (Continued)

DECIDUOUS TREES								
Common Name	**Botanical Name**	**Zone**	**Height**	**Spread**	**Exposure**	**Use**	**Texture**	**Color**
Beech, European	*Fagus sylvatica*	5	60–80'	50–70'	○ or ●	Sp/Sh	M	G
Baldcypress	*Taxodium distichum*	5	50–70'	20–30'	○ or ◗	Sp/Br	F	G
Birch	*Betula sp.*							
Paper	*B. papyrifera*	3	50–60'	30'	○	Sp/A	MF	G
River	*B. nigra*	4	40–70'	30–60'	○ or ◗	Sp	MF	G
White	*B. pendula*	3	40–50'	20–30'	○ or ◗	Sp	MF	G
Black Gum	*Nyssa sylvatica*	5–6	30–50'	20–30'	○ or ●	Sp	MF	G
Buckeye, Ohio	*Aesculus glabra*	4	20–40'	30–40'	○ or ◗	Sp/Sh	MC	G
Corktree, Amur	*Phellodendron amurense*	4	30–45'	30–40'	○	Sp/Sh	M	G
Elm, Chinese	*Ulmus parvifolia*	5	40–50'	30'	○	Sp/Sh	F	G
Ginkgo	*Ginkgo biloba*	5	40–60'	40'	○	Sp/Br	M	G
Goldenraintree, Panicled	*Koelreutaria paniculata*	5	30'	20'	○	Sp	M	G
Hackberry, Common	*Celtis occidentalus*	3	50–70'	50'	○	Sh	M	G
Honeylocust, Common Thornless	*Gleditsia triacanthos var. inermis*	5	75'	40–50'	○	Sp	F	G
Japanese Pagoda Tree	*Sophora japonica*	5	45–70'	30'	○	Sp	MF	B-G
Linden	*Tilia sp.*							
American	*T. americana*	3	60–80'	30–50'	○	Sp/Sh	C	G
Littleleaf	*T. cordata*	3	50–70'	40'	○	Sp/Sh	M	G
Londonplane Tree	*Plantanus x acerifolia*	4–8	70–100'	65–80'	○	Sh	MC	G
Maple	*Acer sp.*							
Japanese	*A. palmatum*	5–6	15–20'	15–20'	○ or ◗	Sp	F–MF	G
Norway	*A. platanoides*	3–4	40–50'	30–50'	○	Sh	MC	Bk-G
Red	*A. rubrum*	3–6	40–60'	30–40'	○ or ●	Sp/Sh	M	G
Silver	*A. saccharinum*	3	50–70'	35–50'	○	Sh*	M	G
Sugar	*A. saccharum*	3	60–120'	50–80'	○ or ◗	Sp/Sh	M	G
Oak	*Quercus sp.*							
Northern Red	*Q. rubra*	3–8	70–90'	60–75'	○	Sp/Sh	M	G
Pin	*Q. palustris*	4–8	60–70'	25–40'	○	Sp/Sh	M	G
Southern Red	*Q. falcata*	7–9	50–60'	50–60'	○ or ◗	Sh	M	G
White	*Q. alba*	3–9	50–80'	50–80'	○	Sh	MC	G
Poplar, Lombardy	*Populus nigra 'Italica'*	3–9	90'	10–15'	○	Sc**	MC	G
Sourwood	*Oxydendrum arboreum*	5–9	25–30'	20'	○ or ◗	Sp	M	G
Sweetgum	*Liquidambar styraciflua*	4	60–90'	40'	○	Sp/Sh	M	G
Tulip Tree	*Liriodendron tulipifera*	4	60–90'	30–40'	○ or ◗	Sp/Sh	M	Y-G
Willow	*Salix sp.*							
Corkscrew	*S. matsudana 'Tortuosa'*	4	20–40'	20–30'	○ or ◗	Sp	F	G
Weeping	*S. babylonica*	6–8	30–40'	30–40'	○ or ◗	Sp	F	G

(Continued)

*fast-growing, softwood
**short-lived

Appendix B (Continued)

EVERGREEN TREES							
Common Name	**Botanical Name**	**Zone**	**Height**	**Exposure**	**Use**	**Texture**	**Color**
Arborvitae	*Thuja*						
American	*T. occidentalis*	4	40–60'	○	Sc/H	MF	G
Oriental	*T. orientalis*	6	18–25'	○	Sc/H	MF	Y-G
Techny	*T. occidentalis cv. techny*	2	8–10'	○ or ◗	Sc/H	MF	G
Cedar, Eastern Red	*Juniperus virginiana*	3	30–40'	○	Sc/H	F	B-G (spring), R-G (summer)
Cryptomeria, Japanese Cedar	*Cryptomeria japonica*	5	50–60'	○	Sp	M	G,B-G
Cypress, Arizona	*Cupressus arizonica*	6	25–40'	○	Sp/Sc	F	G–GG
Douglasfir	*Pseudotsuga menziesii*	4	50–90'	○ or ◗	Sp/Sc	M	B-G,Bk-G
Fir	*Abies sp.*						
Balsam	*A. balsamea*	4	45–75'	○	Sp/G/Br	M	G
White	*A. concolor*	4	30–45'	○	Sp/G/Br	M–C	B-G,Gy-G
Holly	*Ilex sp.*						
American	*I. opaca*	6	20–40'	○ or ◗	F/H/Br	MC	Dark Y-G
Buford	*I. cornuta 'Bufordii'*	6	10–20'	○ or ●	F/H/Br	M	Bk-G
Hume	*I. x attenuata 'Hume #2'*	6	20–25'	○ or ●	F/H/Br	M	Bk-G
Yaupon	*I. vomitoria*	7	10–15'	○ or ●	F/Sp	MF	Bk-G
Laurel, Cherry	*Prunus caroliniana*	7	15–25'	○ or ◗	Sp/H	M	Bk-G
Magnolia, Southern	*Magnolia grandiflora*	7–9	60–80'	○ or ◗	Sc/H/Sh	MC	G
Pine	*Pinus sp.*						
Austrian	*P. nigra*	5	60–90'	○	Sp/Sc/Br	MC	Bk-G
Eastern White	*P. strobus*	3	60–80'	○ or ◗	Sp/H/Sc/Br	MF	B-G
Pitch	*P. rigida*	5	40–50'	○ or ◗	Sc/Br	M	Y-G,Bk-G
Scotch	*P. sylvestris*	2	30–40'	○	Sp/Sc/F	M	B-G
Spruce	*Picea sp.*						
Blue Colorado	*P. pungens f. glauca*	3	70–90'	○ or ◗	Sp/G	M–C	B-G
Colorado	*P. pungens*	3	70–90'	○ or ◗	Sp	M–C	Gy-G,B-G
Norway	*P. abies*	2–7	40–60'	○ or ◗	Sp/Sc	M	G,Bk-G
Weeping White	*P. glauca 'Pendula'*	2	40–50'	○ or ◗	Sp	M	G
White	*P. glauca*	2	30–50'	○ or ◗	Sp	M	G

Appendix C — Landscape Design Examples

Color design courtesy of Matthew Haber, ASLA, Western DuPage Landscaping, Inc.

3 ARROWWOOD VIBURNUM·

3 HUGHES JUNIPER·

8 MOONBEAM COREOPSIS·

SEATWALL W/COLUMNS·

10 HUGHES JUNIPER·

1 RED BUD W/ 96 WINTERCREEPER
IN RAISED PLANTER

9 BLACKEYED SUSAN
8 RUSSIAN SAGE·
4+4 EMERALD ARBORVITAE·

12 PEKING COTONEASTER·

5 FLAGSTONE STEPPERS·

1 BURNING BUSH·

10 MOONBEAM COREOPSIS
5 A.J. SEDUM
1 BLACKHILLS SPRUCE

288 WINTERCREEPER
1 RED SUNSET RED MAPLE
4+5 A.W. SPIREA

8 HUGHES JUNIPER

3 ARROWWOOD VIBURNUM

4+4 DENSE YEW
10 KOBOLD LIATRIS
2 BURNING BUSH

7+7 MOONBEAM COREOPSIS
96 +
100 WINTERCREEPER
1+1 BRADFORD PEAR
W/ 96 WINTERCREEPER EACH

10 BUXWOOD
WALK LIGHT (W6)
124 + 96 WINTERCREEPER

BRUSSELS BLOCK PATIO

DECK

RESIDENCE

FOCAL POINT
(W6)

BRUSSELS
BLOCK
WALK

DRIVE

SOD

SOD

Color design courtesy of Matthew Haber, ASLA, Western DuPage Landscaping, Inc.

NOTES

A TREATED 2×4 EDGING
B WALK
C WOODPILE
D PLAY AREA
E WOOD DECK
F COMPOST PILE
G BENCH
H VEGETABLE GARDEN
I SHED
J PLACE WOOD CHIP MULCH AROUND SHRUBS 4" DEEP

PLANT LIST

1 HAWTHORNE (EXISTING)
2 SILVER MAPLE (EXISTING)
3 ANTHONY WATERER SPIREA
4 BARREN-STRAWBERRY
5 KATSURATREE
6 DENSE YEW
7 STELLA DE ORO DAYLILY
8 DWARF WINGED EUONYMUS
9 COMMON LILAC
10 KOREANSPICE VIBURNUM
11 WILLOW (EXISTING)
12 BOTTLEBRUSH BUCKEYE
13 CANADIAN HEMLOCK
14 MOUNTAINASH (EXISTING)
15 CRABAPPLE (EXISTING)
16 COMPACT AMERICAN CRANBERRYBUSH VIBURNUM
17 KOREAN AZALEA
18 PJM RHODODENDRON

NASTI RESIDENCE

LANDSCAPE PLAN

PLANT LIST

1. DENSE YEW   TAXUS MEDIA 'DENSIFORMIS'
2. ALLEGHANY VIBURNUM   VIBURNUM r RHYTIDOPHYLLOIDES
3. BIGLEAF WINTERCREEPER EUONYMUS   EUONYMUS FORTUNEI 'VEGETUS'
4. RED SUNSET RED MAPLE   ACER RUBRUM 'RED SUNSET'
5. PERIWINKLE   VINCA MINOR
6. KOREAN LITTLELEAF BOXWOOD   BUXUS MACROPHYLLA 'KOREANA WINTERGREEN
7. EASTERN REDBUD   CERCIS CANADENSIS (SINGLE STEM)
8. COREOPSIS
9. PJM RHODODENDRON   RHODODENDRON 'POJKHANENSIS'
10. KOREAN AZALEA
11. SUGAR MAPLE   ACER SACCHARUM
12. GREEN MOUND ALPINE CURRANT   RIBES ALPINUM 'GREEN MOUND'
13. COMPACT AMERICAN CRANBERRYBUSH VIBURNUM   VIBURNUM TRILOBUM 'COMPACTUM'
14. DWARF FRUIT TREES
15. WHITE PINE   PINUS STROBUS
16. WINGED EUONYMUS   EUONYMUS ALATUS
17. FRAGRANT SUMAC   RHUS AROMATICA
18. COMPACT EUROPEAN CRANBERRYBUSH VIBURNUM   VIBURNUM OPULUS 'COMPACTUM'
19. PLANTAIN LILY
20. CORONATION TRIUMPH BUSH CINQUEFOIL   POTENTILLA FRUCTICOSA 'CORONATION TRIUMPH'
21. COMMON LILAC   SYRINGA VULGARIS
22. DAYLILY
23. PEONY
24. MISS KIM LILAC   SYRINGA VELUTINA 'MISS KIM'
25. AUTUMN GOLD GINKGO   GINKGO BILOBA 'AUTUMN GOLD'
26. BARREN-STRAWBERRY   WALDSTEINIA FRAGARIOIDES
27. RED JADE CRABAPPLE

NOTES

A. TREATED 2x4 EDGING
B. DOG RUN
C. PLAY AREA
D. RYERSON STEEL EDGING
E. PERMANENT GAS GRILL
F. REDWOOD DECK
G. BENCH
H. 6' BOARD ON BOARD FENCE
I. PLANTS 5,6,3, AND 10 REQUIRE A SOIL AMENDED WITH PEAT MOSS
J. ◯ INDICATES LANDSCAPE LIGHTING

RYAN RESIDENCE

Appendix D — Professional Landscape and Nursery Associations

Alabama Nursery and Landscape Association

B. James Harwell, III, Executive Director
P.O. Box 9
Auburn, AL 36831-0009
Phone: 334-821-5148
Fax: 334-821-9111
alna51@prodigy.net
www.alna.org

Alaska Horticulture Association

Wayne Vendre
c/o Alaska Cooperative Extension Service
2221 E. Northern Lights Blvd. #8
Anchorage, AK 99508
Phone: 907-279-6575

American Nursery & Landscape Association

Robert J. Dolibois, Executive Vice President
1250 I Street NW, Suite 500
Washington, DC 20005-3922
Phone: 202-789-2900
Fax: 202-789-1893
www.anla.org

American Horticultural Society

7931 East Boulevard Drive
Alexandria, VA 22308
Phone: 703-768-5700
www.ahs.org

American Society of Landscape Architects

David Bohardt
636 Eye Street, NW
Washington, DC 20001-3736
Phone: 202-898-2444
www.asla.org

Arizona Nursery Association

Cheryl Goar, Executive Director
1430 West Broadway Road, Suite A-180
Tempe, AZ 85282-1199
Phone: 480-966-1610
Fax: 480-966-0923

Arkansas Nurserymen's Association

Anne H. Borg, Executive Director
P.O. Box 21715
Little Rock, AR 72221-1715
Phone 501-225-0029
Fax: 501-218-0134
GrowArk@aol.com
www.argia.org

Associated Landscape Contractors of America

Debra H Atkins, Executive Director
150 Elden Street, Suite 270
Herndon, VA 20170
Phone: 703-736-9666
Fax: 703-736-9668
www.alca.org

Atlantic Provinces Nursery Trades Association

Tanya Morrison
130 Bluewater Road, Terra Nova Landscape
Bedford, NS B4B 1G7
CANADA
Phone: 902-835-7387
Fax: 902-835-5498

British Columbia Nursery Trades Association

Jane Stock, Executive Director
5830 176 A Street, Suite 101
Surrey, BC V3S 4E3
CANADA
Phone: 604-574-7772
Fax: 604-574-7773
jstock@idmail.com
www.bclna.com

California Association of Nurserymen and Garden Centers

Elaine Thompson, Executive Director
3947 Lennane Drive, Suite 150
Sacramento, CA 95834-1973
Phone: 916-928-3900
Fax: 916-567-0505
association@cangc.org
www.cangc.org

Canadian Nursery Landscape Association

Victor Santacruz, Executive Director
7856 Fifth Line South
RR4, Station Main
Milton ONT L9T 2X8
CANADA
Phone: 905-875-1399
Fax: 905-875-1840
cnla@canadanursery.com
www.canadanursery.com

Colorado Nursery and Greenhouse Association

Sharon R. Harris, Executive Director
959 S Kipling Pkwy Ste 200
Lakewood, CO 80226
Phone: 303-758-6672
Fax: 303-758-6805
www.coloradonga.org

Connecticut Nursery and Landscape Association

Robert V. Heffernan, Executive Secretary
P.O. Box 414
Botsford, CD 06404-0414
Phone: 203-445-0110
Fax: 203-261-5429
connrsry@aol.com
www.flowersplantsinct.com

Delaware Nursery and Landscape Association

Valann Budischak, Executive Director
P. O. Box 897
Hockessin, DE 19707-0897
Phone: 888-448-1203
Fax: 888-448-1203
dnlainc@comcast.net
www.dnlaonline.org

Florida Nursery, Growers and Landscape Association

Ben Bolusky, Executive Vice President
1533 Park Center Drive
Orlando, FL 32835-5705
Phone: 407-295-7994
Fax: 407-295-1619
info@fnga.org
www.fnga,org

Georgia Green Industry Association

Sherry Loudermilk, Executive Director
Hwy 5 N, Box 369
Epworth, GA 30541-0369
Phone:706-632-0100
sherry@ggia.org
www.ggia.org

Hawaii Association of Nurserymen

Karen Bento
1833 Kalakaua Ave, Suite 211 #203
Honolulu, HI 96815-1500
Phone: 808-545-2257
Fax: 808-545-5026

Idaho Nursery and Landscape Association

Ann Bates
Executive Director
P. O. Box 2065
Idaho Falls, ID 83403-2065
Phone: 208-522-7307
Fax: 208-529-0832
www.inlagrow.org

Illinois Landscape Contractors Association

Patricia Cassidy, Executive Director
2625 Butterfield Road, Suite 204W
Oakbrook, IL 60523
Phone: 630-472-2851
Fax: 630-472-3150
www.ilca.net

Illinois Nurserymen's Association

David Bender, Executive Director
2900 Greenbriar Drive
Springfield, IL 62704-3116
Phone: 217-546-4733
Fax: 217-546-4703
dbender@ina-online.org
www.ina-online.org

Indiana Nursery and Landscape Association

Donna Sheets
6533 Margaret Ct.
Indianapolis, IN 46237
Phone: 317-889-2382
Fax: 317-889-3935
info@inla1.org
www.inla1.org

Iowa Nursery and Landscape Association

Clark Smith, Executive Director
9001 Hackman Road Ste 220
Des Moines, IA 50322
Phone: 515-279-2185
INLA@membermgmt.com
www.iowanla.org

Kansas Nursery and Landscape Association

Mary Gates, Executive Secretary
411 Poplar
Wamego, KS 66547-1446
Phone: 785-456-8338
Fax: 785-456-2066

Kentucky Nursery and Landscape Association

Betsie A. Taylor, Executive Director
216 Pendleton Lane
Frankfort, KY 40601
Phone: 502-848-0055
Fax: 502-848-0013
knla@mis.net
www.knla.org

Landscape Alberta Nursery Trades Association

Nigel Bowles
Executive Director
10215 176th Street
Edmonton, ALB T5S 1M1
CANADA
Phone: 780-489-1991
Fax: 780-444-2152
www.landscape-alberta.com

Landscape Industry Council of Hawaii

Garrett Webb, President
P. O. Box 22938
Honolulu, HI 96823-2938
Phone: 808-325-6251

Landscape Ontario Hort Trades Association

Tony Di Giovanni
Executive Director
7856 5th Line South RR 4, Station Main
Milton, ONT L9T 2X8
CANADA
Phone: 905-875-1805
Fax: 905-875-3942
lo@hort-trades.com

Louisiana Nursery and Landscape Association

Severn C. Doughty, Executive Director
444 Fox Trot Lane
Mansfield, LA 71052
Phone: 318-872-4677
Fax: 318-872-4677
www.lnla.org

Maine Landscape & Nursery Association

Edith Ellis, Executive Secretary
500 N. Parish Road
Turner, ME 04282-3232
Phone: 207-225-3767
Fax: 207-225-3768
melna@megalink.net
www.melna.org

Maryland Nursery and Landscape Association

Vanessa Finely, Executive Secretary
P.O. Box 726
Brooklandville, MD 21022-0726
Phone: 410-823-8684
Fax: 410-296-8288
mnacma@aol.com
www.mnlaonline.org

Massachusetts Nursery & Landscape Association

Rena M. Sumner, Executive Director
1270 Whateley Road
Conway, MA 01341-9772
Phone: 413-369-4731
Fax: 413-369-4962
r10sum@aol.com
www.mnla.com

Michigan Nursery & Landscape Association

Amy Frankmann, Executive Director
2149 Commons Parkway
Okemox, MI 48864-3987
Phone: 517-381-0437
Toll-free: 800-879-6652
Fax: 517-381-0638
educate@mnla.org
www.mnla.org

Minnesota Nursery & Landscape Association

Bob Fitch, Executive Director
1813 Lexington Avenue North
Roseville, MN 55113
Phone: 651-633-4987
Fax: 651-633-4986
www.GardenMinnesota.com

Mississippi Nursery and Landscape Association

Jan Winder
P. O. Box 4190
Brandon, MS 39047
Phone: 601-919-8111
Fax: 601-919-3388
www.msnla.org

Missouri Landscape and Nursery Association

Jewel Hoffman
344 Hearses Ctr
Columbia, MO 65211-0001
Phone: 573-882-4038
Fax: 573-882-1953
NunnJA@missouri.edu
www.muconf.missouri.edu

Montana Nursery and Landscape Association

Robin L. Childers, Executive Director
P.O. Box 4553
Missoula, MT 59806-4553
Phone: 406-251-5232
Fax: 406-251-5270
www.plantingmontana.com

Nebraska Nursery and Landscape Association

Helen Adams
4200 Witherbee Blvd.
Lincoln, NE 68510
Phone: 402-450-7192
Fax: 402-489-4215
www.nnla.org

Nevada Landscape Association

Debra Rae Drew, Executive Director
P.O. Box 7431
Reno, NV 89510-7431
Phone: 702-673-0404
Fax: 702-673-5828

New England Nursery Association

M. Virginia Wood, Executive Director
8D Pleasant Street
South Natick, MA 01760
Phone: 508-653-3112
Fax: 508-653-4112
NensyAssn@aol.com
www.NEnsyAssn.org

New Hampshire Plant Growers Association

Chris Robarge
56 Leavitt Road
Hampton, NH 03842-3938
Phone: 603-225-0653

New Jersey Nursery & Landscape Association

Carl Nordstrom, Executive Director
605 Farnsworth Avenue
Bordentown, NJ 08505-2028
Phone: 609-291-7070
Fax: 609-291-1121
njnla@ix.netcom.com
www.gardennj.net

New Mexico Association of Nursery Industries

Linda McClean
Box 30003, Department 3Q
Las Cruces, NM 88003-8003
Phone: 505-880-0326
Fax: 505-880-0326
befdbd@msn.com
www.nmani.org

New York State Nursery and Landscape Association

Kim Tiberia, Executive Director
24 Martin Road
Voorheesville. NY 12186
Phone: 315-635-5008
Fax: 315-635-4874
nysnla@aol.com
www.nysnla.org

North Carolina Association of Nurserymen

Ronald E. Gelvin, Executive Director
968 Trinity Road
Raleigh, NC 27607-4940
Phone: 919-816-9121
Fax: 919-816-9118
ncnurserymen@mindspring.com
www.ncan.com

North Dakota Nursery & Greenhouse Association

Mary Holm
P. O. Box 34
Neche, ND. 58265-0034
Phone: 701-886-7673

Ohio Landscapers Association

Sandy Manley, Executive Director
9238 Broadview Road
Broadview Heights, OH 44141
Phone: 440-717-0002
Fax: 440-717-0004
ola@bright.net
www.ohiolandscapers.org

Ohio Nursery & Landscape Association

William Stalter, Executive Director
72 Dorchester Square
Westerville, OH 43081-3350
Phone: 614-899-1195
Fax: 614-899-9489
onlagreen@aol.com
www.onla.org

Oklahoma Nursery and Landscape Association

Carroll Emberton, Executive Director
400 North Portland Street
Oklahoma City, OK 73107-6110
Phone: 405-942-5276
Fax: 405-945-3382
OklahomaONLAOGGA@aol.com
www.oknurserymen.org

Oregon Association of Nurseries

John J. Aguirre, Executive Director
29751 SW Town Center Loop W
Wilsonville, OR 97070-9460
Phone: 503-682-5089
Fax: 503-682-5099
info@oan.org
www.oan.org

Pennsylvania Landscape and Nursery Association

Gregg Robertson, Executive Vice President
1707 South Cameron Street
Harrisburg, PA 17104-3148
Phone: 717-238-1673
Fax: 717-238-1675
plna@plna.com
www.plna.com

Rhode Island Nursery and Landscape Association

Kenneth A. Lagerquist, Executive Secretary
64 Bittersweet Drive
Seekonk, MA 02771-1103
Phone: 508-761-9280
Fax: 508-761-9260
www.rinla.org

Saskatchewan Nursery Trades Association

Tim Van Duyvendyk
685 Reid Road
Saskatoon, SASK S7N 3J4
CANADA
Fax: 306-249-0151

South Carolina Nursery and Landscape Association

Donna Shealy Foster, Executive Secretary
332 Sunward Path
Inman, SC 29349-8266
Phone: 864-592-3868
Fax: 864-592-3857
scplant@bellsouth.net
www.scnla.com

South Dakota Nursery and Landscape Association

Julie Hoffmann, Executive Director
5659 Dakota South
Huron, SD 57350-6550
Phone: 605-352-4414
Fax: 605-352-8836

Southern Nursery Association

Sam Gallo way
Bldg 4, Suite 100
1827 Powers Ferry Road
Atlanta, GA 30339-5621
Phone: 770-953-3311
Fax: 770-953-4411
mail@mail.sna.org
www.sna.org

Tennessee Nursery and Landscape Association, Inc.

Louree Walkter, Executive Director
115 Lyon Stree
P.O. Box 57
McMinnville, TN 37111-2545
Phone: 931-473-3951
Fax: 931-473-5883
tnurseryassn@clomand.net
www.tnla.com

Texas Nursery & Landscape Association

Eddy D. Edmond son, President
7730 South IH-35
Austin, TX 78745-6621
Phone: 512-280-5182
Fax: 512-280-3012
info@tnlaonline.org
www.tnlaonline.org

Utah Nursery & Landscape Association

Diane Jones, Executive Director
P.O. Box 526314
Salt Lake City, UT 84152-6314
Phone: 801-463-4426
Fax: 801-463-0026
info@utahgreen.org
www.utahgreen.org

Vermont Association of Professional Horticulturists

Kristina Mackulin
P.O. Box 92
North Ferrisburg, VT 05473
Phone: 802-425-5117
Fax: 802-425-5122
admin@vaph.org
www.vaph.org

Virginia Nursery and Landscape Association

Jeffrey B. Miller, Executive Director
383 Coal Hollow Road
Christiansburg, VA 24073-6721
Phone: 540-382-0943
Fax: 540-382-2716
info@VNLA.org
www.VNLA.org

Washington State Nursery & Landscape Association

Jeanne McNeill, Executive Director
34400 Pacific Hwy S Ste 2
Federal Way, WA 98003-7830
Phone: 253-661-6055
Fax: 253-661-6058
www.wsnla.org

West Virginia Nursery and Landscape Association, Inc.

Bradford C. Pearce, Executive Director
1517 Kingwood Pike
Morgantown, WV 26508-3938
Phone: 304-292-2440
Fax: 304-292-2488
wvnla@prodigy.net
www.growit.com

Western Nursery and Landscape Association

Sarah Woody Bidens, Executive Director
1210 Frederick Avenue
St. Joseph, MO 64501-2334
Phone: 816-233-1481
Fax: 816-233-4774
wbaacnts@ponyexpress.net
www.wnla.org

Wisconsin Nursery and Landscape Association

Brian Swingle, Executive Director
12342 W. Layton Avenue
Greenfield, WI 53228-3347
Phone: 414-529-4705
Fax: 414-529-4722
membership@toriiphillips.com
www.wgif.net

Glossary

accelerator—a chemical to speed the hardening process.

accent—special emphasis provided by a striking or prominent feature.

accent lighting—when small lights are used to highlight a particular plant, small garden element, or work of art.

acidity—a pH below 7.0.

aerifier—a piece of power equipment which punches small holes in the turf's surface.

aesthetic injury level—the point where visible plant damage in the landscape justifies using pest control techniques.

aesthetic value—a benefit of the landscape which is sensitive to art and beauty.

algae—a group of small, primitive, filamentous, green plants that manufacture their own food and are found under very wet conditions.

alkaline—a pH over 7.0.

Ames lettering instrument—a tool used to draw eight parallel guidelines for lettering.

annual—a herbaceous plant that germinates from seed, grows to maturity, flowers, and produces seed in one growing season.

anti-transpirant—seals the stomata and reduces transpiration which can help prevent leaf scorch or leaf burn.

arboretum—a natural setting of trees, shrubs, and vines.

arboriculture—the culture of trees.

arborist—professional tree care specialist.

Architect's scale—a measuring instrument used for scale measurements of 1/16", 1/8", and 1/4".

area measurements—those made of the surface.

art—the production or expression of beauty.

backflow prevention device—a safety device that eliminates the movement of irrigation water back into its source, a potable water system, which could become contaminated.

bacteria—small, one-celled organisms that have a primitive nucleus.

balance—implied equilibrium.

balled and burlapped (B&B)—a harvesting technique where a plant is dug keeping a ball of soil around the root system and covering it with burlap to hold the soil and roots together.

baluster—a vertical piece of wood between the top and bottom rails in a deck.

bare root (BR)—a harvesting technique where a plant is dug without taking soil from the field.

base plan—a drawing of the house on the lot.

bay—the distance between two posts.

beam—a large board that connects the posts and provides the support for the joists in deck construction.

bedding plant—a flower already growing in a container and ready to begin blooming, rather than grown from seed.

bed edging—the area where the landscape bed joins the lawn area.

bed pattern—a border that outlines where plants are planted.

berm—a mound of soil.

bid—a fixed price placed on the work to be done.

biennial—a plant species that normally requires two growing seasons to flower and produce seed.

biological pest management—using living organisms that are predators to manage pests.

border garden—a site on a fence or wall that can viewed from one side.

botanical garden—a plant collection habitat.

branch bark ridge—a raised line of bark that forms on the upper side of where the branch joins the trunk.

broadcasting—involves the wide distribution of material on the surface of the soil.

broom finish—the process of dragging a broom over concrete before it hardens to create a rough, nonskid surface.

bulb—a short, flattened stem that bears fleshy storage leaves and is normally underground.

callus—protective growth of tissue; an undifferentiated mass of cells.

candle stage—new growth on pines which resembles candles.

capillary water—water held between the soil particles against the force of gravity.

career success—actions that help a person succeed in their career.

cement—a mixture of lime, clay, iron, and silica.

chain saw—a gas powered or electric saw with a continuous loop cutting chain.

chlorosis—yellowing of plant leaves caused by the absence of chlorophyll.

circle template—an instrument used as a guide to draw circles and curves.

cleat—a short board attached to posts for beams to rest on.

closing—last step of the sales process in which an agreement between the customer and the salesperson is reached.

collar—swollen trunk tissue surrounding the base of a tree branch.

color—has greatest visual impact of all the design qualities; subdivided into warm and cool colors.

color rendering—the process of adding color to a landscape plan.

color rotation—cycle of several floral displays in one growing season.

communication—individuals participate in exchanging information.

compartmentalization—the formation of a chemical barrier by a tree to seal a wound.

compass—a tool used to make large circles and curves not possible when using the circle template.

complete metamorphosis—four distinct changes in an insect life cycle (egg, larvae, pupae, and adult).

computer assisted design (CAD)—refers to the use of computer hardware and software to produce drawings.

computer spreadsheet—an all-purpose computer program used for almost any task involving the organization of numbers based on columns and rows.

contact herbicide—a chemical that kills only the portions of the plants that it contacts.

container grown—a cultural method where plants are grown in containers filled with a special soil mix.

container nursery—grows nursery crops to marketable size in containers.

contingency costs—the unforeseen expenses associated with a project, such as theft of materials at the work site, mechanical breakdowns, or rain outs.

contour lines—represent the vertical rise or fall of the land; how the terrain changes elevation.

contract—a legal document representing agreement between two parties.

cool humid region—a turfgrass region suited to cool season grasses, such as bluegrass, ryegrass, fescue, or bentgrass.

cool season turfgrass—a grass that grows best in a temperature range of 60 to 75°F.

corner planting—plants placed at the corners of the house.

cost summation—the total expenses for a job, including labor, materials, overhead, and contingencies.

covenant—an agreement made between two or more parties to do or keep from doing a specific thing.

cross lighting—when two or more spotlights are shown down onto the same general area but from different angles.

cubic yard—a volume measurement 3 feet wide, 3 feet long, and 3 feet high.

cultivar—a plant with a distinguishing characteristic from other plants in the species but does not transfer that characteristic to its offspring through sexual reproduction.

cultural pest management—the use of management techniques to limit pest populations.

cure—hardening of concrete.

cut—describes removing or excavating soil from an area.

dead zone—the region in the center of a plant that, when exposed to light, seldom produces new shoots.

deciduous—those plants that lose their leaves in the fall.

deck—wooden surface area raised above the ground level.

deck boards—those that cover joists and provide the flooring surface of a deck.

desiccation—water loss from tissues resulting in tissue death.

design/build landscape companies—companies that design and install landscapes.

doorway planting—plants located on either side of the entry door.

down-lighting—the lighting of an object, area, or surface from above.

drawing paper—white vellum or tracing paper.

drip irrigation device—an irrigation emitter that produces a short throw, zero radius, or ultra-low volume water distribution.

drop-crotch pruning—a method effectively used to shorten tree limbs and to reduce the size of a tree.

drought tolerance—refers to the ability of a plant to live and grow with low amounts of moisture.

dry fertilizer—nutrients packaged in dry form, commonly granular.

eased—shape of boards whose edges have been rounded.

ecosystem—a confined community; all the parts of a particular environment, such as all the contents of a lily pond.

elevation view—a view of a house from the front.

emphasis—dominance of some elements of the design over others.

enclosure—the wall of the outdoor living room; the term used to describe both fences and walls in the landscape.

Engineer's scale—a measuring instrument used for scale measurements divided by tenths.

entry garden—consists of plantings at the entrance of the house that are more developed than a typical doorway planting.

environmental stress—problems or conditions that can damage turfgrass plants, such as cold temperatures, high temperatures, drought, heavy foot traffic, and disease problems.

erasure shield—a thin metal plate used to protect lines while erasing.

estimate—an approximate price for the work to be done.

estimate sheet—a form for calculating prices.

evergreen—a plant that keeps its leaves year round.

exoskeleton—external skeleton.

exposed aggregate—the gravel used to make concrete exposed by washing away some of the cement just before the concrete hardens in the finishing process.

family inventory survey—a form on which the customer provides information on factors that affect the landscape project.

fence—an enclosure having posts, rails, and infill.

fertilizer analysis—the composition of the active ingredients in the formulation.

fertilizer capsule—a solid form of fertilizer implanted in a tree trunk after drilling a hole just under the bark.

fertilizer spike—hardened form of dry fertilizer in the shape of a stake which is driven into the soil.

field nursery—grows nursery crops to marketable size in fields.

fill—describes the addition of soil to an area.

filtration system—pool filters and pump to remove impurities and keep the water clean and clear.

final grade—the elevation of the soil surface after completing all grading operations.

float—a tool used to initially smooth the surface of liquid concrete after screeding.

flower bed—a planting bed that only contains flowers.

flower border—flowers planted in front of shrubs in the planting bed with the shrubs providing the back drop.

focal point—point of emphasis of a well-designed landscape.

form—a frame or mold that holds liquid concrete to shape until it has set; the three-dimensional shape of the plant.

formal balance—the exact same plants on each side of a view.

foundation plant—shrubs placed around the foundation of a house.

French curve—an instrument used as a guide to draw irregular curves.

frost line—the maximum depth that the ground will freeze in winter.

fungi—small, one-celled, filamentous, spore-bearing organisms having no chlorophyll that grow on or in a plant.

fungicide—a chemical used to manage fungi populations.

garden accessory—an item in the landscape that attracts attention and provides interest, such as a sculpture, pool, or lawn ornament.

garden center—a retail store that specializes in selling plant materials and supplies for landscape gardening.

gate—a moveable barrier in a fence.

gate post—the post to which a gate is attached.

genus—a closely related group of plants comprised of one or more species.

geotextile—woven strips of plastic landscape fabric that allow the movement of air, water, and fertilizer into the soil.

golf course design and maintenance—the planning, establishment, and maintenance of golf course turf and landscaped areas.

goose egg plan—a small sketch of the house and lot with rough ovals or circles to represent activities, such as lawn games, play area, patio or deck, vegetable garden, plantings, shed, screen, water garden, service area, or public area; sometimes referred to as functional diagrams.

grade—slope of the land.

grading—the moving of soil and the reshaping of the land.

gravitational water—water that drains down through the soil to the pore spaces because of gravity.

green industry—reference to the ornamental horticulture industry because of the use of green plants.

ground cover—a woody or herbaceous plant that forms a mat less than 1 foot high covering the ground.

ground fault circuit interrupter (GFCI)—a safety device designed to protect people using electricity in areas that may be wet or have water.

group planting—one consisting of several different species of shrubs and trees.

guying—supporting a tree by driving three equally-spaced stakes around the tree trunk and attaching a wire or cable from each stake to the trunk. The wire between stake and the trunk is split in the middle with a turnbuckle.

hand pruner—a hand-held scissor or anvil-style hand pruning tool.

hardiness—refers to the ability of a plant to withstand cold temperatures.

hardpan—densely, compacted layer of soil.

hardscape—physical features, such as fences, terraces, retaining walls, patios, walks, drives, irrigation systems, or pools

hardscaping—describes installing non-plant landscape features, such as fences, patios, walks, pools, or walls.

hardware—describes the computer equipment.

hardy plant—one that is less sensitive to temperature extremes.

heading back—involves the shortening of individual plant stems.

heading cut—a cut made between nodes on the stem to promote branching or to direct growth.

hedge—a group of all one type of shrub that defines space, ties other landscape elements together, and may screen views; may be clipped or unclipped.

hedge shear—a hand operated scissor-type cutter, or electric or gas powered cutter used to trim hedges and shape shrubs in a formal garden.

herbaceous perennial—a perennial plant of soft tissue that dies back each year.

herbaceous plant—a non-woody plant that dies back to the ground each year.

herbicide—a chemical used to kill or prevent weed growth.

high interest planting—a planting designed to capture the attention of the viewer and to provide interest to the garden.

high visual energy—the ability of a plant to attract attention.

high-voltage—conventional 120 volt electricity.

horticultural garden—an arranged garden with a variety of horticultural plants.

host plant—one that provides a pest with food.

hygroscopic water—water that forms a thin film around individual soil particles.

incomplete metamorphosis—the gradual change in an insect's life cycle from the egg through the nymph to the adult.

infill—the material fastened to the rails of a fence that ensure security and privacy.

infiltration—the process of the water soaking into the soil.

informal balance—different plants and different sized plants on each side of a view, but the visual weights of these plants balance one another.

inorganic mulch—one that was never living, such as volcanic rock or river gravel.

insect—an animal with three distinct body parts; head, thorax, and abdomen.

insecticide—a chemical used to kill insects or insect forms.

instar—the shedding of the external skeleton in the life cycle of insects with incomplete metamorphosis.

integrated pest management (IPM)—using cultural, biological, mechanical, and chemical techniques to limit pest populations with the least disruption to the environment.

irrigation controller—a device which regulates and electrically controls solenoid valves in the a sprinkler system.

island bed—a landscape bed in center of a yard with tall plants in the middle and shorter plants toward the edge.

J.U.L.I.E.—Joint Utility Location and Information Exchange finds and marks all underground utilities at the construction site.

joist—a board run at a 90-degree angle to beams that flooring (deck boards) is attached to.

knits down—sod establishing its roots into the soil at a new site.

landscape architect—a person trained in engineering, graphic arts, and architectural technology to design landscapes ranging from small gardens to entire cities.

landscape construction—the segment of landscaping that involves the installation of materials identified in the landscape design.

landscape contractor—the person hired to install the landscape.

landscape design—the practice of creating a plan to make the best use of available outdoor space in the most attractive way.

landscape designer—a person trained in the art of design and the science of growing horticultural plants whose work is primarily residential landscape designs.

landscape fabric—a plastic sheet placed in the landscape bed to reduce weed competition.

landscape maintenance—the care and upkeep of the landscape materials after installation.

landscape maintenance technician—a person who has been trained in landscape maintenance skills.

landscape proposal—a complete description of the materials and services to be provided in a landscaping job.

landscape service contract—a legal document binding the client and the landscaper.

landscape service proposal—a document prepared for the client where proposed services to be provided are identified, along with the total cost.

landscape supervisor—the person responsible for the crew.

landscaping—the segment of the green industry that focuses on the beautification of outdoor terrain and, to some extent, interior settings.

larvae—the worm-like stage of an insect with complete metamorphosis.

lethal dose (LD$_{50}$)—pesticide toxicity given in milligrams of pesticide per kilogram of body weight that will kill 50 percent of a test population.

leaching—gravitational water moving through the soil carrying with it dissolved minerals, chemicals, and salts.

leader—a central branch that dominates over other branches on a tree.

leadership—the ability to influence other people to meet individual or group goals.

line—the outline of plants, plant parts, and physical features.

linear measurements—those made of a line.

line post—a post between corner and/or gate posts.

lines of force—dominant lines created by such features as corners, windows, chimneys, and doors which have visual energy that extend into the landscape.

lopper—a larger, hand operated scissor-style pruning tool.

low-voltage—stepped-down 24 volt electricity.

macroclimate—concerns the temperature, precipitation, humidity, and wind over large areas or regions.

main post—a post located at a corner or gate.

mechanical pest management—using tools or equipment to limit pest populations.

microclimate—the temperature, precipitation, humidity, and wind on the landscape site.

microirrigation—a closed irrigation system characterized by low operating pressure and small orifice size.

mirror lighting—a technique using reflected light on water to add interest in the landscape.

mono-stand—contains only one cultivar of turfgrass.

mortarless block wall system—a block wall system that uses precast concrete blocks stacked on top of one another without mortar to hold them together.

moss—tangled green mats composed of a branched, thread-like growth over the soil surface usually found in highly acidic, excessively shaded, improperly watered, or low fertility compacted conditions.

mulch—material used around plants to reduce water loss, prevent weed growth, keep soil temperatures uniform, or prevent erosion.

mulching—the practice of spreading a material over the surface of the soil.

National FFA Organization—a student organization for individuals enrolled in secondary school agricultural education classes.

National Junior Horticultural Association—an organization for young people interested in horticulture that is not school-based.

native plant—a plant growing naturally, not introduced by people.

nematicide—a chemical used to reduce nematode populations.

nematode—an appendageless, non-segmented worm-like invertebrate with a body cavity and complete digestive tract, including mouth, alimentary canal, and anus.

night-landscaping—describes the use of ornamental lighting to enhance the landscape after dark.

non-selective herbicide—a chemical that kills all vegetation without regard to species.

nurseries—grow many different varieties of trees, shrubs, and bedding plants.

nursery production—producing plants in fields and containers for transplanting into landscapes.

nutrient—chemical substance that supports the life processes.

nutrient ratio—shows the relationship of nitrogen, phosphorus, and potassium to each other in a bag of fertilizer.

nymph—the stage of the life cycle of an insect with incomplete metamorphosis that looks similar to the adult, only differing in appearance by size and color.

opening—the first meeting of the salesperson and the customer.

ordinance—a governmental regulation or statute.

organic mulch—one that originated from plant material, such as wood chips, shredded wood bark, or pine needles.

ornamental grass—an annual or perennial grass plant valued for its texture and color in the landscape.

ornamental horticulture—uses plants and other materials for decorative purposes.

ornamental plant—a plant planted by people for its attractive characteristics.

ornamental tree—a smaller tree having high visual interest.

outdoor living area—includes all of the property to the rear of the house except the service area.

overhead costs—general costs in running a business.

parasite—usually a multi-celled organism that lives in or on other organisms.

path lighting—walk lights to improve the safety of pedestrians while providing an interesting lighting effect in the landscape; safety lighting.

pathogen—a biological agent or virus that can cause disease.

patio—permanent hard surface, such as brick, concrete, or flagstone, that is level with the ground.

paver blocks—specially made units constructed from molded and compressed concrete or molded clay into many types, styles, colors, and sizes.

paving—covering the soil with a hard surface material to prevent soil erosion and compaction from traffic.

percolation—the downward movement of water through the soil.

perennial—a plant that has a life cycle of more than two growing seasons.

permeable—a quality of soil that allows water movement by infiltration and percolation.

personal growth—social, citizenship, and self-esteem skills.

pesticide—a chemical used in managing pests.

pest—anything that causes injury or loss to a plant.

pH scale—a 14-point scale used to explain acidity or alkalinity.

pheromone—a chemical sexual attractant for insects.

photocell—a light-sensitive switch.

photosynthesis—the process that green plants use to convert light energy into chemical energy.

pilaster—a rectangular support or pier projecting partially from a wall.

plains region—a turfgrass region that is dry and where buffalo grass grows naturally.

planimeter/digitizer—a computer device to accurately and quickly calculate linear feet, area, and volume.

plant disease—any abnormal conditions in plants that interfere with its normal appearance, growth, structure, or function.

planting bed—describes the area in the landscape where shrubs and flowers are planted.

planting plan—a drawing developed by the landscape designer which shows the exact location for plant materials, includes a plant materials list, and hardscape features. Contours and spot elevations may also be included.

plant nomenclature—the common and botanical names of plants.

plan view—a view of the house and lot from above looking down.

plate compactor—a mechanical plate vibrator used to compact base materials and pavers.

plat of survey—a legal document indicating exact locations of physical structures on a piece of property and the exact dimensions of the property.

plug—a small block or square of turf including soil that is used to vegetatively propagate warm season turfgrasses, such as zoysia.

point-of-connection—the location where the irrigation line is connected to the household water supply.

polyethylene (PE)—a tough, black waxy plastic material derived by combining hydrogen and carbon that is commonly used to make flexible pipe which is used in landscape irrigation and drainage.

polyvinyl chloride (PVC)—a tough, rigid plastic material, commonly used to make rigid pipe, made by combining coke, lime, and salt.

pop-up rotating sprinkler—one that has a pair of nozzles that raise and revolve to distribute water over the area of coverage.

pore spaces—holes in the soil between soil particles.

portfolio—design work and photos of previous landscape projects.

postemergence—after plant emergence.

postemergent—(see postemergence)

preemergence—before plant emergence but after planting.

preemergent—(see preemergence)

preformed pool—a ready-made pond of plastic or fiberglass material.

preparation—first step in the sales process that involves a number of factors before the sale is actually conducted.

presentation—the sales step where the designer introduces the service or product meeting the customer's needs as identified earlier in the sales process.

private area—includes all the property to the rear of the house except the service area; also known as the outdoor living area.

probing—a practice of thoroughly investigating a customer's wants, needs, and problems.

profit—the amount of money leftover after deducting all expenses.

pruning—selective removal or reduction of certain plant parts.

pruning saw—a hand saw with widely spaced large teeth used to remove tree branches.

public area—the portion of the property that is in full view of the public.

pupae—the transformation stage in the life cycle of an insect with complete metamorphosis.

rejuvenation pruning—complete removal of all stems to 4- to 6-inch stubs.

renewal pruning—the selective removal of older plant stems.

repetition—repeating forms, textures, and colors of the plants throughout the design.

respiration—the chemical process in which cells, including root cells, convert sugars into energy.

retaining wall—an enclosure constructed to retain or hold soil in place.

retarder—a chemical to slow the hardening process.

rhizome—a horizontally growing underground stem.

riser—the elevating vertical part of a step.

rootstock—the root system used in the grafting process.

root circling—occurs if a plant grows too long in a container; also called pot bound.

root zone—the area in which plant roots are growing.

rough grade—establishing the approximate grade or slope of the terrain and should closely parallel the proposed final grade but is usually 3 to 6 inches below the final or finish grade.

sale—the exchange of goods or services at a price mutually agreed upon by the parties involved.

scaffold branch—one that grows laterally from a tree trunk.

scale—the proportion of one object to another.

scion—the top growth (stem) used in the grafting process.

screeding—leveling the liquid concrete surface with a straight edge by moving the excess concrete from the high spots and filling in the low spots.

screen—a solid mass of one type of shrub serving as a living wall that effectively blocks views.

security lighting—when light is used to protect property from vandalism or theft.

selective herbicide—a chemical used to kill only certain plant species.

sequence—the uniformity of change from one item in the landscape to the next.

service area—area to the rear or the side of the house set aside for strictly functional purposes.

shade tree—a large tree with a spreading canopy which screens the sun.

shadow lighting—lights a plant to create a distinct pattern of light and shadow on a plain wall or backdrop.

shearing—the removal of a shrub's surface by clipping in order to achieve a desired shape.

shrub—a multi-stem, woody plant that does not exceed 20 feet in height.

shrub border—a mass of many shrubs on the border of the property which helps to create the outdoor living room, screens views, and serves as a backdrop for flower borders.

silhouette lighting—a light installation that is directed at a wall or other plain backdrop in the background to show off the silhouette of a plant or statue in the foreground.

site analysis plan—an accurate sketch of the house and lot on which observations are recorded.

soaker hose—oozes water providing a slow application.

sod—the surface layer of turf, including the plants and a thin layer of soil.

sod production—producing sod for transplanting in a landscape.

soft paving—covering the soil with loose aggregates.

software—the programs (instructions) which make computer equipment function.

soil—the outer part of the earth's crust in which plant root systems grow.

soil amendments—materials added to the soil to improve drainage, moisture holding ability, and aeration.

soil ball—the soil surrounding the root system of a plant.

soil pH—a measure of the amount of alkalinity or acidity in the soil.

soil structure—the arrangement of soil aggregates in the soil.

soil texture—the proportion of different sized particles in the soil described as sand, silt, and clay.

soil water needle—a device that is used to supply water directly to the root zone of a plant.

solenoid valve—turns irrigation water on and off with electricity which allows remote clocks to time cycles.

soluble fertilizer—dissolved, liquid form.

species—plants that show characteristics that distinguish them from other groups in the genus.

specifications—written descriptions of materials, work, and time schedules for a project.

specimen plant—one displaying outstanding form, texture, and color.

spotlighting—a technique giving focal glow to an object within the landscape by directing an intense beam of light toward it.

spray head sprinkler—one that emits single or double fans of water in a fixed pattern.

sprigs—pieces of grass stems (rhizomes and stolons) without soil used to vegetatively propagate warm season turfgrasses, such as Bermuda grass.

sprinkler—provides moisture to a large area.

stake the site—describes writing plant names on small wooden or plastic stakes that are driven into the ground to show the exact center of each planting hole.

staking—supporting a tree by driving two or three long stakes next to the soil ball and attaching a wire between the stakes and the three trunk.

station—a single electric switch in an irrigation controller that turns on or off a solenoid valve.

stolon—a horizontally growing aboveground stem.

stomata—small openings in the epidermal layer of plant tissue where transpiration occurs.

subordination—involves cuts made that slow the growth of a branch.

subsoil—lighter colored layer of soil below the topsoil.

sucker—a soft, green shoot that develops at the base of a tree.

sun calculator—a drawing that can be placed under the tracing paper and centered on the area to be shaded to help locate trees in the landscape with the angles suggested to block the sun's rays for a particular time of day.

sunscald—describes a condition in which bark blisters from the intense winter sunlight; winter burn.

supervised agricultural experience (SAE)—planned work experiences related to in-school instruction and supportive of FFA achievement.

systematic herbicide—a chemical absorbed into a plant's vascular and root system, destroying the entire plant.

tender plant—one more sensitive to temperature extremes.

terrain—describes the rise and fall of the land.

texture—the appearance of a plant in terms of coarseness or fineness, roughness or smoothness, heaviness or lightness, denseness or thinness.

thatch—describes the accumulation of excess grass stems and roots in the turf.

thinning cut—a cut that removes a branch from the parent stem or trunk.

tines—the hollow tubes of a core aerifier which are driven into the soil removing ½-inch diameter plugs of soil.

title block—space or location on a landscape plan that provides the name of the individual for whom the plan was prepared and other information about the plan.

topdressing— covering turfgrass with 1/4" to 3/8" of soil.

topography—a record of an area's terrain.

topsoil—soil found near the surface.

transition zone—an area between major climate zones.

transpiration—the loss of water in the form of water vapor from the plant through the leaves.

trash paper—often a buff color, this tracing paper is lightweight and inexpensive and is used by the designer to sketch ideas on when laid on top of the base plan without marking the quality tracing paper beneath.

tread—the level part of the step on which the foot is placed.

tree—a single-stem, woody, perennial plant reaching the height of 12 feet or more.

trowel—a tool used to bring a thin film of cement to the top after concrete has initially set, making a very smooth surface.

turf—the plants in a ground cover and the soil in which the roots grow.

turfgrass—a collection of grass plants that form a ground cover.

turfgrass blend—a combination of different cultivars of the same species.

turfgrass maintenance—keeping a stand of turfgrass in an attractive and healthy condition.

turfgrass mixture—a combination of two or more different species.

unity—a look of oneness.

unity of three—involves the use of anything in multiples of three.

up-lighting—a general term used for light sources which shine upward.

urban forester—a forester who works with ornamental trees in city settings.

U-shaped crotch—tree branches that exhibit a 45- to 90-degree angle of attachment.

variety—contrast in the design by selecting some plants with different qualities from the mass of plants; plants within a species that show a significant difference from other plants in the species and inherit those characteristics through sexual reproduction.

video imaging—a technique that uses computer technology to superimpose a landscape design over a photograph of the customer's undeveloped site.

vine—a woody or herbaceous plant that requires some type of support which climbs on objects or creeps along the ground.

viruses—infective living agents of microorganisms, some with characteristics of nonliving matter, that can multiply only in connection with living cells and are regarded both as living organisms and as complex proteins sometimes involving nucleic acid, enzymes, etc.

volume measurements—those of size or amount in three-dimensions.

V-shaped crotch—tree branches that exhibit a sharp, less than 45-degree angle of attachment.

wall—an upright structure serving to enclose, divide, support, or protect an area.

warm arid and semi-arid regions—turfgrass regions that will only support warm season grasses with irrigation to supplement the low natural rainfall.

warm humid region—a turfgrass region suited to warm season grasses, such as Bermuda grass, zoysia, or St. Augustine grass.

warm season turfgrass—a grass that grows best in a temperature range of 80 to 95°F.

water bag—a bag filled with water which has tiny holes to allow the water to slowly seep into the ground.

water requirement—refers to the amount of water plants need to live and grow.

watersprout—a soft, green shoot that typically grows vertically from existing tree branches.

water zone—an area in a landscape based on the amount of water needed by the plants.

weed—a plant growing out of place or any unwanted plant.

weep hole—a hole made through a wall to release the built-up water pressure.

wilting—the drooping of a plant due to a lack of firmness in the plant tissues.

winter burn—describes a condition in which bark blisters from the intense winter sunlight; sunscald.

wrought iron—an iron that contains some slag and very little carbon.

xeriscape—water conservation through creative, appropriate landscaping and water management.

xeriscaping—using a landscape design that is water efficient.

Bibliography

Biondo, Ronald J., and Jasper S. Lee. *Introduction to Plant and Soil Science and Technology*. Danville, Illinois: Interstate Publishers, Inc., 2003.

Biondo, Ronald J., Michael G. White, and Eric Reutter. *Biological Science and Agriculture*. Danville, Illinois: Professional Educators Publications, Inc., 2006.

Damrosch, Barbara. *The Garden Primer*. New York, New York: Workman Publishing Company, Inc., 2008.

Dirr, Michael A. *Manual of Woody Landscape Plants*. Champaign, Illinois: Stipes Publishing Company, 1998.

Dock, Katie and Fiona Wild, ed. *Learn to Garden*. New York, New York: DK Publishing, 2008.

Giles, Floyd. *Pruning and Care of Trees and Shrubs*. Urbana: Vocational Agriculture Service, University of Illinois, Publication U5040.

Giles, Floyd. *Landscape Construction Procedures, Techniques, and Design*. Illinois: Stipes Publishing Company, 1999.

Gilman, Edward F. *An Illustrated Guide to Pruning*. New York: Delmar Publishers, 2002.

Hall, Larry, editor. "The Kindest Cut of All." Wheeling, Illinois: Hendrickson, The Care of Trees. *Arbor Topics*, Volume XXV, Fall and Winter, 1992-93.

Nelson, William. R. *Landscaping Your Home*. University of Illinois Cooperative Extension Service Circular 1111.

Nelson, William R., *Planting Design: A Manual of Theory and Practice.* Champaign, Illinois: Stipes Publishing Company, 1985.

Noland, Dianne A., and Kirsten Bolin. *Perennials for the Landscape.* Danville, Illinois: Interstate Publishers, Inc., 2000.

Phipps, Lloyd J., Glen M. Miller, and Jasper S. Lee. *Introduction to Agricultural Mechanics*, 2nd ed. Upper Saddle River, New Jersey: Pearson Prentice Hall Interstate, 2004.

Powell, Kim. *Pruning Trees, Flushcuts and Wound Dressings.* North Carolina Cooperative Extension Service, Leaflet Number: 602, October, 1992.

Schroeder, Charles B., Eddie Dean Seagle, Lorie M. Felton, John M. Ruter, William Terry Kelley, and Gerard Krewer. *Introduction to Horticulture.* Boston, Massachusetts: Pearson Prentice Hall Interstate, 2009.

Schroeder, Charles B., and Howard B. Sprague. *Turf Management Handbook.* Danville, Illinois: Interstate Publishers, Inc., 1996.

Turgeon, A. J. *Turfgrass Management*, 7th ed. Upper Saddle River, New Jersey: Pearson Prentice Hall, 2005.

_____ *Conducting an Agricultural Sales Call.* Urbana: Vocational Agricultural Service, University of Illinois, 1990.

_____ "Interview with Robert S Hursthouse." R.S. Hursthouse & Associates, Inc., Naperville, Illinois, 1996.

_____ "Interview with John F. Mitten." Church Landscape, Lombard, Illinois, 1996.

_____ *Landscaping.* Reston, Virginia: Associated Landscape Contractors of America.

_____ *Selecting Plants & Trees.* Lisle, Illinois: The Morton Arboretum, 1991.

_____ *The Value of Landscaping.* Tacoma, Washington: Weyerhaeuser Nursery Products Division.

Index